z

560d

NUMERICAL ANALYSIS

NUMERICAL ANALYSIS

BY

D. R. HARTREE, F.R.S.

Plummer Professor of Mathematical Physics
University of Cambridge

OXFORD
AT THE CLARENDON PRESS

Oxford University Press, Amen House, London E.C.4

GLASGOW NEW YORK TORONTO MELBOURNE WELLINGTON
BOMBAY CALCUTTA MADRAS KARACHI CAPE TOWN IBADAN

Geoffrey Cumberlege, Publisher to the University

FIRST PUBLISHED 1952
REPRINTED LITHOGRAPHICALLY IN GREAT BRITAIN
AT THE UNIVERSITY PRESS, OXFORD
FROM CORRECTED SHEETS OF THE FIRST EDITION
1955

PREFACE

THIS book is based on a course of lectures on Numerical Analysis which I have given in the Mathematical Laboratory of the University of Cambridge for several years. It is intended to be introductory, in the sense that no previous knowledge of the theory and practice of systematic numerical work is assumed, but it is not 'elementary' in the sense of using only school mathematics. It assumes familiarity with the calculus up to Taylor's theorem and partial derivatives, acquaintance with differential equations and, in the chapter on linear simultaneous algebraic equations, with some of the simpler properties of matrices. But in all these cases what is wanted is mainly an understanding of the ideas involved rather than technical facility in manipulating algebraical or analytical expressions.

I have deliberately tried to restrict the algebraical and analytical work to the treatment of those methods which are useful in practice when numbers are substituted for the literal symbols of a general treatment, and to avoid developments which are of purely formal interest. Such developments may be elegant mathematics, or may make the formal presentation more complete, but they are not contributions to numerical analysis, and are distracting rather than helpful to the reader who wants practical information about what calculations to make to obtain the results he requires, and how to carry them out. For a similar reason, I have tried to give prominence to the importance of checking in numerical work. Mistakes can occur in such work, and it follows that some process of checking is necessary to ensure that any results obtained are not vitiated by undetected mistakes. A treatment of numerical methods which does not pay some attention to this aspect of the subject seems to me to be quite unrealistic. In some worked examples I have deliberately introduced mistakes in order to show how, by suitable checking procedure, they can be detected, diagnosed, and corrected.

For similar practical reasons I have deliberately omitted some examples of numerical work which seem to have become almost classical, for example the evaluation of an approximation to $\frac{1}{4}\pi$ by application of Gregory's quadrature formula to the integral $\int_0^1 dx/(1+x^2)$. This particular calculation I regard as an example of how *not* to do numerical work; not because the method is wrong, but because it is not the most suitable for obtaining the required result (see § 6.51); use of it is therefore an example of bad practice, and should not be presented as if it were an example of satisfactory numerical procedure. Much could be written on how *not* to do numerical calculations. I have mentioned in the text some procedures which should, in general, be avoided, mostly because they are not the most suitable for obtaining the results sought, but some because they are dangerous in that, if used without precautions, they may give wrong results. I have refrained from giving numerical illustrations of the dangers of such methods, except in one case (§ 5.81) in which it seemed advisable to give a warning, by means of a horrid example, of the dangers of a method for inverse interpolation which might at first sight appear attractive, and which has in fact been given in print as a usable method without any mention of the dangers.

An introductory treatment such as that of this book cannot cover the subject completely; several of the chapters from Chapter IV onward could well be expanded to form a volume each. In particular, this book hardly begins to touch the needs of the specialist or research worker in the subject of numerical analysis; its purpose is rather to give an introduction to the subject to workers in other fields of pure or applied science who may have to carry out calculations of a non-trivial magnitude. In such contexts the accuracy of the approximations or measurements underlying the calculation to be done do not usually justify working to a greater accuracy than six or seven figures, and often a smaller number will be adequate. On the other hand, the amount of calculation to be done to this accuracy may be considerable. In so far as the appropriate method for carrying out a calculation depends on the number of figures kept in it, emphasis is therefore placed on methods suitable for calculations of substantial extent to moderate accuracy, rather than for a few calculations to many figures. My personal experience of such work extends over 35 years, and most of this work has been concerned with calculations involving numerical approximations to some of the limiting processes of analysis, in particular integration (including the integration of differential equations). On the basis of this experience, I believe this to be one of the most important practical fields for the use of numerical methods, and have deliberately given it considerable prominence.

In the past few years there has been considerable development of high-speed automatic general-purpose digital calculating machines. This development has given practical importance to the study of the process of organizing calculations for these machines, a process usually referred to as 'programming'. This study can be regarded as a branch of numerical analysis, and it is one which is likely to grow in importance as more of these machines become available. I have therefore included an introductory chapter on this subject (Chapter XII). There are several systems of programming, and for brevity in an introductory account such as this, and to avoid confusing the reader with a number of alternatives, it seems best to adopt one particular system in presenting illustrative examples. I have adopted the one with which I myself am most familiar, and which I think is one of the simplest to follow. But this must not be regarded as more than a means for illustrating in a simple form some of the general ideas involved in programming. For various reasons, some of which are mentioned in § 12.8, numerical methods which are convenient for hand calculation with the assistance of a desk machine are not the most suitable for an automatic machine, and vice versa. But this book is intended to provide an introduction to numerical analysis for those who will mainly be concerned with methods suitable for hand calculation, and little or no reference is made to other methods some of which might be more suitable for automatic machines.

In the Bibliography I have included, as suggestions for further reading, some books and papers not referred to in the text, but I have not attempted to compile a complete bibliography of numerical analysis, or to give references to the history of the subject; the reader who is interested in early references should consult *The Calculus of Observations* by Whittaker and Robinson.

On matters concerning the use of desk calculating machines, I am conscious of a considerable debt to the late Dr. L. J. Comrie; the processes of §§ 2.25, 4.45, 4.46, and Example 7 I learnt from him, though whether he originated them I do not know; and there may well be other examples of his influence of which I am unconscious. Some of Dr. Comrie's long and varied experience in numerical work is incorporated in *Chambers's Six-figure Mathematical Tables*, but it is much to be regretted that he did not live to write a fuller work on the art of numerical calculation.

In the derivation of central-difference interpolation formulae, I have followed a treatment which I learnt from J. G. L. Michel, and in the examination of truncation errors of interpolation and integration formulae I have followed a treatment which I learnt from Professor W. E. Milne while I was serving as Acting Chief of the Institute for Numerical Analysis of the U.S. National Bureau of Standards.

I wish to express my thanks to Dr. J. Howlett, of the Computing Section, A.E.R.E., who read the first draft typescript of this book, and to Mr. A. S. Douglas, who read the proof sheets, for many valuable comments and suggestions, and for a number of corrections. Also I wish to thank Mr. P. Farmer for the photographs from which the drawings for Figs. 1, 2, and 3 were made, Mrs. Valerie Taylor for making the drawings themselves, my daughter for her skill in typing much of the text, and Dr. M. V. Wilkes, Director of the Mathematical Laboratory, Cambridge, for permission to avail myself of the services of Mr. Farmer, Mrs. Taylor, and my daughter, all members of the staff of the Laboratory. It is a pleasure also to thank those members of the staff of the Clarendon Press who have been concerned with the production of this book.

D. R. H.

CAVENDISH LABORATORY
    CAMBRIDGE
        May 1952

ADDENDUM TO PREFACE

WITH the co-operation of the Clarendon Press, I have taken the opportunity, provided by a new impression of this book, to make a number of corrections and two substantial alterations. Two sections (§§ 5.61 and 8.53) have been completely rewritten, as experience of calculations of the kind considered in these sections has led me to the conclusion that, for the readers for whom this book is mainly written, the methods now given are preferable to those given in the first impression.

I wish to thank various correspondents, and particularly Mr. R. E. Beard, Mr. D. R. Bland, and Mr. G. A. Erskine, who have written to draw my attention to points requiring correction or modification. It is a pleasure to renew my thanks to the staff of the Clarendon Press for their co-operation.

D. R. H.

CAVENDISH LABORATORY
    CAMBRIDGE
    JULY 1954

CONTENTS

I

INTRODUCTION

1.1. What numerical analysis is about

THE subject of numerical analysis is concerned with the science and art of numerical calculation, and particularly with *processes* for getting certain kinds of numerical results from certain kinds of data. The following are some simple typical problems for which we may require processes for obtaining numerical solutions:

   (i) Tabulate $(\sinh x - x)/x^3$ to five decimals for $x = 0(0.1)3$.†
  (ii) Given such a table,

      (*a*) find, as accurately as possible, the value of x for which

$$(\sinh x - x)/x^3 = 0.2;$$

      (*b*) construct a table at intervals of 0.02.
 (iii) What values of x, y, z satisfy the equations

$$xyz = 6, \qquad x^2 - y^2 + z^2 = 6, \qquad x + 2y + 3z = 10?$$

 (iv) Tabulate $\int_0^\infty e^{-(x-w^2)^2}\, dw$ for $x = -2(0.1)2$.

  (v) For what values of λ has the equation

$$y'' + (\lambda - e^{-x^2})y = 0$$

got a solution for which $y \to 0$ as $x \to \pm\infty$ and for which

$$\int_{-\infty}^{\infty} y^2\, dx = 1,$$

and what are the corresponding solutions?

Although from the point of view of numerical analysis the end to be attained is always a numerical result or set of results, the subject is not concerned with the *results*, that is to say *answers* to specific problems themselves, but with the *processes* by which those results can be obtained. And although the end is a numerical result, algebra and analysis are involved in the development of these processes. In so far as these processes, and the arguments by which they are derived, are general and independent of the particular values of the numbers to which they may be

† This is a standard notation for 'from $x = 0$ to 3 inclusive at intervals of 0.1 in x'; see § 2.3.

           B

applied, the subject may properly be regarded as a branch of mathematics.† But the algebra and analysis must be aimed at providing or
establishing *practical methods of obtaining numerical results*; otherwise
it may be elegant mathematics, but is not a contribution to numerical
analysis.

This emphasis on *practicable numerical processes* requires a considerable
change in attitude from that of ordinary algebra and analysis, to which
the idea is quite foreign. Algebraical or analytical results which are
formally complete answers may be almost or quite useless for numerical
purposes. Consider, for example, the solution of a system of simultaneous
linear algebraic equations. Any textbook of algebra shows how this can
be expressed in terms of ratios of determinants, and this result is often
presented in a form which seems to imply that there is nothing more to
be said on the subject. But direct evaluation of the solution in this form
is certainly not the practical answer to the problem of finding a *numerical*
solution of a set of simultaneous equations.

As another example, consider the solution of

$$\frac{dy}{dx} = 1 - 2xy, \qquad y = 0 \text{ at } x = 0. \tag{1.1}$$

The standard textbook treatment gives

$$y = e^{-x^2} \int_0^x e^{x^2}\, dx, \tag{1.2}$$

and regards this as a complete answer. And so, for numerical purposes,
it is, *provided* one has a table of $\int_0^x e^{x^2}\, dx$. But in order to obtain such a
table it is much easier to reverse the process and solve the differential
equation (1.1) by numerical methods, and then to evaluate the integral
by using (1.2) in the form

$$\int_0^x e^{x^2}\, dx = e^{x^2} y,$$

than to evaluate $\int_0^x e^{x^2}\, dx$ numerically directly. Again the formal text-
book answer is of no practical use if numerical results are wanted in the
end. As in these two examples, practical numerical considerations which
are irrelevant to formal mathematics may require alternative methods

† A. N. Whitehead has written (*Introduction to Mathematics*, p. 15): 'Mathematics as a
science commenced when first someone, probably a Greek, proved propositions about
any things or *some* things, without specification of definite particular things.' The
methods of numerical analysis, as distinct from the details of their application in particular cases, have that degree of generality which entitles them to be considered part of
mathematics.

for treating problems for which complete formal solutions may already be known.

Another matter in which there is much greater emphasis in numerical analysis than in formal analysis is the checking of numerical work. Numerical results which are not reliable are of little or no value, and for this reason any process for obtaining them should include checking procedures for confirming that the alleged results are free from mistakes. This is considered further in § 1.3.

As already mentioned, numerical analysis is concerned with *processes*. It is an active subject, one in which things *happen* in the course of carrying out numerical processes, and it cannot be learnt properly simply by reading about it, by following examples already worked, or even by watching examples being worked, any more than one can learn golf, tennis, or violin-playing by watching others play, without ever handling a club, racket, or violin. There is a great deal of difference between only *thinking* about processes for carrying out numerical calculations and actually carrying them out with numbers in the place of the algebraical symbols of a general treatment, and the student who wishes to get a feeling for the subject *must* work examples of the processes for himself. This is an essential part both of study and research in the subject. Also, probably, he must make his own mistakes and spend time finding them and correcting them and their consequences before he really appreciates the importance of adequate checking.

The processes of numerical analysis are necessarily *finite* processes. Ideas such as limiting processes, Dedekind sections, formal convergence, scarcely play any part in the numerical processes themselves, though they may be involved in the analytical arguments by which the numerical process is established. Related to this is the approximate nature of much of numerical analysis. In most applications of numerical analysis, almost no problems have answers which are rational numbers. But our system of representation of numbers is not suitable for numerical operations on irrational numbers, so that in most cases we have to be satisfied with approximations. And even when the answers are rational numbers, we shall often be content with decimal approximations to these rational numbers, if indeed we would not prefer them.

It will be as well to end this section by explaining what numerical analysis is *not*.

First, it is *not* necessarily concerned with the analysis of numbers obtained by observation in the course of some branch of experimental science; secondly, it is *not* closely related to statistics. Certainly numerical analysis may be involved in the analysis of observational material, whether statistical or obtained by measurement, and the analysis of observations consisting of measurements may involve consideration of the statistics of errors of the measurements. But the subject itself is distinct from these two particular applications of it, just as it is distinct from its particular applications, for example, to the evaluation of super-sonic fluid flow or to the structures of atoms or stars.

1.2. The main types of problems in numerical analysis

The main kinds of operations which have to be carried out in the course of a numerical calculation, and for which numerical processes are required, are the following:

(a) Evaluation of formulae.
(b) Solution of non-linear equations in one unknown.
(c) Solution of systems of linear simultaneous equations.
(d) Inversion of matrices.
(e) Determination of characteristic values and characteristic vectors of matrices.
(f) Solution of systems of non-linear simultaneous equations.
(g) Tabulation of standard functions.
(h) Interpolation and subtabulation.
(i) Integration and differentiation of a given function.
(j) Smoothing.
(k) Integration of ordinary differential equations.
(l) Integration of partial differential equations.
(m) Solution of integral equations.
(n) Harmonic analysis.
(o) Frequency analysis (periodogram analysis).

Of these, (j), (n), and (o) are often concerned with analysis of *observed data*, which is not primarily the subject of numerical analysis as pointed out at the end of the previous section.

A single calculation may involve a number of these operations. For example, evaluation of the solution of an ordinary differential equation may well involve any one or more of (a), (b), or (h) as well as the integration process (k) itself.

The subjects in this list have been arranged more or less in order from less to more 'advanced'; they will not, however, be taken in this order, since some of the ideas required in treating later items of this list are also valuable in the earlier ones.

1.3. Errors, mistakes, and checking

There are three reasons for which the results of a numerical calculation may differ from the exact answer to the mathematical question concerned:

(i) One (or more) of the formulae which are evaluated in the course of the work is derived by cutting off an infinite series after a finite number of terms; the errors introduced in this way are called 'truncation errors';

(ii) Only the more significant decimal digits of a number are retained, the less significant beyond a certain point being rejected: this process is called 'rounding off' and the errors introduced in this way are called 'rounding errors' or 'rounding-off errors';

(iii) Mistakes are made in carrying out the sequence of operations required to obtain the results sought.

The distinction made here between an 'error' and a 'mistake' is this. A 'mistake' is due to fallibility, either human on the part of the individual carrying out the calculation, or technical on the part of the mechanical or electrical aids used in the course of it, and is in principle avoidable. 'Errors', in some degree, are unavoidable, except in some cases of calculations concerned entirely with integers or rational numbers; such calculations may occur, for example, in connexion with number theory, but are otherwise exceptional. 'Truncation errors' are unavoidable in any process which takes the place in numerical work of a limiting process of analysis; integration and differentiation are two important examples. 'Rounding errors' are inevitable in division when the answer is a non-terminating decimal, and in the use of values of functions other than polynomials with rational coefficients, and are often incurred in multiplication also, since although it is possible to retain the $(m+n)$ digits of the product of two numbers, one of m and the other of n digits, it is only exceptionally that all these digits are wanted; if one or both of the numbers being multiplied is subject to rounding error, some of the less significant digits in the product will be valueless anyway.

It is necessary to check that the final results of a calculation are not vitiated either by errors or by mistakes, and in a substantial calculation it will usually be advisable to include a number of checks of intermediate results as well. It is often possible to estimate the magnitude of truncation errors and so ensure that they are kept below a specified tolerance depending on the calculation and the accuracy required in the final results. Rounding errors can often be rendered innocuous by carrying one or two,

or sometimes more, extra figures, known as 'guarding figures', in intermediate stages of the calculation; for example in calculating a compound
interest table of
$$f(p) = (1 \cdot 0325)^p$$
for $p = 0(1)100$, to five decimals, by repeated use of the recurrence
relation
$$f(p+1) = 1 \cdot 0325 f(p),$$
rounding errors greater than 6 in the sixth decimal can be avoided by
keeping eight decimals in the intermediate values of $f(p)$. A full analysis
of the effect of rounding errors in any but a simple calculation may be
fairly elaborate.

Intermediate and final results of a calculation will usually be influenced
by rounding errors at previous stages of the work, and in some cases the
accumulated effects of rounding errors will result in checks not being
satisfied exactly. Let y be the correct value of a quantity and y^* the
calculated value of it. Then there may be a range of values of $y-y^*$
which can be accepted as being results of rounding (and possibly truncation) errors and not as indicating mistakes. The term 'tolerance' (in the
sense in which it is used in machining work in engineering) will be used
for this acceptable range of $y-y^*$. For example, if a check consists of
the equality of two numbers calculated by different processes, and the
tolerance of each is ± 2 in the last digit, a difference of 3 between them
in this digit is within the tolerance on this difference, and can be passed.

Anyone intending to undertake a serious piece of calculation should
realize that adequate checking against *mistakes* is an essential part of any
satisfactory numerical process. No one, and no machine, is infallible, and
it may fairly be said that the ideal to aim at is not to avoid mistakes
entirely, but to find all mistakes that *are* made, and so free the work from
any *unidentified* mistakes. This of course is an ideal. It does not seem
possible to eliminate mistakes with absolute certainty; it is always possible that a mistake might be made in the check itself in such a way as
to cancel the effect of an error it was devised to find. But with properly
designed checking procedures and care in working, the probability of this
should be negligibly small.

Provision of adequate checks is not, however, to be regarded as an
excuse for mistakes or a justification of carelessness in carrying out the
details of numerical work. Location and diagnosis of a mistake, and
correction of the mistake itself and of subsequent calculations vitiated
by it, is often a time-consuming job, and a tiresome one at that; and
moreover, if mistakes are too frequent, the probability of a mistake in
a check masking a mistake which the check should detect may become

appreciable. Numerical work should always be done with care to avoid mistakes, and checks regarded as insurance against the occasional mistakes which may occur even in careful work.

Many calculations consist of the same group of arithmetical operations applied repeatedly to different data. For example, if it were required to evaluate the function y defined by

$$y = \tfrac{1}{2}x^2 + \frac{3}{5!}x^5 + \frac{3 \cdot 6}{8!}x^8 + \frac{3 \cdot 6 \cdot 9}{11!}x^{11} + \dots \qquad (1.3)$$

for a set of values of x, say $x = -3\cdot0(0\cdot1)3\cdot0$, by evaluating and summing the separate terms of the series, the process of calculating y is the same for each value of x (except that for the smaller values of x more terms of the series are negligible and do not have to be evaluated explicitly). Such a systematic set of calculations is easier to check than one in which no step is similar to any other. A *single* value of the function y would be difficult to check adequately; a systematic set of values can be checked comparatively easily. In this case, for instance, a check might be based on the fact that y defined by (1.3) is a solution of the differential equation $y'' = 1 + xy$ (for an example, see § 3.3), but use of such a check depends on the behaviour of y *as a function of* x, and is not applicable to a single isolated value of y.

Mistakes in such a calculation are of two kinds, systematic (that is, the same mistake is made at the same point in each repetition of the sequence of arithmetical operations) and random. These can be illustrated from one method of evaluating the above series (1.3). Suppose the $(n+1)$th term is evaluated by multiplying the nth by $x^3/(3n+1)(3n+2)$; then

$$\text{(third term)} = (x^3/56) \times \text{(second term)},$$

and the denominator here might be taken as 54 instead of 56 throughout the whole calculation for all values of x; this would be a systematic mistake. On the other hand, one too many or one too few zeros between the decimal point and the first significant figure might be taken in a single one of the terms of the series for a single value of x; this would be a random mistake.

It is recognized by those with extensive experience of numerical work that there are two kinds of random mistake which are particularly easy to make. One is an interchange of adjacent digits; for example, 28575 may be read or recorded as 25875. The other is repeating the wrong digit in a number in which two adjacent digits are the same; for example 36609 may be read or written as 33609 or 36009. The error introduced by a mistake of the first of these kinds is always a multiple of 9 in terms of the less significant of the two interchanged digits as unit; this may often help in locating and identifying a mistake of this kind. These are not, of course, the only kinds of mistakes that can be made: but if a check indicates the presence of a random mistake, knowledge that it is likely to be of one of these kinds may assist in diagnosing it.

In the calculation of the function y defined by (1.3) by evaluation of the series, the calculations for different values of x are independent, so that a mistake in the calculation for one value of x does not affect those for later values of x.

But in many calculations, such as a calculation of this same function y by numerical integration of the differential equation $y'' = 1 + xy$ satisfied by it, a mistake at one stage vitiates all subsequent work. In such a case, it is important to have a *current* check on the work as it progresses rather than only an overall check carried out when the calculation is completed, otherwise the amount of work that has to be repeated if a mistake is made may become very considerable. All the time spent on work subsequently found to be vitiated by a mistake is just wasted, and a few experiences of this kind may be found severely discouraging, although really the moral should be simply that an adequate current check is needed.

One kind of 'check' is so inadequate as to be almost worthless, namely, repetition of a calculation by the same individual that did it originally. It is much too easy to make the same mistake twice; and indeed it may be that having made a mistake once, one is conditioned to make it again on repeating the work. An *independent* repetition of the work by a second individual is better than no check, but should not be regarded as adequate. The only really satisfactory check is one which obtains or verifies a result by *a different sequence of arithmetical operations, or a sequence involving different numbers, from that by which it was obtained*. For example, values of $\cosh x$ and $\sinh x$ interpolated from tables may be checked by use of the identity $\cosh^2 x - \sinh^2 x = 1$ (this does not check that they are not both interpolated for the wrong value of x, but this can probably be checked in some other way, depending on the rest of the calculation for which values of $\cosh x$ and $\sinh x$ are wanted); and the values of y calculated from the series (1.3) can be checked by use of the differential equation satisfied by y.

1.4. Arrangement of work

In most numerical work, a working sheet will be used for recording data and intermediate results of the calculation. A clear and orderly arrangement of this working sheet is a great help both in avoiding mistakes and in locating and correcting any that do happen to be made. Numerical work should not be done on odd scraps of rough paper, but laid out systematically and in such a way as to show how the intermediate and final results were obtained; and the numbers entered on the work sheet should be written neatly and legibly. Use of ruled paper is a help in keeping the layout of the work neat and clear. It is advisable to use loose sheets rather than a book since it is rather easy to make mistakes in copying from one page to another of a book; with loose sheets the number to be copied from one sheet, and the place to which it is to be copied on another, can more easily be brought close together, and the copy made and checked more easily.

For work of any permanent value, it is advisable to record on the working sheet enough explanation of the different entries, and how they were obtained, for the working to be followed after the lapse of a period of years.

1.5. Accuracy and precision

In contexts in which numerical work is carried out in connexion with scientific and technical problems, we are often concerned with the numerical solution of one or a set of algebraic, differential, or integral equations. Then it may be convenient to distinguish between the accuracy to which the equations, or data used in obtaining a solution of them, represent the real situation to which they refer, and the accuracy to which the results of the numerical work represent the solution of these equations with these data, supposed exact. The latter is sometimes distinguished by being called the 'precision' or 'nominal accuracy' of the numerical work.

Calculations are often carried out deliberately to a nominal accuracy known or expected to be higher than the accuracy of the approximations made in deriving the equations, or higher than that of the data used in their solution. There are several reasons why this may be done. We may be interested in the differences between the results of observation and of calculation, whether for the purpose of assessing the accuracy to which the equations do give an account of the observations, or in order to analyse these differences so as to derive more accurate equations or data to use in them. Then we want to be sure that the difference between the results of observation and of calculation are significant, and are not merely consequences of the limited nominal accuracy of the calculations.

Or we may want to determine the difference between two solutions of the equations with different values of some parameters, and to obtain this difference we may have to calculate the separate solutions to a nominal accuracy higher than that of the data. Or the results may be only intermediate results on which some extensive interpolation, perhaps in two or three variables, is going to be carried out. Both for the interpolation process and for checking purposes, it is then desirable that these intermediate results should be smooth and of a nominal accuracy higher than required in the final results.

In a hand calculation, however, greater nominal accuracy means more work, more writing in recording intermediate results, more possibilities of mistakes, and a longer time for the calculation. It is advisable, therefore, to watch lest the calculation is being carried to an unnecessarily high nominal accuracy. In this connexion a warning may be given concerning the use of desk machines. Since with a desk machine it is possible to work to eight or ten figures, there is a tendency to get into a habit of working with eight or ten figures when four or five would be adequate. This is bad practice, and a habit which the serious student of numerical work should avoid for his own sake.

II

THE TOOLS OF NUMERICAL WORK AND HOW TO USE THEM

2.1. The main tools of numerical work

FOR carrying out the numerical details of a calculation there are four main kinds of tools:

(*a*) Desk machines.　　　　(*c*) Slide rule.

(*b*) Tables.　　　　　　　(*d*) Graph paper.

Of these the first and second are much the most important.

2.2. Desk machines

A desk calculating machine is the most important single tool for numerical work and anyone intending to study numerical analysis seriously should become familiar enough with the main kinds to use them with facility, without more deliberate thought for the details of operating the machine than a good typist gives to the operation of individual keys of the typewriter.

There are several kinds of desk machine, some being primarily adding machines whereas others have facilities for multiplication; the former are sometimes called 'adding machines' as distinct from 'calculating machines' to emphasize this feature. The latter are the more important and will be considered first; adding machines are considered in § 2.26. Of the calculating machines some are considerably different in appearance and operation from others, but all are broadly similar in general principle. All have four main components:

(i) A setting mechanism by which a number can be set on the machine.

(ii) A register in which results of additions, subtractions, and multiplications are accumulated; this will be called the 'accumulator'; other names for it are 'result register' and 'product register'.

(iii) A counting register, sometimes called 'multiplier register', on which a count is kept of the number of additions or subtractions made.

(iv) An operating handle (in hand machines) or key-operated switch (in electrically-driven machines).

The setting mechanism and registers have means for setting them to zero; this is called 'clearing'.

Three kinds of desk calculating machines are illustrated in Figs. 1, 2, and 3. Three different kinds of setting mechanisms are represented in these three machines, and this is the main reason for the difference in appearance between them.

On the Brunsviga (Fig. 1), the setting mechanism consists of a series of levers, one for each digital position, each lever having ten positions corresponding to the decimal digits 0–9. On the Marchant (Fig. 2) the setting mechanism consists of a keyboard on which there is a set of nine keys, corresponding to the digits 1–9, in a column in each digital position; a number is set by pressing the appropriate key in each column. On the Facit (Fig. 3) there is a keyboard of only ten setting keys, corresponding to the digits 0–9; a number is set by pressing these keys in an order corresponding to the order of the digits in the number, beginning with the most significant.

The accumulator can be traversed relative to the setting mechanism, so that the least significant digital position of the adding mechanism corresponds to different digital positions of the accumulator. Shifting the accumulator one place to the *right* corresponds to multiplication by 10.

On all these machines multiplication is carried out by repeated addition and shifting. Machines which carry out multiplication directly, by use of a built-in multiplication table, have been constructed, but some machines carrying out multiplication by repeated addition are now so fast that, for work in which numbers are supplied manually to the machine, there is little purpose in making machines using direct multiplication.

On hand-operated machines, addition is carried out by rotating the handle through one turn in one direction (clockwise, looking along the handle towards the body of the machine) and subtraction by rotating it through one turn in the other direction. Most machines have a lock on the handle so that once a turn has been started it must be completed, and often have mechanical interlocks to prevent incorrect operation. On an electrically-driven machine the rotation is supplied by an electric motor instead of directly by the operator's hand, and the motor is controlled by a set of key-operated switches.

This is not the place for an account either of the internal mechanism or of the details of operation of different machines; the operating procedure is given in booklets supplied with the machine or obtainable from the makers or agents, but can perhaps be best acquired from personal demonstration by someone already familiar with the machine. The

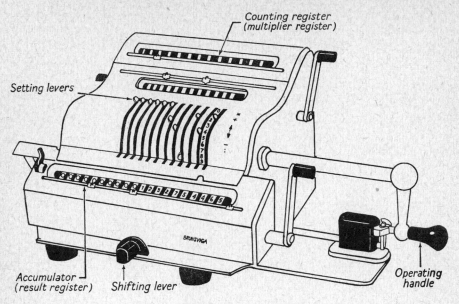

FIG. 1. Brunsviga (hand-operated).

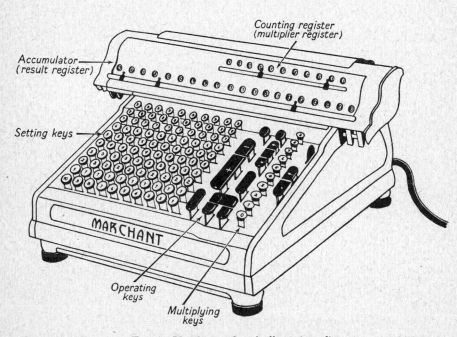

FIG. 2. Marchant (electrically operated).

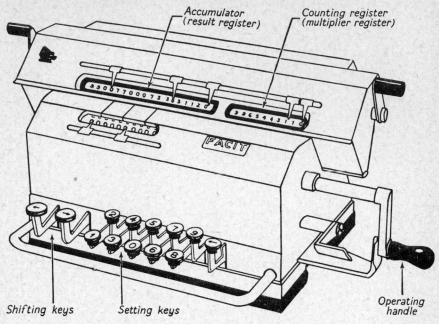

Fig. 3. Facit (hand-operated model).

following sections deal with some general points of procedure applicable to most machines.

2.21. Addition and subtraction

Addition is carried out by setting the addend on the setting levers or keys and turning the handle once positively, or on an electric machine by pressing the $+$ key or by multiplying by 1 with the shift-control set to 'non-shift'; on some machines the latter procedure is necessary when it is required to hold the number set, since this is cleared after addition when the $+$ key is used. The number set up is then added to the content of the accumulator. The position of the decimal point needs watching if the number of digits after the decimal point is different in the addend and in the content of the accumulator. Decimal-point markers are furnished on all machines (their form is different on different machines); in single arithmetical operations it is often unnecessary to use them, but they are very useful in helping to keep the position of the decimal point correct in carrying out sequences of operations on the machine without writing down intermediate results, as is sometimes possible.

Subtraction is carried out similarly to addition, except that the handle is turned in the opposite direction. The result of subtracting a greater number from a smaller is as follows. Let $\bar{a}$ be written for a contribution $(-a)$ in any digital position, so that, for example, the number 90 can be written $1\bar{1}0$ and the number 88 as $1\bar{1}\bar{2}$. Then the negative number -23 (for example) which is

$$-23 = -1{,}000+977 = -10{,}000+9{,}977 = -1{,}000{,}000+999{,}977$$

can be written

$$-23 = \bar{1}997 = \bar{1}9977 = \bar{1}999977, \text{ etc.} \tag{2.1}$$

The number 999...99977, to the full capacity of the accumulator of the machine, is called the 'complement' of 23, or the 'complementary form' of the number -23; it can be regarded as a representation of the number -23 in the form (2.1), with the digit $\bar{1}$ to the left of the most significant digital position of the accumulator. In a number in complementary form, the digits to the right of the row of 9's are the significant figures.

Negative results appear in such a complementary form, and, in some machines, a carry-over from the most significant digital position of the accumulator is indicated by the ringing of a bell.

Recording of negative numbers will usually be in terms of sign and *modulus*, not in their complementary form. The translation from the complementary form to the modulus can be done in two ways:

(i) Translate mentally by subtracting each digit of the complement *except the last* from 9 and subtracting the last from 10. Set the result on the setting levers or keys, add into the accumulator, and *verify that the content of the accumulator is now zero*. This checks the translation and should *always* be done before the result is recorded. If the number in complementary form is wanted in the accumulator for further numbers to be added to it, it can be recovered by subtracting the number on the setting levers.

(ii) Transfer the number in complementary form from the accumulator to the setting levers or keys (see § 2.22), and subtract from zero. This will give some spurious 9's on the extreme left of the accumulator, but it will be easy to distinguish these from the significant figures of the result.

2.22. Transfer from accumulator to setting keys or levers

In some calculations it is necessary to transfer to the setting levers or keys a number formed in the accumulator as the result of previous calculations. For example, in the calculation of a continued product, an intermediate product formed in the accumulator has to be transferred to the setting levers or keys to be ready for multiplication by the next factor; and as already mentioned in the previous section, such a transfer is a step in one method of obtaining the modulus of a negative number expressed in complementary form.

Some machines are provided with facilities for direct transfer from accumulator to setting levers or keys. In using one that is not, the following procedure should be followed.

Copy on to the setting keys or levers the number to be transferred, *subtract it from the content of the accumulator, and verify that the result is zero.* This checks that the number has been copied correctly on to the setting mechanism, and this check should *always* be used.

On an electric machine, the subtraction must be done in such a way as *not* to clear the keyboard after subtraction.

2.23. Multiplication

Multiplication is carried out by repeated addition in each digital position of the multiplier, the accumulator being traversed one place right or left between successive digits of the multiplier. In most cases it is best to carry out multiplication starting with the *most* significant digit of the multiplier, as then the order of the digits is the natural one, in which it is easy to remember the multiplier while the multiplication is being carried out.

In a few machines, mainly older models, in which the mechanism for carrying-over in addition does not extend to the full capacity of the accumulator, this procedure will occasionally lead to incorrect results. The best way to test whether a machine has this objectionable feature is to subtract 1 from 0 with the accumulator in the extreme left position, and see if the carry-over produces 9's right to the extreme left-hand digital positions of the accumulator. If not, the best way of avoiding trouble is not to use such a machine; but if none other is available the possibility of incorrect results from this cause must be kept in mind. In multiplication they can be avoided by starting from the least significant digit of the multiplier, but this is inconvenient as it means taking the digits in the opposite order to that in which they will naturally be remembered.

Appreciable time can be saved in multiplication on a hand machine by a procedure known as 'short-cutting'. If, as in § 2.21, a bar over a digit is used to represent a negative digit *in that digital position only*, we have, for example:

$$\left.\begin{array}{ll} 183 = 2\bar{2}3 & (\text{l.h. } 12, \text{ r.h. } 7) \\ 2879 = 3\bar{1}2\bar{1} & (\text{l.h. } 26, \text{ r.h. } 7) \\ 369175 = 4\bar{3}\bar{1}2\bar{2}\bar{5} & (\text{l.h. } 31, \text{ r.h. } 17) \end{array}\right\}. \qquad (2.2)$$

Multiplication by one of these numbers can be carried out by using as multiplier the number in the form given on the right-hand side of the equalities in (2.2), and using both positive and negative directions of turning the handle; an appreciable number of turns may be saved in this way; this is the process of 'short-cutting'. The numbers of turns taken to carry out a multiplication by each of the numbers in the example (2.2), in its form on the left-hand side and in its form on the right-hand side of the equality sign, are shown in brackets. 'Short-cutting' should be used on digits over 5, and on a 5 if flanked on either side by a digit over 5; for users of hand machines, it should become the natural way of carrying out multiplications; it needs a little practice at first to become proficient and reliable, but ease in using it is certainly worth attaining.

In a few old models of machines, which have not carry-over (sometimes called 'tens-transmission') mechanism in the multiplier register, only the moduli of the individual digits are indicated (in some machines the negative digits are indicated in red). Such machines should be avoided, or, if they have to be used, short-cutting must be used with discretion and particular attention should be paid to checking.

Some electric machines are fitted with means by which multiplication by any digit of the multiplier and the succeeding shift of the accumulator can be carried out by pressing one of a set of ten keys; these machines are so fast that short-cutting is unnecessary. On others the complete multiplier can be set and transferred to a register, then the multiplicand set and the multiplication carried out automatically; in these machines the operator is not concerned at all with the process of multiplication by individual digits.

2.24. Division

Division can be carried out in three ways:

First, by multiplication by the reciprocal of the divisor. This is particularly useful when the result of the division is required to be in the accumulator, either in order to have further numbers added to it or for transfer to the setting levers or keys. In the other methods of division, the quotient appears in the multiplier register, and no machine has transfer facilities from there to the setting levers or keys; this transfer has to be done by hand and there is no adequate means of checking it, whereas if a result is in the accumulator its transfer to the setting levers or keys can be made mechanically or checked (see § 2.22).

Secondly, by successive subtraction, starting from the *most* significant digit. In this process, the dividend, if not already in the accumulator as a result of previous operations, is set and added into the accumulator which has previously been cleared. *The multiplier register must then be cleared* (this is automatic in the case of automatic division on some electrical machines); this is a step which is rather easily overlooked. The divisor is then set and subtracted in the most significant position until the remainder is less than the divisor; the accumulator is then shifted one place left, and the subtraction followed by a shift is repeated. The result appears in the multiplier register. In order to make full use of the capacity of this register, the divisor should normally be set in such a position on the setting levers or keys that the quotient has a non-zero digit in the extreme left digital position of the multiplier register.

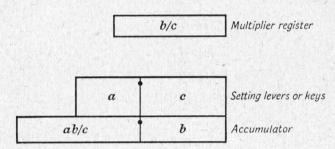

FIG. 4. (Dots • show decimal-point markers used as separators.)

Thirdly, by successive addition (sometimes called division by 'building up'). In this process the accumulator is cleared, the divisor set on the setting levers or keys, and *multiplied* by such a number x that the result in the accumulator is the dividend. This multiplication is done by a process which is essentially one of trial, but can be quite fast, and in which short-cutting can be used to some extent. It is useful when the same divisor is used with a number of dividends, as then this divisor can be set up once for all and need not be disturbed to set the new dividend. It is sometimes also useful for forming ab/c in one operation, if the number of digits involved is not too large. If a is set at one side of the setting mechanism and c at the other, and b/c is found by building up c to b, then the handle has been turned a number of times corresponding to (b/c), and a has been multiplied by that number. The arrangement is shown diagrammatically in Fig. 4. Another application of the process of division by building up is in the calculation of $|a/b|$, where a is a negative number standing in the accumulator (in complementary form) as the result of a previous calculation. If $|b|$ is set, and the content of the accumulator built up to zero, the multiplier register will read $|a/b|$.

Most electric machines are provided with facilities for automatic division; the dividend is placed in the accumulator, either by adding it in after clearing the accumulator, or by forming it there as a result of previous calculations. The divisor is then set and the 'automatic division' key pressed; the division then proceeds without further manipulation on the part of the operator.

2.25. Other calculations

With a machine of sufficient capacity, and numbers of a few digits, it is possible to do two calculations simultaneously, one with numbers set on the extreme left and the other with numbers set on the extreme right of the setting levers or keyboard; an example has already been given in the calculation of ab/c in one operation. The following are two other examples:

(i) $\sum\limits_{n} a_n$ *and* $\sum\limits_{n} a_n b_n$ *simultaneously.* Set 1 on the extreme left and the numbers b_n successively on the extreme right; for each b_n multiply by the corresponding a_n. Then in the accumulator $\sum\limits_{n} a_n$ is formed on the left and $\sum\limits_{n} a_n b_n$ on the right.

(ii) $\sum\limits_{n} a_n^2$ *and* $\sum\limits_{n} a_n b_n$ *simultaneously.* Set a_n on the extreme left and b_n on the extreme right, multiply by a_n, and repeat for each value of n. Then in the accumulator $\sum\limits_{n} a_n^2$ is formed on the left and $\sum\limits_{n} a_n b_n$ on the right. If the multiplier register is *not* cleared between each multiplication, $\sum\limits_{n} a_n$ is accumulated there, but this is hardly satisfactory, as it is then impossible to check after each multiplication that the right multiplier has been used. An overall check can be provided by setting the pairs of numbers a_n, b_n in succession and multiplying each pair by the corresponding b_n. This would give $\sum\limits_{n} a_n b_n$ and $\sum\limits_{n} b_n^2$; the latter is likely to be wanted in contexts in which $\sum\limits_{n} a_n^2$ and $\sum\limits_{n} a_n b_n$ are wanted, and the agreement of the two values of $\sum\limits_{n} a_n b_n$ would check that the right multiplier values had been used in each calculation; it does not check the setting of the values of a_n in the first, or of b_n in the second, of the calculations.

2.26. Adding machines

In adding machines the position of the accumulator relative to the keyboard is fixed, and there is no multiplier register. Most of them have keyboard setting, and many have electrical operation controlled through a set of keys.

The most useful of these machines are those which make a printed record of each number added into the accumulator. There are two operations by which a total standing in the accumulator can be printed. If a key marked 'total' is operated, the total is printed and the accumulator is *cleared*; if a key marked 'sub-total' is operated the total is printed and retained in the accumulator. A particular application of the latter operation is in the evaluation of an integral $\int_a^x f(w)\, dw$ as a function of its upper limit x, by successive addition of contributions from successive intervals of x. After each contribution is added, a sub-total is taken, then the next contribution is set and added. The printed record consists of a sequence of entries, alternately contributions to the integral and values of the integral itself. The contributions actually used by the machine can then be checked against the values which should have been set.

It should be a convention in using a machine of this kind that it is left with the accumulator clear; but in case this has not been done, it is advisable, before using it, always to ensure that the accumulator is clear by taking a total.

2.3. Mathematical tables

Mathematical tables form a very important aid to numerical work. Many calculations involve the use of values of standard functions such as exponentials, logarithms, circular functions, Bessel functions, the gamma function, and though it would be possible to calculate the required function values from scratch as they were wanted, this would usually lengthen the calculation so much as to make it impracticable. In fact, if tables of these functions did not already exist, it would often be worth constructing them as a first step in the calculations for which values of these functions are wanted.

The most important tables are the following:

> *Comrie and Milne-Thomson's Standard 4-Figure Tables*; *Chambers's 6-Figure Mathematical Tables* (1948-9), edited by Comrie; *Barlow's Tables of Squares, Cubes, Reciprocals, etc.*, edited by Comrie; *Interpolation and Allied Tables* (H.M. Stationery Office).

The first two of these include tables of circular functions for argument in radians, and also tables of inverse trigonometric and hyperbolic functions; of the two volumes of Chambers's 6-figure tables, the second with so-called 'natural' values is much the more useful for work with machines.

Interpolation and Allied Tables contains a great deal of information on formulae and methods for interpolation and other numerical processes and is a very useful and inexpensive booklet.

For functions other than the elementary functions, the following are useful:

> Dale, *5-Figure Tables of Mathematical Functions*; Jahnke-Emde, *Tables of Functions with Formulae and Graphs*; British Association *Tables of Bessel and Airy Functions*.

The amount of tabular material available in various volumes of tables and scattered among various journals is very considerable. The nature and location of most of this material published up to the end of 1944 has been classified and tabulated in an *Index of Mathematical Tables*† which is a most valuable volume and should be known to all undertaking any extensive numerical work, or even small calculations involving functions other than the elementary functions, since if a function has been tabulated, knowledge of this fact and an adequate reference will usually avoid duplicating the calculation of it.

An important source of information, particularly regarding recent or current work on tabulation of functions, is the journal *Mathematical Tables and Aids to Computation* (generally referred to as *M.T.A.C.*).

In describing a table, it is convenient to have a compact notation for specifying the range and interval of the argument. The notation $x = x_1(\delta x)x_2$ has come to be adopted as the standard abbreviated form for 'for values of x from x_1 to x_2 inclusive at intervals δx'. The notation mD or nS is often used for a table to m decimals, or n significant figures.

2.31. Critical tables

Most tables give the values of the function $f(x)$, rounded off to a certain number of decimals, for a sequence of equally spaced exact values of the argument x. Occasionally another type of table is more convenient, namely, one giving the *range* of x for which the function $f(x)$, rounded off to a certain number of decimals, has a specified value. Such a table is called a *critical table*, and is convenient for slowly varying functions, and also for functions which have a limited range and for which accuracy in the last figure is important; in using a critical table no interpolation is required, and the possibility of an error of a unit in the last figure in interpolation in an ordinary table is avoided.

As an example, consider a table of $\frac{1}{6}x(x-\frac{1}{2})(x-1)$, which occurs in a

---

† By A. Fletcher, J. C. P. Miller, and L. Rosenhead (Scientific Computing Service, Ltd., London 1946). A second edition is in preparation.

formula for non-linear interpolation, as a function of x. A portion of a critical table of this function to four decimals is as follows:

x	$f(x)$
0·1621	
	+0·0077
0·1691	
	0·0078
0·1777	
	0·0079
0·1897	
	0·0080
0·2334	
	0·0079
0·2462	

The values of $f(x)$ are on lines intermediate between those on which the values of x stand, and the values of x between which a value of $f(x)$ stands mark the limits of the range of x for which that is the rounded value of $f(x)$. These values of x are rounded values of the inverse function $f^{-1}(y)$ for values of $y = f(x)$ halfway between the tabular values. For example, the above table indicates that for values of x between 0·1777 and 0·1897 the function $f(x)$ has the value +0·0079 to four decimals; and the value of x for $f(x) = 0·00785$ is 0·1777 to four decimals.

It is a convention in critical tables that if x has exactly the tabular value, the value of $f(x)$ to be taken is that standing *above* the line on which $f(x)$ stands; a reminder of this convention is often given in such tables by the words 'in critical cases ascend'.

2.32. Auxiliary variables in tables

An important aspect of mathematical tables is the use of auxiliary variables to simplify interpolation. This is especially important (i) in the neighbourhood of a singularity, where the ordinary interpolation formulae, applied directly to the function values, cease to be valid, (ii) for large values of the argument, and (iii) for oscillating functions when the table has to cover a large number of periods of the oscillation. Use of auxiliary variables may both simplify interpolation and lessen the amount of material which has to be calculated and printed to provide a useful table.

The most usual step is to tabulate an auxiliary function, but in some cases an auxiliary independent variable may be used instead or in addition. The following are examples of the tabulation of auxiliary functions:

(i) $\log\{(\sin x)/x\}$ and $\log\{(\tan x)/x\}$ for small x, in place of logsin x and logtan x which are infinite at $x = 0$ and cannot be interpolated by standard formulae near $x = 0$.

(ii) If $f(x)$ is oscillatory, it may be possible to determine an 'amplitude function' $A(x)$ and a 'phase function' $\phi(x)$ such that

$$f(x) = A(x)\cos\{\phi(x)\}$$

and that $A(x)$ and $\phi'(x)$ vary much more slowly than $f(x)$. Then $A(x)$ and $\phi(x)$ can be tabulated at wider intervals than $f(x)$, and interpolation of $A(x)$ and $\phi(x)$ is easier than that of $f(x)$ itself. This is particularly convenient when two functions can be expressed as the real and imaginary parts of $A(x)\exp\{i\phi(x)\}$. An important example is provided by the Bessel functions, for which

$$A(x) = x^{\frac{1}{2}}[\{J_n(x)\}^2 + \{Y_n(x)\}^2]^{\frac{1}{2}} = x^{\frac{1}{2}}|H_n^{(1)}(x)|$$

and $\qquad \phi(x) = \tan^{-1}[Y_n(x)/J_n(x)] = \arg[H_n^{(1)}(x)]$

form a convenient pair of auxiliary functions except for small values of x.

An example of the joint use of auxiliary functions and an auxiliary independent variable is provided by the elliptic integral

$$K(k) = \int_0^\pi (1 - k^2\sin^2\theta)^{-\frac{1}{2}}\, d\theta$$

near $k = 1$. If $k' = (1-k^2)^{\frac{1}{2}}$ and

$$K(k) = K_1\log(4/k') + K_2,$$

K_1 and K_2 are regular functions of k' near $k = 1$, and a convenient tabulation is K_1 and K_2 against k' as argument.

2.4. Slide rule

A slide rule is an instrument of limited accuracy, and of limited scope since it cannot easily be used for addition and subtraction; but within its limitations it is a valuable tool of numerical work. Two contexts in which it is particularly useful are the following:

(i) When a function is tabulated at intervals too large for linear interpolation between tabular values, more elaborate interpolation formula have to be used; these will be considered in Chapter V. In many of these, the interpolated value is expressed as the sum of the value which would be obtained by linear interpolation, and some other terms which can be regarded as contribution to a 'correction' to this value. For some or all of these contributions, the accuracy attainable with a slide-rule may be adequate, and then it is a useful tool.

(ii) When in the solution of a linear differential equation a particular integral P and a complementary function C have been evaluated, and a small constant multiple of C, say γC, has to be added to P to give a solution satisfying specified conditions, the calculation of γC may often be carried out to adequate accuracy on a slide-rule. This is a quick calculation, because after a single setting of γ, all the values of γC can be read off without resetting.

As well as the usual straight slide-rule with a 10-inch scale, there is another form, with two cursors and a single scale in the form of a helix on a movable cylinder. In the Fuller slide-rule this scale is 50 feet long, and this enables an accuracy of 1 in 10,000 to be obtained without difficulty, and 1 in 20,000 with care. Such an instrument is cheap compared with a desk machine and may be found very useful in work for which its accuracy is adequate and in circumstances in which the cost of a desk machine is prohibitive. With one of these slide-rules and an adding machine much useful numerical work can be done, especially in contexts involving empirical or experimentally determined functions not specified to more than four- or five-figure accuracy.

2.5. Graph paper

Graph paper is more generally useful as a means of presenting results than as a tool for obtaining them. But there are occasions when it is useful as a means of doing calculations, e.g. for obtaining approximate results which can later be refined by more accurate methods.

Before being used for anything more than qualitative or the roughest of quantitative work, graph paper should be examined for uniformity of ruling. Paper ruled in two colours (e.g. blue for the main ruling, with red for every tenth line) should be examined for the registration of the two colours. Paper which is ruled with every fifth or tenth line thick should be examined to see that the intervals between the *centres* of the lines are uniform, and not the intervals between the *edges* of the lines, a remarkable fault in some papers.†

2.6. Other machines

There are other aids to numerical work of various kinds, but mostly large or special pieces of equipment which are unlikely to be available to most of those for whom this book is primarily intended. The more important may, however, be mentioned here.

First, there is the 'National' machine,‡ developed from an accounting machine. This is an adding machine with keyboard setting mechanism

---

† See Jeffreys and Jeffreys, *Methods of Mathematical Physics*, chap. 9.
‡ See, for example, L. J. Comrie, *Journ. Roy. Stat. Soc., Supplement*, **3** (1936), 87.

and six registers, with facilities for adding or subtracting the number set on the keyboard, or the number standing in any register, into any combination of registers. The mechanical arrangement for controlling these transfers is such that it can only be used effectively in calculations in which the same set of operations has to be repeated successively on different sets of numbers; but many calculations have just this character, and for such calculations this machine can be very valuable.

Secondly, there are two groups of machines for carrying out arithmetical operations on numbers represented by punchings on cards, the 'Hollerith' and 'Powers-Samas' machines. The main machines of each group are a 'tabulator' which is a multi-register adding machine with printing mechanism, a sorter, and a multiplying punch which can take a card with two numbers punched on it, and calculate and punch their product. The use of these machines, and the organization of calculations for them, is a special technique of its own,† and hardly appropriate for an introductory book like the present.

Thirdly, there are various high-speed automatic calculating machines which can carry out, automatically, long sequences of operations once they have been supplied with operating instructions in a suitably coded form. A short account of the principles of these machines and of the process of organizing calculations for them is given in Chapter XII.

2.7. The organization of a calculation

The organization of a calculation is represented diagrammatically in Fig. 5. There are three kinds of equipment the computer has to assist him; these are represented by rectangular blocks in the figure. One is a desk machine, another is a set of tables, and the third is the working sheet on which intermediate and final results will be recorded and on which should be written enough data to identify the calculation and to summarize the calculating procedure.

When the method for doing a calculation has been decided, the detailed process of carrying it out consists of (i) a sequence of arithmetical operations carried out on the machine, or perhaps on a slide-rule as auxiliary equipment, or mentally in the case of simple operations such as multiplication or division by 2 or addition of pairs of numbers, and (ii) transfer of numbers between the three blocks represented in Fig. 5. For example, suppose that in the course of a calculation it is required to obtain the value of $y \sin ax$ where a is a constant whose value has been entered in the work sheet as part of the data of the calculation, and x and y are

† See W. J. Eckert, *Punched Card Methods in Scientific Computation* (Columbia University, 1940).

numbers which have been calculated as intermediate results in the course of the calculation and noted on the working sheet. First x must be transferred to the machine and multiplied by a. The value of ax will probably be transferred to the working sheet for reference; this will be necessary if the machine is going to be used for interpolation of the value

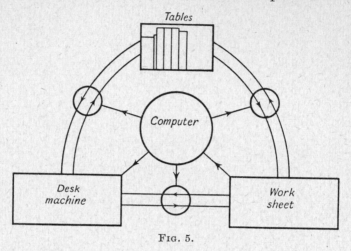

Fig. 5.

of $\sin(ax)$, since the value of ax in the accumulator will be lost in the process. The value of ax will certainly be used as argument in a table of sines, and if interpolation in this table is involved, a subsidiary calculation is necessary for that purpose. The value of $\sin(ax)$ will probably be recorded on the working sheet, and certainly transferred to the machine for the multiplication required to form $y \sin ax$.

The transfers and the arithmetical operations are controlled by the individual who is carrying out the calculation, who is represented by the large circle in Fig. 5; the controls he exerts are represented by directed lines from the controller to small circles representing control of the transfer of numbers, and to the desk machine. He also takes from the working sheet information about the arithmetical operations to be carried out and their sequence; this is represented by the directed line from the work sheet to the controller.

III

EVALUATION OF FORMULAE

3.1. The significance of formulae in numerical work

THE evaluation of a given formula is the simplest kind of problem in numerical analysis. In a sense most problems reduce to this, as the numerical work itself almost always consists in substituting particular numerical values into a process or sequence of operations which could be expressed in the form of a sequence of formulae to be evaluated, even if they are not explicitly so expressed. In most cases the real question of numerical analysis is, What is the best formula or set of formulae to evaluate in order to obtain the required result?, and it is with this question that we shall primarily be concerned in later chapters. But equally important questions for practical work are how to evaluate the formulae and how to check the results.

A formula for a calculation to be carried out numerically has a significance rather different from that of a formula in formal algebra or analysis. For example, the formula

$$y = (x^2+1)/2x \tag{3.1}$$

regarded as an algebraical formula states a *relation* between the quantities on the two sides of the sign of equality, and is completely equivalent to

$$x^2-2yx+1 = 0$$

or

$$x = y\pm(y^2-1)^{\frac{1}{2}}, \tag{3.2}$$

which are different ways of expressing the same relation. But formula (3.1) regarded as a formula for a numerical calculation specifies a *process* to be carried out for determining the value of y given the value of x, whereas formula (3.2) specifies a *process* to be carried out for determining the value of x given the value of y. These processes are different from one another, the data used in them are different and the results required are different. This aspect of a formula, as representing a *process* consisting of a set of operations to be carried out in a definite sequence, plays little part in formal analysis, but is fundamental in numerical work. Even the formulae

$$x = y-z \quad \text{and} \quad z = y-x$$

mean quite different things when regarded as specifications of numerical calculations to be carried out; and the process specified by the formula

$$y = \tfrac{1}{2}[x + (1/x)] \tag{3.3}$$

is different from that specified by formula (3.1).

A striking example is discussed in § 11.3, where it is shown that of two ways of writing the recurrence relation for the Bessel functions, namely,

$$J_{n+1}(x) = (2n/x)J_n(x) - J_{n-1}(x)$$

and

$$J_n(x) = (x/2n)[J_{n+1}(x) + J_{n-1}(x)]$$

which are formally completely equivalent (for $n > 0$, $x > 0$), the first specifies a numerical process which is quite impracticable as a general method for calculating $J_n(x)$ for $n > x > 0$, whereas the second gives a quite practicable iterative process.

There may be various ways of evaluating even simple formulae, and the best way may depend on the equipment available for carrying out the numerical work. For example, in the evaluation of $(abc...)/(uvw...)$ by means of a slide rule it is best to take multiplications and divisions alternately, expressed by writing this fraction in the form

$$[\{(a/u) \times b\}/v] \times c....$$

But with a desk machine it is best first to evaluate the denominator $D = uvw...$ and record this, then form the continued product $abc...$, and finally divide the result by D. In forming these continued products, no intermediate results need be written down; the only numbers to be recorded are D and the final result.

In using a machine it is worth while planning the calculation in such a way that as much as possible of the work is done on the machine without recording intermediate results, so as to reduce the amount of writing, with the possibilities of mistakes in recording and reading the written results, to a minimum demanded by the need for clarity in presentation of the calculation and for checking. Transfers from the counting register to the setting levers or keys should also be avoided if possible.

For example, if e^x were given, $2(\cosh x - 1)$ could be calculated from

$$2(\cosh x - 1) = e^x + (1/e^x) - 2;$$

this would require a reciprocal to be calculated, recorded, and reset on the machine (or at least transferred from the counting register to the setting levers or keys). But if it is calculated from

$$2(\cosh x - 1) = (e^x - 1)^2/e^x,$$

this can all be done by a sequence of operations on the machine alone;

it also has the advantage that for small x it does not calculate the result as the small difference of two relatively large quantities.

3.2. Evaluation of polynomials

Expressions consisting of a number of additions and multiplications can usually be evaluated in various ways, of which the best to use in any case may depend on particular features of that case. For example, a polynomial

$$y = a_0 x^n + a_1 x^{n-1} + \ldots + a_{n-1} x + a_n \qquad (3.4)$$

may be evaluated by calculating the separate terms and adding. When x has a simple numerical value ($r = 1, 2,$ or 10 for example) this may be the best method, especially if the coefficients are small integers. If this method is used for evaluating a polynomial both for positive and for negative values of x, a convenient procedure is first to sum separately all the terms involving odd powers of x and all those involving even powers of x, for positive values of x only, then for each value of x to add and subtract these two sums.

If x has not a simple numerical value it may be better to write

$$y = [\{(a_0 x + a_1)x + a_2\}x + a_3]x + \ldots \qquad (3.5)$$

and carry out an addition and a multiplication alternately as indicated by this expression. That is, construct the sequence y_j defined by

$$y_0 = a_0, \qquad y_j = y_{j-1} x + a_j \quad (j > 0); \qquad (3.6)$$

the result required is y_n. This process requires n multiplications and n additions, and no recording of intermediate results. Care is necessary with the decimal point; use of the decimal point markers is a great help here.

The process for checking the results will depend on the calculation of which the evaluation of the polynomial forms part. It is unlikely that just a single value of a polynomial will be wanted; the evaluation of the polynomial is much more likely to form part of a larger calculation, which may well include means of checking the value obtained for the polynomial.

If a set of values y of a polynomial (3.4) for a set of values of x is calculated, then

$$\sum y = a_0 \sum x^n + a_1 \sum x^{n-1} + \ldots \qquad (3.7)$$

where the sum is over all values of x for which the polynomial has been calculated. One way of checking such a set of values of y is to evaluate the right hand side of (3.7) and compare the result with $\sum y$; the results should not differ by more than the tolerance for rounding errors.

We shall see later (§4.42) that if a polynomial has simple coefficients and is of not too high order, its values for a set of equally-spaced values of x can be obtained simply and conveniently by a sequence of additions, without any multiplication at all.

3.3. Evaluation of power series

To evaluate the sum of a power series

$$y = a_0 + a_1 x + a_2 x^2 + \ldots \tag{3.8}$$

it is often most convenient to write each term as a multiple of the preceding one, thus:

$$y = a_0 + \left(\frac{a_1}{a_0} x\right) a_0 + \left(\frac{a_2}{a_1} x\right) a_1 x + \left(\frac{a_3}{a_2} x\right) a_2 x^2 + \ldots$$

and to evaluate each term from the previous one by the appropriate multiplications. Series containing odd powers only or even powers only can be treated similarly. If several values of y, at equal intervals of x, are calculated, evaluation of the finite differences (§4.2) of the values of y probably provides the best check.

Example: To evaluate

$$y = \tfrac{1}{2}x^2 + \frac{1}{2.4.5} x^5 + \frac{1}{2.4.5.7.8} x^8 + \frac{1}{2.4.5.7.8.10.11} x^{11} + \ldots$$

to six decimals for $x = 1 \cdot 0(0 \cdot 1)1 \cdot 4$.

It is convenient to write this

$$y = \tfrac{1}{2}x^2 \left[1 + \frac{1}{4.5} x^3 + \frac{1}{4.5.7.8} x^6 + \frac{1}{4.5.7.8.10.11} x^9 + \ldots\right] \tag{3.9}$$

and first to sum the series in the square bracket and then multiply the sum by $\tfrac{1}{2}x^2$.

If the ratios of successive coefficients in the series are written $b_1, b_2, \ldots$ then

$$(n\text{th term}) = b_n x^3 [(n-1)\text{th term}]; \tag{3.10}$$

the values of the first few b's are

$$b_1 = \frac{1}{4.5} = \frac{1}{20}, \qquad b_2 = \frac{1}{7.8} = \frac{1}{56}, \qquad b_3 = \frac{1}{10.11} = \frac{1}{110}, \ldots,$$

and in general

$$b_n = \frac{1}{(3n+1)(3n+2)}.$$

The denominator in this fraction is a quadratic function of n, hence the second differences (see §4.2) of its values are constant, and this can be used to check these values:

20		56		110		182		272		380
	36		54		72		90		108	
		18		18		18		18		

A similar check can usually be applied if the ratios of successive coefficients can be expressed as the ratio of the two polynomials of low degree in n. The work can conveniently be arranged as follows:

x	.	.	.	1·0	1·1	1·2	1·3	1·4
x^3	.	.	.	1·000	1·331	1·728	2·197	2·744
		b_n						
				1·000000,00	1·000000,00	1·000000,00	1·000000,00	1·000000,00
$1/20 =$ ·05								
				0·050000,00	0·066550,00	0·086400,00	0·109850,00	0·137200,00
$1/56 =$ ·01785714								
				892,86	1581,75	2666,06	4309,65	6722,80
$1/110 =$ ·00909091								
				8,12	19,14	41,88	86,08	167,70
$1/182 =$ ·005495								
				0,04	0,14	0,40	1,04	2,53
$1/272 =$ ·003676								
				0,00	0,00	0,00	0,01	0,03
sum	.	.	.	1·050901,02	1·068151,03	1·089108,34	1·114246,78	1·144093,06
$\frac{1}{2}x^2$	.	.	. 0·5	0·605	0·72	0·845	0·98	
y (to six decimals)		0·525451		0·646231	0·784158	0·941539	1·121211	
$\delta^2 y$	.	.	.	17147	19454	22291		
$y'' = 1 + xy$	.	.	1·52545	1·71085	1·94099	2·22400	2·56970	
$\delta^2 y''$	.	.	.	4474	5287	6269		
$\delta^4 y''$	.	.	.		169			
$y'' + \frac{1}{12}\delta^2 y'' - \frac{1}{240}\delta^4 y''$				1·7145$_8$	1·9453$_9$	2·2292$_2$		

Notes: (i) The entries in the third to eighth lines are the values of the terms in the square bracket in formula (3.9). Each is calculated from the preceding one by formula (3.10); if the decimal values of b_n given on the left are used, these terms can be calculated entirely by multiplication and transfer.

(ii) To obtain six decimals in the final result, it is advisable to keep eight decimals in the individual terms, that is, to retain two guarding figures.

(iii) The function y defined by the series (3.9) satisfies the equation $y'' = 1 + xy$. The second differences (see § 4.2) of y can be calculated from the values of y (see § 4.45) and compared with the values calculated from y'' by formula (4.19); this provides a close check on the results.

3.4. Kinds of formulae to avoid

There are two kinds of formulae to be avoided if possible, namely those that express the result required as

   (i) the ratio of two small numbers,

   (ii) the difference of two large, nearly equal, numbers.

When one or other of these situations occurs, it often, though not always, means that the method adopted for calculating the result is not the most suitable, and it is usually worth examining whether there is a more suitable alternative.

The following are some examples:

(a) *Exponential extrapolation*

Three numbers y_0, y_1, and y_2 are known to differ from the required result Y by amounts which are in geometrical progression; to find Y (see Fig. 6). This process is called 'exponential extrapolation'; it is useful in some methods of successive approximation (see § 9.32).

Since y_0-Y, y_1-Y, and y_2-Y are in geometrical progression,
$$(y_2-Y)/(y_1-Y) = (y_1-Y)/(y_0-Y)$$
and solution for Y gives
$$Y = (y_0 y_2 - y_1^2)/(y_2 - 2y_1 + y_0). \tag{3.11}$$
But if $y_0 = y_1 = y_2$ this gives $Y = 0/0$ which is useless for numerical work; and if y_0, y_1, and y_2 are only slightly different from Y, it gives Y as the ratio of two small numbers, the numerator and denominator being both of order (y_0-Y).

But if Y is written as the best approximation y_2 plus a correction, thus:
$$Y = y_2 - (y_2 - y_1)^2/(y_2 - 2y_1 + y_0), \tag{3.12}$$
the numerator of the 'correction' is of order $(y_0-Y)^2$ whereas the denominator is of order (y_0-Y); the correction is therefore of order (y_0-Y) and is zero in the case $y_0 = y_1 = y_2$, and is small if y_0 is nearly equal to Y. Its evaluation gives no trouble.

This illustrates the way in which two expressions, formally equivalent, may be very different when assessed from the point of view of the ease of practical numerical evaluation.

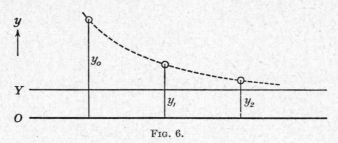

FIG. 6.

(b) *Solution of a quadratic equation when the ratio of the roots is large*

Let x_1 be the larger and x_2 the smaller of the roots of the equation
$$x^2 - 18x + 1 = 0.$$
Use of the standard general formula for the root gives
$$x_1, x_2 = 9 \pm \sqrt{80}. \tag{3.13}$$
If $\sqrt{80}$ is taken to four decimals (five figures) this gives
$$x_1, x_2 = 17{\cdot}9443,\ 0{\cdot}0557.$$
Here x_2 is obtained as the small difference of two relatively large numbers 9 and $\sqrt{80} = 8{\cdot}9443$; the first two significant figures in the value of $\sqrt{80}$ are lost, and from a five-figure value only a three-figure result is obtained.

On the other hand if x_2 is obtained not from (3.13) but from the relation (for this equation) $x_1 x_2 = 1$, the value of x_2 is obtained to full five-figure accuracy without requiring that $\sqrt{80}$ should be obtained to any greater accuracy than for $\dot{x}_1$. Here again we see a marked difference, from the point of view of numerical evaluation, between two formally equivalent formulae.

3.5. Evaluation of a function in the neighbourhood of a value of the argument at which it becomes indeterminate

In the neighbourhood of a value of the argument at which a function becomes indeterminate, some form of series expansion will usually be available.

Consider, for example, the function y defined by

$$\begin{cases} y = (1/\sin x) - (1/x) & (0 < |x| < \pi) \\ y(0) = 0. \end{cases}$$

To evaluate this for small values of x, it is convenient to write it

$$y = x\frac{x - \sin x}{x^3} \bigg/ \frac{\sin x}{x}$$

$$= \frac{x}{6}\left[1 - \frac{x^2}{4.5} + \frac{x^4}{4.5.6.7}\cdots\right] \bigg/ \left[1 - \frac{x^2}{2.3} + \frac{x^4}{2.3.4.5}\cdots\right].$$

It would be possible to carry out the division of one series by the other algebraically, but if more than the first two or three terms have to be included, it is easier to evaluate the two series separately and carry out the division numerically.

IV

FINITE DIFFERENCES

4.1. Functions of a continuous variable in numerical analysis

IN numerical work we may be concerned with two different ways of specifying functions of a continuous variable. First, a function may be specified by a formula which can, in principle, be evaluated for any value of x as required: examples of such functions are polynomials, circular, exponential, and other functions defined or expressed in terms of convergent power series, and functions defined by definite integrals such as the gamma-function

$$\Gamma(x) = \int_0^\infty e^{-t} t^{x-1}\, dt. \tag{4.1}$$

Secondly, there are those functions which are specified only by tables of values; these may often be tables expressing some empirical physical relationship, such as the relation between grid voltage and anode current in an electronic valve, or between velocity and resistance for a projectile; or they may be results of previous calculations.

In practice, there is not much difference between functions specified in these two ways, for usually one obtains values of functions of the first kind from tables rather than by evaluating the defining formulae. In fact, mathematical tables are made precisely for the purpose of enabling function values to be determined without going back to first principles and evaluating the defining formulae each time a function value is required; if we require $\Gamma(1\cdot27836)$ we interpolate in tables of $\Gamma(x)$, rather than evaluate the integral in formula (4.1) for $x = 1\cdot27836$, unless it happens that no tables to the number of figures required are available. Thus in either case we are concerned in practice with functions specified by tables, and with the properties of functions so specified.

A function $f(x)$ specified only at discrete tabular values of the independent variable x is not formally defined for intermediate values. If the tabular values of x include zero and are at equal intervals δx, and $g(x)$ is any function (not necessarily even continuous) which is finite at the tabular values of x, then $f(x) + g(x)\sin(\pi x/\delta x)$ has the same values as $f(x)$ at the tabular values of x. Further, the tabular values of $f(x)$ are usually subject to rounding errors, so that the function may not be accurately defined even at the tabular values of x.

On the other hand, a table of a function of a continuous variable x

would often be of little value unless it were possible to determine values of the function for values of x between the tabular values (to an approximation depending, of course, on rounding errors). In order to do this, some understanding is necessary about the behaviour of the function between its tabular values, an understanding which may be justified formally in cases of functions of the first kind mentioned at the beginning of this section, but may have to remain an assumption in the case of empirical functions. This understanding may be expressed qualitatively by saying that the function is 'smooth' over the range concerned. 'Smoothness' of a function is a property which it is difficult to define in a quantitative way; it is discussed further in § 11.4. It implies differentiability to some high order, and smallness of high-order derivatives. An example will illustrate this.

We shall later (Chapter V) derive interpolation formulae for use when the interval of tabulation is too large for linear interpolation between tabular values of the function. It will be found that it is possible to interpolate $\sin x$, not only roughly but to any required accuracy, from its values at interval $\delta x = \frac{1}{2}\pi$:

$$
\left.
\begin{array}{cccccccc}
x & -\frac{3}{2}\pi & -\pi & -\frac{1}{2}\pi & 0 & +\frac{1}{2}\pi & \pi & \frac{3}{2}\pi \\
y = \sin x & 1 & 0 & -1 & 0 & 1 & 0 & -1
\end{array}
\right\} \quad (4.2)
$$

or even from its values at intervals $x = \frac{2}{3}\pi$:

$$
\begin{array}{cccccccc}
x & -2\pi & -\frac{4}{3}\pi & -\frac{2}{3}\pi & 0 & +\frac{2}{3}\pi & \frac{4}{3}\pi & 2\pi \\
y = \sin x & 0 & \frac{1}{2}\sqrt{3} & -\frac{1}{2}\sqrt{3} & 0 & \frac{1}{2}\sqrt{3} & -\frac{1}{2}\sqrt{3} & 0
\end{array}
$$

Let us inquire what particular property the function $y = \sin x$ has which selects it from all other functions with the tabular values (4.2) as the one for which the interpolation formula is accurate. Suppose, for simplicity, that we know that y is an odd function of x, periodic with period 2π. Then it can be expanded in a sine series in the interval $-\pi \leqslant x \leqslant \pi$:

$$
y = a_1 \sin x + a_2 \sin 2x + a_3 \sin 3x + \ldots \tag{4.3}
$$

where, to give the value of y at $x = \frac{1}{2}\pi$

$$
1 = a_1 - a_3 + a_5 - a_7 + \ldots . \tag{4.4}
$$

We shall require a measure of the nth derivative of y; this derivative varies with x, but a convenient single quantity giving an overall measure of its magnitude is its mean square value

$$
\frac{1}{2\pi} \int_{-\pi}^{\pi} (y^{(n)})^2 \, dx = \frac{1}{2}(a_1^2 + 2^n a_2^2 + 3^n a_3^2 + \ldots).
$$

As $n \to \infty$, the minimum value of this quantity, subject to the condition (4.4), is given by $a_1 = 1$, $a_m = 0$ $(m > 1)$. Thus the relevant property of the function $y = \sin x$ is this, that of all functions which are odd and have period 2π, it is the one for which, to put it roughly, the high-order derivatives are as small as possible.

In the great majority of cases, functions are tabulated at equal intervals of the independent variable, which is often called, in this context, the 'argument' of the table. For the present, we will only consider such sets of function values.

4.2. Finite differences

The most important property of a function specified by a table consists of what are called its 'finite differences'. The following example illustrates what is meant by this term:

x	$f(x) = 1/x$	First differences	Second differences	Third differences
3·0	·33333			
		−1075		
3·1	·32258		67	
		−1008		−6
3·2	·31250		61	
		− 947		−5
3·3	·30303		56	
		− 891		−6
3·4	·29412		50	
		− 841		−2
3·5	·28571		48	
		− 793		
3·6	·27778			

The 'first differences' are obtained by subtracting each function value from that for the next *greater* tabular value of x; the 'second differences' are obtained by carrying out a similar set of subtractions on the first differences, and so on.

Values of *odd* order differences should be written on levels intermediate between those of function values, and of *even* order differences on the same lines as function values, and normally these values are written in terms of the last digital position as unit, decimal points, and zeros before the first significant digit, being omitted. They can conveniently be distinguished from function values by being written or printed smaller.

The finite differences of tabular functions play a very important part both in the analytical and in the numerical manipulation of such functions. Use of them enables formulae for operations on such functions, such as interpolation and integration, to be expressed compactly and in a form convenient for practical use. When the tabular values provide all the information we have about a function, all processes involving this function have to be expressed as operations on the tabular values; one of the most important operations on a set of values at equal intervals of the independent variable is that of differencing, and we shall later in this Chapter, and in Chapters V and VI, see that most of the other operations can be expressed in terms of this one.

It will be seen that the values of the third differences in the above table are noticeably irregular; this is an effect of rounding errors in the function value, which will be considered more fully in § 4.44.

In order that a function shall be well determined by a table, the average value of the nth order differences should tend to zero, or at least become small, as n increases. We have seen examples in which this does not appear to be the case; for the function $y = \sin x$, at interval $\frac{1}{2}\pi$ in x (see (4.2)), the $2n$th differences have extreme values $\pm 2^n$, but this function is still well defined by these values, in the sense that accurate intermediate values can be interpolated between them. But this is a peculiar property of the function $y = \sin x$ alone out of all the functions with these tabular values; given these function values *alone*, without the knowledge that they are intended to represent $\sin x$, one could not be at all confident about the results of any attempt to interpolate between them. Eight values per cycle is about the smallest number which can in practice be regarded as specifying an oscillating function adequately, and at least twelve values per cycle is preferable.

4.21. Notation for finite differences

Let x_0 be one of the tabular values of x, $x_j = (x_0 + j\,\delta x)$ a set of other tabular values, and $f_j = f(x_j)$ the values of $f(x)$ at the tabular values of x.

There are two kinds of notation for finite differences. In one the differences of a function f are written δf or Δf, so that the symbol δ or Δ stands for an *operation* carried out on the values of the function f. In the other the symbol δ or Δ is used for the *differences themselves*.

The former seems much the preferable, both for use in the derivation and manipulation of formulae in finite differences and in application of them. It is more nearly self-explanatory, and many formulae with which we shall be concerned express relations between differences of two different functions (for example a function of x and its derivative), and if a symbol is used to represent a difference itself rather than a difference-operator, differences of different functions cannot be distinguished except by introducing new symbols, which are unnecessary. In this notation, repetition of an operation is expressed by the use of an index (as in δ^2, Δ^3).

The use of the symbol δ or Δ for the differences themselves is a convenient shorthand in cases in which it is unambiguous, and is sometimes preferred by those carrying out the details of the numerical work. In this notation the use of dashes (Δ'') or Roman superiors (as $\Delta^{(\mathrm{vi})}$) is preferable to the use of numerical indices to indicate orders of differences.

In this book, the former usage will be adopted throughout, so that δ

and Δ must be regarded as finite-difference *operators*. Consistently with this notation, δx will be used for the interval in the independent variable (other notations for this are h and w).[†]

The first difference $f_1 - f_0$ may be associated with the argument value x_0, with the argument value x_1, or symmetrically with these two argument values, and assigned a corresponding suffix. A different symbol for the finite-difference operator is used to distinguish these three cases:

$$\left. \begin{aligned} f_1 - f_0 &= \Delta f_0 \\ &= \nabla f_1 \\ &= \delta f_{\frac{1}{2}} \end{aligned} \right\} . \tag{4.5}$$

This is generalized in the following three schemes for a difference table:

(a) Forward differences

x	f	Δf	$\Delta^2 f$	$\Delta^3 f$
x_{-2}	f_{-2}		$\Delta^2 f_{-3}$	
		Δf_{-2}		$\Delta^3 f_{-3}$
x_{-1}	f_{-1}		$\Delta^2 f_{-2}$	
		Δf_{-1}		$\Delta^3 f_{-2}$
x_0	f_0		$\Delta^2 f_{-1}$	
		Δf_0		$\underline{\Delta^3 f_{-1}}$
x_1	f_1		$\Delta^2 f_0$	
		Δf_1		$\Delta^3 f_0$
x_2	f_2		$\Delta^2 f_1$	

(b) Backward differences

f	∇f	$\nabla^2 f$	$\nabla^3 f$
f_{-2}		$\nabla^2 f_{-1}$	
	∇f_{-1}		$\nabla^3 f_0$
f_{-1}		$\nabla^2 f_0$	
	∇f_0		$\nabla^3 f_1$
f_0		$\nabla^2 f_1$	
	∇f_1		$\nabla^3 f_2$
f_1		$\nabla^2 f_2$	
	∇f_2		$\nabla^3 f_3$
f_2		$\nabla^2 f_3$	

(c) Central differences

f	δf	$\delta^2 f$	$\delta^3 f$	$\delta^4 f$
f_{-2}		$\delta^2 f_{-2}$		$\delta^4 f_{-2}$
	$\delta f_{-1\frac{1}{2}}$		$\delta^3 f_{-1\frac{1}{2}}$	
f_{-1}		$\delta^2 f_{-1}$		$\delta^4 f_{-1}$
	$\delta f_{-\frac{1}{2}}$		$\delta^3 f_{-\frac{1}{2}}$	
f_0		$\underline{\delta^2 f_0}$		$\underline{\delta^4 f_0}$
	$\delta f_{\frac{1}{2}}$		$\underline{\delta^3 f_{\frac{1}{2}}}$	
f_1		$\delta^2 f_1$		$\delta^4 f_1$
	$\delta f_{1\frac{1}{2}}$		$\delta^3 f_{1\frac{1}{2}}$	
f_2		$\delta^2 f_2$		

In any particular numerical case the *numbers* will be the same in each table; what is different is the general notation for these numbers, the notation which expresses the value of x with which each difference is associated.

Differences with the same suffix value in table (a) are called 'forward differences'; they lie on a downward-slanting line on the table, such as those underlined. The forward differences from the first entry in a table are sometimes called 'leading differences'. Those differences with the same suffix value in table (b) are called 'backward differences'; an example is indicated similarly. Those with the same suffix in table (c) are called 'central differences'.

Central differences are much the most useful in practice. Many formulae in central differences involve only alternate orders of differences, whereas the corresponding formulae in forward or backward differences involve all orders of differences; also the coefficients of higher terms in central-difference formulae usually decrease more rapidly with the order n of the differences than do the coefficients in formulae involving forward or backward differences. Further, this notation gives a much more natural relation between finite differences and derivatives.

[†] It is sometimes convenient to distinguish between the general symbol δx for the interval length and the particular value which it has in a particular calculation.

In the analytical work of deriving formulae for interpolation, integration, etc., in terms of differences, use of forward differences leads to rather simpler algebra; but in order to get from the results the central-difference formulae which are most convenient for practical use, it may be necessary to do some rather laborious algebra, which may then only give the coefficients of the central-difference formulae term by term, and be difficult to generalize to give the general term. It seems best to work throughout in terms of central differences, and so obtain directly the formulae for interpolation, integration, etc., in the forms in which they are most useful for practical work.†

It will be seen that in the central-difference scheme (c) on p. 38, only the *even*-order differences have integral suffixes. It is sometimes convenient to take the arithmetic mean of two adjacent differences and to write

$$\mu\,\delta f_0 = \tfrac{1}{2}(\delta f_{\frac{1}{2}} + \delta f_{-\frac{1}{2}})$$

and in general

$$\mu\,\delta^n f_j = \tfrac{1}{2}(\delta^n f_{j+\frac{1}{2}} + \delta^n f_{j-\frac{1}{2}})$$
$$= \tfrac{1}{2}(\delta^{n-1} f_{j+1} - \delta^{n-1} f_{j-1}).$$

Then the available differences are *odd*-order differences with $(\text{integer}+\tfrac{1}{2})$ suffixes, and *even*-order differences and *odd*-order *mean* differences with integral suffixes. A set of successive function values f_j from $j = J-k$ to $J+k$ inclusive is said to be 'centred on' the argument value x_J or on the function value f_J; similarly for a set of differences $\delta^n f_j$.

4.3. Finite differences in terms of function values

It is sometimes convenient to have differences expressed in terms of the function values from which they are derived. We have in succession

$$\delta f_{\frac{1}{2}} = f_1 - f_0 \tag{4.6}$$

$$\delta^2 f_0 = \delta f_{\frac{1}{2}} - \delta f_{-\frac{1}{2}} = (f_1 - f_0) - (f_0 - f_{-1})$$
$$= f_1 - 2f_0 + f_{-1} \tag{4.7}$$

$$\delta^3 f_{\frac{1}{2}} = \delta^2 f_1 - \delta^2 f_0 = (f_2 - 2f_1 + f_0) - (f_1 - 2f_0 + f_{-1})$$
$$= f_2 - 3f_1 + 3f_0 - f_{-1},$$

and in general

$$\delta^n f_j = \sum_{k=0}^{n} (-1)^k \frac{n!}{k!(n-k)!} f_{j+\frac{1}{2}n-k} \tag{4.8}$$

as can be proved by induction; for an alternative proof see § 4.6. The coefficients of the function values in $\delta^n f_j$ are those in the binomial expansion of $(1-z)^n$.

† The symbol Δ is then left free for another use, to indicate the difference between the data or between the results of two similar calculations.

In particular, the differences of the function

$$\begin{cases} f_m = 0 & m \neq 0 \\ f_0 = 1 \end{cases}$$

are the binomial coefficients:

x	f	δf	$\delta^2 f$	$\delta^3 f$	$\delta^4 f$
x_{-2}	0		0		1
		0		1	
x_{-1}	0		1		-4
		1		-3	
x_0	1		-2		6
		-1		3	
x_1	0		1		-4
		0		-1	
x_2	0		0		1

The effect of an error ϵ in a function value on the difference table builds up in the same way:

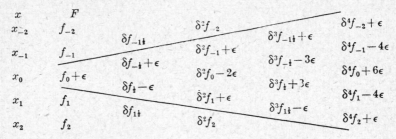

This is the basis of an important application of differences to *checking* tables, and sometimes for correcting isolated errors, which will be considered shortly (§ 4.42).

4.4. Simple applications of differences

The simplest applications of differences are:

(a) Building up polynomials;
(b) Checking tables;
(c) Smoothing.

Of these, (a) and (b) will be considered here and (c) in § 11.4.

4.41. Differences of a polynomial

An important property of finite differences is that for a polynomial of degree n, the nth order differences are constant. One proof of this is by induction.

Suppose that $\qquad \delta^m(x^m) = m! \, (\delta x)^m \qquad\qquad$ (4.9) for all integral values of m up to $m = n$, say; then it will be proved that (4.9) holds for $m = n+2$. Since for $p < m$

$$\delta^m(x^p) = \delta^{m-p}(\delta^p x^p),$$

(4.9) implies that $\delta^m(x^p) = 0 \quad \text{for } p < m.$ (4.10)

Now from (4.7)

$$\delta^2(x^{n+2}) = (x+\delta x)^{n+2} - 2x^{n+2} + (x-\delta x)^{n+2}$$

$$= (n+2)(n+1)(\delta x)^2 x^n + \text{terms of lower degree},$$

so

$$\delta^{n+2} x^{n+2} = \delta^n(\delta^2 x^{n+2})$$

$$= (n+2)(n+1)(\delta x)^2 \, \delta^n[x^n + \text{terms of lower degree}]$$

$$= (n+2)(n+1)(\delta x)^2 \, \delta^n(x^n) \quad [\text{by (4.10)}]$$

$$= (n+2)(n+1)(\delta x)^2 n! \, (\delta x)^n \quad [\text{since (4.9) holds for } m = n]$$

$$= (n+2)! \, (\delta x)^{n+2}.$$

Now (4.9) holds for $m = 1$ and $m = 2$, hence the induction succeeds, and (4.9) holds for all integral m.

It follows that for a polynomial of degree m, say

$$p_m(x) = a_0 x^m + a_1 x^{m-1} + \dots,$$

the mth differences are constant and equal to $a_0 m! \, (\delta x)^m$.

Another derivation, which depends on some properties of a set of functions to which reference will be made later, is as follows. Consider the polynomials:†

$$\psi_0(\xi) = 1$$

$$\psi_m(\xi) = \prod_{k=0}^{m-1} [\xi + \{\tfrac{1}{2}(m-1) - k\}];$$ (4.11)

$\psi_m(\xi)$ is a polynomial of degree m in ξ, and its argument value is the mean of the extreme factors. The first few such functions are

$$\psi_0(\xi) = 1,$$
$$\psi_1(\xi) = \xi,$$
$$\psi_2(\xi) = (\xi + \tfrac{1}{2})(\xi - \tfrac{1}{2}) = (\xi^2 - \tfrac{1}{4}),$$
$$\psi_3(\xi) = (\xi + 1)\xi(\xi - 1) = \xi(\xi^2 - 1),$$
$$\psi_4(\xi) = (\xi + \tfrac{3}{2})(\xi + \tfrac{1}{2})(\xi - \tfrac{1}{2})(\xi - \tfrac{3}{2})$$
$$= (\xi^2 - \tfrac{1}{4})(\xi^2 - \tfrac{9}{4}).$$

For intervals $\delta\xi = 1$, the first differences of ψ_m are

$$\delta\psi_m(\xi + \tfrac{1}{2}) = \psi_m(\xi + 1) - \psi_m(\xi)$$

$$= [\xi + \tfrac{1}{2}(m+1)][\xi + \tfrac{1}{2}(m-1)]\dots[\xi - \tfrac{1}{2}(m-3)] -$$

$$- \underbrace{[\xi + \tfrac{1}{2}(m-1)]\dots[\xi - \tfrac{1}{2}(m-3)]}[\xi - \tfrac{1}{2}(m-1)].$$

† Sometimes called 'factorial polynomials'.

The common factor of the two terms, indicated by a bracket, is a polynomial of the set (4.11); it has $(m-1)$ factors and the mean of its extreme factors is $(\xi+\tfrac{1}{2})$, so it is $\psi_{m-1}(\xi+\tfrac{1}{2})$. Hence, for $m > 0$,

$$\delta\psi_m(\xi+\tfrac{1}{2}) = [\{\xi+\tfrac{1}{2}(m+1)\}-\{\xi-\tfrac{1}{2}(m-1)\}]\psi_{m-1}(\xi+\tfrac{1}{2})$$
$$= m\psi_{m-1}(\xi+\tfrac{1}{2}), \tag{4.12}$$

and $\delta\psi_0 \equiv 0$.

Repeating the operation we have

$$\delta^2\psi_m(\xi) = \delta\psi_m(\xi+\tfrac{1}{2})-\delta\psi_m(\xi-\tfrac{1}{2})$$
$$= m[\psi_{m-1}(\xi+\tfrac{1}{2})-\psi_{m-1}(\xi-\tfrac{1}{2})]$$
$$= m\,\delta\psi_{m-1}(\xi)$$
$$= m(m-1)\psi_{m-2}(\xi),$$

and ultimately
$$\delta^m\psi_m(\xi) = m!$$
$$\delta^{m+1}\psi_m(\xi) = 0.$$

Any polynomial $p_m(x) = a_0 x^m+a_1 x^{m-1}+\dots$ tabulated at intervals (δx) in x, can be written
$$p_m(x) = a_0(\delta x)^m[\psi_m(\xi)+b_1\psi_{m-1}(\xi)+b_2\psi_{m-2}(\xi)+\dots]$$
where $\xi = x/\delta x$, so $\qquad \delta^m p_m(x) = a_0\,m!\,(\delta x)^m$
as already shown.

This result, that the mth differences of any polynomial of degree m are constant, and its $(m+1)$th differences are zero, corresponds, in finite differences, to the result in differential calculus that the mth *derivative* of such a polynomial is constant and its $(m+1)$th derivative zero. The functions $\psi_m(x)$ take the place, in finite differences, of the function x^n in differential calculus, as the polynomials whose form remains unchanged on differencing.

These functions will appear later in another context, for which some further properties of them will be required. From the definition (4.11) it follows that
$$\psi_m(-\xi) = (-)^m\psi_m(\xi).$$
Hence for odd values of m

$$\psi_{2n+1}(\xi)+\psi_{2n+1}(1-\xi) = \psi_{2n+1}(\xi)-\psi_{2n+1}(\xi-1)$$
$$= (2n+1)\psi_{2n}(\xi-\tfrac{1}{2}) \tag{4.13}$$

by (4.12), whereas

$$\psi_{2n+1}(\xi)-\psi_{2n+1}(1-\xi) = \psi_{2n+1}(\xi)+\psi_{2n+1}(\xi-1)$$
$$= [(\xi+n)+(\xi-n-1)]\psi_{2n}(\xi-\tfrac{1}{2})$$
$$= (2\xi-1)\psi_{2n}(\xi-\tfrac{1}{2}). \tag{4.14}$$

4.42. Building up polynomials

The constancy of the mth differences of an mth order polynomial can be used to construct a table of values of the polynomial by building up successively the lower orders of differences from the higher by repeated addition. It is necessary to calculate at least m function values to give a set of leading differences from which to start the construction of the difference table, and it is advisable to take one or two more to provide a check.

Example: To evaluate the polynomial $y = x^3 - 5x^2 + 6x + 1$ for $x = 0(1)10$:

x	x^3	$-5x^2$	$+6x$	$+1=$	y	δy	$\delta^2 y$	$\delta^3 y$
-2	-8	-20	-12	$+1=$	-39			
						$+28$		
-1	-1	-5	-6	$+1=$	-11		-16	
						12		6
0	0	0	0	$+1=$	1		-10	start
						2		6
1	1	-5	6	$+1=$	3		-4	
						-2		6
2	8	-20	$+12$	$+1=$	1		2	
						0		6
3					1		8	
						8		6
4					9		14	
						22		6
5					31		20	
						42		6
6					73		26	
						68		6
7					141		32	
						100		6
8					241		38	
						138		6
9					379		44	
						182		
10	1000	-500	$+60$	$+1=$	561			check

Here five function values, from $x = -2$ to 2 (the simplest ones to evaluate) have been calculated to provide a start for building up the differences. We know from (4.9) that the third differences must have the constant value 6, and this provides a check on the starting values. From the constant third differences of 6 the second differences are built up, then the first differences, and finally the function values. The function value at $x = 10$ is easy to calculate directly, and is so calculated to provide a check on the successive additions.

It will be noted that intermediate values of y are calculated by *addition only*: this process can be carried out very effectively on an adding machine fitted with a printing mechanism (§ 2.26). For example, in summing the second differences to give the first differences, after adding each second difference the resulting value of the first difference, which is the current total, is printed without clearing by taking a 'sub-total'. The results appear in the form of alternate values of second differences and first differences; the former can be checked against the table of values and the latter then summed similarly to give the function values.

It is necessary in using this process to keep all figures without rounding off, although final results may not be wanted to this accuracy.

Example: To evaluate the polynomial $y = x^3 - 5x^2 + 6x + 1$ for $x = 0(0\cdot01)0\cdot1$; four decimals required.

x	x^3	$-5x^2$	$+6x$	$+1$	$=$	y		$\delta^2 y$		y rounded off to four decimals		
$-0\cdot02$	$-\cdot0000,08$	$-\cdot0020$	$-0\cdot12$	$+1$	$=$	$\cdot8779,92$				$\cdot8780$		
							61507				615	
$0\cdot01$	$-\cdot0000,01$	$-\cdot0005$	$-0\cdot06$	$+1$	$=$	$\cdot9394,99$		-1006		$\cdot9395$		-10
							60501		6		605	
0	0	0	0	$+1$	$=$	$1\cdot0000,00$		-1000	6	$1\cdot0000$		-10
							59501		6		595	
$0\cdot01$	$+\cdot0000,01$	$-\cdot0005$	$+0\cdot06$	$+1$	$=$	$1\cdot0595,01$		-994	6	$1\cdot0595$		-10
							58507		6		585	
$0\cdot02$	$+\cdot0000,08$	$-\cdot0020$	$+0\cdot12$	$+1$	$=$	$1\cdot1180,08$		$-\cdot988$	6	$1\cdot1180$		-10
							57519		6		575	
$0\cdot03$						$1\cdot1755,27$		-982	6	$1\cdot1755$		-9
							56537		6		566	
$0\cdot04$						$1\cdot2320,64$		-976	6	$1\cdot2321$		-101
							55561		6		465	
$0\cdot05$						$1\cdot2876,25$		-970	6	$1\cdot2786$		$+171$
							54591		6		636	
$0\cdot06$						$1\cdot3422,16$		-964	6	$1\cdot3422$		-100
							53627		6		536	
$0\cdot07$						$1\cdot3958,43$		-958	6	$1\cdot3958$		-9
							52669		6		527	
$0\cdot08$						$1\cdot4485,12$		-952	6	$1\cdot4485$		-10
							51717		6		517	
$0\cdot09$						$1\cdot5002,29$		-946	6	$1\cdot5002$		-9
							50771				508	
$0\cdot10$						$1\cdot5510.00$				$1\cdot5510$		

Notes: (i) Although the third difference of 6 in the sixth decimal is smaller than the rounding error in the four-decimal values finally required, it must not be neglected on that account, as this would be a *systematic* rounding error which would accumulate and ultimately affect the results wanted. Omission of it would be equivalent to omitting the x^3 term in the polynomial, and the error would already be 10 in the fourth decimal at $x = 0\cdot1$.

(ii) Here a typical copying mistake (78 for 87) has been made in the column of rounded-off values, which are those finally required. It is a mistake which is easy to make at this stage; all the calculations have been done, and all that is wanted is to copy the four decimals required with the appropriate rounding off; unconsciously one may relax some of the care with which the rest of the calculation has been carried out, and then a mistake of this kind can easily occur. Such a mistake is easily identified by *differencing the rounded-off results* and such a check should *always* be used. As will be seen in the following section, the irregular differences not only locate the erroneous value unambiguously, but strongly suggest the correction.

4.43. Checking by differences

We have seen in § 4.4 that an isolated error ϵ in a function value makes:

a maximum error	ϵ in the first differences
2ϵ	second differences
3ϵ	third differences
6ϵ	fourth differences
10ϵ	fifth differences
20ϵ	sixth differences

whereas the magnitude of the differences themselves normally decreases with the order of differences; if it does not, the function is not well defined by the table. Hence an error shows up more and more as the order of the differences is increased. Examination of the differences of a function is one of the best checks against *random* errors; it will not necessarily check against *systematic* errors.

The differences which are affected by an error spread fanwise from the incorrect function value (see § 4.3), and this can be used to locate an error.

Example:

x	y		$\delta^2 y$		$\delta^4 y$	corrections to $\delta^4 y$
0	358					
		12				
1	370		15			
		27		12		
2	397		27		− 1	
		54		11		
3	451		38		− 1	
		92		10		
4	543		48		− 1	
		140		9		
5	683		57		− 19	+ 18
		197		−10		
6	880		47		+ 71	− 72
		244		+61		
7	1124		108		−109	+108
		352		−48		
8	1476		60		+ 71	− 72
		412		23		
9	1888		83		− 19	+ 18
		495		4		
10	2383		87		− 1	
		582		3		
11	2965		90			
		672				
12	3637					

The last column is $18 \times (1, -4, 6, -4, 1)$.

Notes: (i) The existence *and location* of an error is unambiguously shown by the table.

(ii) A change Δy in a function value y makes changes $(1, -4, 6, -4, 1)$ times Δy in successive values of the fourth difference, centred on the changed value of y. A few trials show that a change $\Delta y = +18$ will make all the fourth differences -1. The error can often be corrected in this way.

(iii) A transposition of two adjacent digits differing by m will produce an error of $9m$ in terms of the less significant of the digits as unit. It has already been mentioned that transpositions form a common type of mistake; values of Δy which are multiples of 9, or nearly, probably arise from mistakes of this kind. This can be checked from the values of the digits involved. Here $\Delta y = 18$, hence $m = 2$ in the last figure. The value $y = 1124$ at $x = 7$ should read $y = 1142$.

(iv) In this case the fourth difference of the corrected table is exact; the location and correction of the mistake is not affected by rounding errors.

Example: Here the values of y are alleged to be rounded off from a table of $x^{\frac{1}{4}}$:

x	y	δy	$\delta^2 y$	Correction to $\delta^2 y$	Revised $\delta^2 y$	Correction to $\delta^2 y$	Corrected $\delta^2 y$
38	6·1644						
		806					
39	·2450		−10		−10		−10
		796					
40	·3246		−11		−11		−11
		785					
41	·4031		−9		−9		−9
		776					
42	·4807		−36	+27⎫	−9		−9
		740					
43	·5547		+45	−54⎬	−9		−9
		785					
44	·6332		−35	+27⎭	−8		−8
		750					
45	·7082		0	−9⎫	−9		−9
		750					
46	·7832		−5	+18⎬	+13	−20⎫	−7
		745					
47	·8577		−40	−9⎭	−49	+40⎬	−9
		705					
48	6·9282		+13		+13	−20⎭	−7
		718					
49	7·0000		−7		−7		−7
		711					
50	·0711		−8		−8		−8
		703					
51	·1414		−6		−6		−6
		697					
52	·2111						

Notes: (i) Here a succession of seven values of $\delta^2 y$ is irregular. The first obviously wrong value, −36 at $x = 42$, indicates a mistake at $x = 43$; the value of $\delta^2 y(42)$ would be expected to be −8, −9, or −10; that is, the correction is +28, +27, or +26. The value +27 suggests a transposition of two digits differing by 3, and reference to the function values shows that the end digits *do* differ by 3.

(ii) Correction of this mistake then makes the differences smooth, apart from slight irregularities which can be ascribed to rounding errors in the function values, as far as $\delta^2 y(44)$ inclusive. The next *four* second differences are irregular, indicating mistakes in both the values $y(45)$ and $y(46)$. The value of $\delta^2 y(45)$ would be expected to be −8 or −9; that is the correction is −8 or −9; the latter suggests an interchange of two digits differing by 1, and when the corresponding correction has been made, we have the series of second differences given in the column headed 'Revised'.

(iii) The next three second differences should be about −8, and to give them all this value we would require corrections (−21, +41, −21); the corrections arising from a single change in y must be in the ratio (1 : −2 : 1), so the error in $y(47)$ is +20 or +21. The former would be produced by doubling the wrong one of two digits differing by 2, and as such digits do occur in $y(47)$ in the right place, the error can be ascribed to this cause with fair certainty.

These examples show that it is possible to use differences not only for detection and location of errors in tables, but for correcting them, when the nature of the error is clear from the behaviour of the differences, or for indicating a probable correction when it is not. In the case of the second example just given, it would of course be much better to use the differences simply to *indicate* the erroneous values, and to refer back to a table of $x^{\frac{1}{3}}$ to *correct* them.

4.44. Effect of rounding errors on differences

In most tables almost every function value will be in error to some degree, on account of rounding errors. Although the rounding error in a function value may not be more than $\frac{1}{2}$ in the least significant figure, the effect of an error is exaggerated in the higher differences, which unavoidably become somewhat irregular, and the more so the higher the order of differences. It is important to realize this, otherwise irregularities in differences which are due to rounding errors may be taken as indicating mistakes, and time may be spent trying to find mistakes and to make changes in function values which cannot be improved except by taking more significant figures.

The greatest effects of rounding errors will occur when alternate function values are rounded off by $+\frac{1}{2}$ and $-\frac{1}{2}$ alternately. Then departures of the nth differences from those for unrounded function values may be up to $\pm 2^{n-1}$ in the last place tabulated and alternate departures will be of alternate signs; though such large irregularities will be rarer the higher the order n of the differences. It is useful to have a working criterion for the magnitude of the fluctuations in the different orders of differences which can be expected as the result of rounding errors. Comrie† gives the following limits for various values of n:

n	1	2	3	4	5	6	8	10
	± 1	± 2	± 3	± 6	± 12	± 22	± 80	± 300

Differences having fluctuations less than these limits can be accepted; only those having greater fluctuations should be regarded as suspicious.

The example overleaf illustrates the way in which irregular differences may occur in the most accurate rounded-off values of a smooth function.

From examination of the differences in the table, one would be very inclined to 'correct' the rounded values of $y(5)$ and $y(8)$ to 393 and 777 respectively, giving the third differences shown on the extreme right; but reference to the exact values of y shows that this would be incorrect.

† *Chambers's 6-Figure Mathematical Tables*, vol. 2 (1949), Introduction, p. xxxi.

x	y	δy	$\delta^2 y$	$\delta^3 y$	$\delta^4 y$	y	δy	$\delta^2 y$	$\delta^3 y$	to $\delta^3 y$	$\delta^3 y$
						Values of y rounded off to nearest unit				'*Corrections*'	
0	61·24					61					
		4581					46				
1	107·05		897			107		9			
		5478		109			55		1		1
2	161·83		1006		53	162		10			
		6484		162			65		1		1
3	226·67		1168		52	227		11			
		7652		214			76		4	−1	3
4	303·19		1382		51	303		15			
		9034		265			91		0	+3	3
5	393·53		1647		50	394		15			
		10681		315			106		6	−3	3
6	500·34		1962		49	500		21			
		12643		364			127		1	+1 +1	3
7	626·77		2326		48	627		22			
		14969		412			149		7	−3	4
8	776·46		2738		47	776		29			
		17707		459			178		2	+3	5
9	953·53		3197		46	954		31			
		20904		505			209		6	−1	5
10	1162·57		3702		45	1163		37			
		24606		550			246		5		5
11	1408·63		4252			1409		42			
		28858					288				
12	1697·21					1697					

This example illustrates that smoothness of differences of rounded values of a function is *not* a guarantee that these values give the best representation of that function. The adjustment of function values by differences cannot be depended on to ± 1 unit in the last place; it is possible, as in this example, to make the differences over-smooth.†

4.45. Direct evaluation of second differences

It is sometimes convenient to be able to evaluate second differences directly from function values without the intermediate step of calculating first differences. This can be done on a machine as follows.

Suppose first that the second differences of f are positive; $\delta^2 f_j$ is calculated from the formula
$$\delta^2 f_j = f_{j-1} + f_{j+1} - 2f_j,$$
the terms being taken in this order; then f_j is set ready for the calculation of
$$\delta^2 f_{j+1} = f_j + f_{j+2} - 2f_{j+1},$$
and so on.

If the second differences are negative, this process will give them in complementary form; then it is more convenient to obtain
$$-\delta^2 f_j = 2f_j - f_{j-1} - f_{j+1},$$

† For a further discussion of checking by differences, see J. C. P. Miller, *M.T.A.C.* **4** (1950), 3.

the terms being taken in this order so that when $-\delta^2 f_j$ has been obtained, f_{j+1} is already set for the calculation of

$$-\delta^2 f_{j+1} = 2f_{j+1} - f_j - f_{j+2}.$$

If the function values are negative, their moduli are set, and the signs of the machine operations altered accordingly.

This is a useful process for checking values of a function built up from second differences by summing the second differences to form the first differences, and then summing first differences to give the function values. The direct calculation of second differences provides a good check of these two successive summations.

4.46. Building up from second differences

A function can be built up directly from its second differences, without calculation of the first differences, by a process which is the converse of that of the previous section. If the function is positive, we have

$$f_{j+1} = 2f_j - f_{j-1} + \delta^2 f_j;$$

this is transferred to the setting levers, and used in the first step in forming

$$f_{j+2} = 2f_{j+1} - f_j + \delta^2 f_{j+1}.$$

If f_j is negative, it is more convenient to form

$$(-f_{j+1}) = 2(-f_j) - (-f_{j-1}) - \delta^2 f_j.$$

If this process of building up a function from its second differences is used, the method of the previous section should *not* be used for checking; the processes are too nearly alike for one to be a good check of the results of the other.

One machine, the Brunsviga 20, has two facilities which are very convenient for building up a function from its second differences; these are transfer from the accumulator to the setting levers, and an arrangement for clearing only the right-hand half of the accumulator, leaving the left-hand half unaffected. The latter feature is known as 'split clearance', and has the effect of furnishing the machine with two registers.

In the present application, the first differences are accumulated in the right-hand half of the accumulator (R.H. for short) and the function itself in the left-hand half (L.H.) Let $\delta f_{j-\frac{1}{2}}$ be in R.H. and f_j in L.H.; then $\delta^2 f_j$ is set on the setting levers (S.L.), and added into R.H., which then contains $\delta f_{j+\frac{1}{2}}$. This is transferred to S.L., and the operation of clearing it from R.H. does not affect L.H.; it is added back into R.H. and also, after shifting the accumulator, into L.H.; R.H. now contains $\delta f_{j+\frac{1}{2}}$ and L.H. contains f_{j+1}. The accumulator is now shifted back, $\delta^2 f_{j+1}$ set, and the process repeated. The only quantities needing setting are the second differences $\delta^2 f_j$.

4.5. Differences and derivatives

We have seen that functions defined by analytical formulae are adequately represented by tables only in ranges away from singularities and discontinuities, and that if a table is the only information we have about a function, we may regard the function represented by the table as being differentiable as many times as we require. We will therefore suppose that in any application of numerical methods to functions specified by a table, the function can be expanded in a Taylor series over the range with which we are concerned.

Then we have

$$f_{\pm 1} = f_0 \pm (\delta x)f_0' + \frac{1}{2!}(\delta x)^2 f_0'' \pm \frac{1}{3!}(\delta x)^3 f_0''' + \dots \qquad (4.15)$$

and in general

$$f_{\pm n} = f_0 \pm (n\,\delta x)f_0' + \frac{1}{2!}(n\,\delta x)^2 f_0'' \pm \frac{1}{3!}(n\,\delta x)^3 f_0''' + \dots, \qquad (4.16)$$

the remainder term being of order $(\delta x)^m$ if the series is cut off after m terms. We shall only derive a few relations directly from these expansions, as we shall shortly see a quicker and more effective way of deriving relations of the kind we require in practical work.

Substitution of series such as (4.15), (4.16) into the formulae giving differences in terms of function values gives a set of relations for *differences in terms of derivatives*; for example, if terms of order $(\delta x)^6$ are included,

$$\delta^2 f_0 = f_1 - 2f_0 + f_{-1} = 2\left[(\delta x)^2 \frac{1}{2!}f_0'' + \frac{1}{4!}(\delta x)^4 f_0^{iv} + \frac{1}{6!}(\delta x)^6 f_0^{vi}\right] + O(\delta x)^8$$

$$= (\delta x)^2[f_0'' + \tfrac{1}{12}(\delta x)^2 f_0^{iv} + \tfrac{1}{360}(\delta x)^4 f_0^{vi}] + O(\delta x)^8, \qquad (4.17)$$

and similarly

$$\delta^4 f_0 = f_2 - 4f_1 + 6f_0 - 4f_{-1} + f_{-2} = (\delta x)^4[f_0^{iv} + \tfrac{1}{6}(\delta x)^2 f_0^{vi}] + O(\delta x)^8. \qquad (4.18)$$

From the symmetry of the coefficients in formula (4.17) it follows that even-order differences $\delta^{2n} f_0$ involve only even-order derivatives at x_0.

It follows from (4.17), (4.18) that

$$\lim_{\delta x \to 0} [\delta^2 f_0 / (\delta x)^2] = f_0'',$$

$$\lim_{\delta x \to 0} [\delta^4 f_0 / (\delta x)^4] = f_0^{iv},$$

and similarly for higher orders of differences; thus finite difference *ratios* are closely allied to derivatives. But in using differences, it is the differences themselves that enter into most formulae, rather than difference ratios.

The relations (4.17), (4.18) and similar ones for higher-order differences can be regarded as equations for derivatives in terms of differences, and solved for these. A more important relation, however, is one between the second difference of f and its second derivative and its differences.

From (4.17) applied to the function f'' we have

$$\delta^2 f_0'' = (\delta x)^2 [f_0^{iv} + \tfrac{1}{12}(\delta x)^2 f_0^{vi}] + O(\delta x)^6,$$

$$\delta^4 f_0'' = (\delta x)^4 f_0^{vi} + O(\delta x)^6,$$

so that

$$(\delta x)^2 f_0^{iv} = \delta^2 f_0'' - \tfrac{1}{12}\delta^4 f_0'' + O(\delta x)^6,$$

$$(\delta x)^4 f_0^{vi} = \delta^4 f_0'' + O(\delta x)^6,$$

and substitution into (4.17) gives

$$\delta^2 f_0 = (\delta x)^2 [f_0'' + \tfrac{1}{12}\delta^2 f_0'' - \tfrac{1}{240}\delta^4 f_0''] + O(\delta x)^8. \tag{4.19}$$

Similarly,

$$\mu \, \delta f_0 = \tfrac{1}{2}(f_1 - f_{-1}) = (\delta x)\left[f_0' + \frac{1}{3!}(\delta x)^2 f_0''' + \frac{1}{5!}(\delta x)^4 f_0^{v} \right] + O(\delta x)^7 \tag{4.20}$$

and application of (4.17), (4.18) to f' gives

$$\delta^2 f_0' = (\delta x)^2 [f_0''' + \tfrac{1}{12}(\delta x)^2 f_0^{v}] + O(\delta x)^6,$$

$$\delta^4 f_0' = (\delta x)^4 f_0^{v} + O(\delta x)^6;$$

and substitution in (4.20) gives

$$\mu \, \delta f_0 = (\delta x)[f_0' + \tfrac{1}{6}\delta^2 f_0' - \tfrac{1}{180}\delta^4 f_0'] + O(\delta x)^7. \tag{4.21}$$

As we shall see later, the first two terms in the square bracket here give the formula usually known as 'Simpson's rule' for numerical quadrature.

For relations involving *even*-order differences, and *odd*-order *mean* differences, the expansions (4.15), (4.16) in f and its derivatives at $x = x_0$ is the most convenient. For corresponding relations involving *odd*-order differences and *even*-order *mean* differences, it is often more convenient to expand in terms of f and its derivatives at $x = x_{\frac{1}{2}}$.

4.6. Finite difference operators

A powerful method of obtaining formulae for interpolation, integration, etc., in terms of finite differences is by means of finite difference operators. We have already recognized that the symbol δ or Δ prefixed to a symbol representing a function can be regarded as representing an *operation* performed on that function. We will now extend this idea, and first define some further operators.

The operator E is defined by

$$Ef(x) = f(x + \delta x)$$

or shortly
$$Ef_j = f_{j+1}. \tag{4.22}$$

This operator advances the argument from one value to the next of the finite difference table, and is sometimes called the 'shift operator' or 'forward shift operator'. Its inverse, written E^{-1} or $1/E$, the 'backward shift operator', steps the argument back from one value to the previous one in the difference table; that is

$$E^{-1}f_j = f_{j-1}. \tag{4.23}$$

If D is the differential operator $D \equiv d/dx$, Taylor's expansion can be written symbolically

$$f_1 = f(x_0 + \delta x) = e^{(\delta x)D}f_0,$$

so that, formally
$$Ef_0 = e^{(\delta x)D}f_0 \tag{4.24}$$

for all functions f for which the right-hand side is significant. A relation such as this, between results of different operations, which is independent of the function f operated on, is often written as a relation between the *operators*, without an operand explicitly indicated. We follow this usage, and, in accordance with it write (4.24) as

$$E = e^{(\delta x)D}. \tag{4.25}$$

Two operators of which we shall make considerable use are $E^{\frac{1}{2}}$ and its inverse $E^{-\frac{1}{2}}$. $E^{\frac{1}{2}}$ is the operator which, applied twice to f_0, gives f_1, independently of the particular form of the function f; that is to say, it is an operator such that for any operand f,

$$E^{\frac{1}{2}}[E^{\frac{1}{2}}f_0] = f_1 = Ef_0.$$

It is clear that an operator which advances the argument value by *half* the tabular interval satisfies this condition; that is

$$E^{\frac{1}{2}}f(x) = f(x + \tfrac{1}{2}\delta x)$$

or
$$E^{\frac{1}{2}}f_0 = f_{\frac{1}{2}}. \tag{4.26}$$

From Taylor's series $\qquad f_{\frac{1}{2}} = e^{\frac{1}{2}(\delta x)D}f_0$

which is consistent with (4.25).

The 'forward difference operator' Δ is defined by

$$\Delta f(x) = f(x + \delta x) - f(x) = Ef(x) - f(x)$$

or shortly
$$\Delta f_0 = f_1 - f_0 = (E - 1)f_0$$

which, expressed as a relation between operators, is

$$\Delta = E - 1. \tag{4.27}$$

The 'backward difference operator' ∇ is defined correspondingly by

$$\nabla f(x) = f(x) - f(x - \delta x)$$

or
$$\nabla = 1 - E^{-1} = (E - 1)/E. \tag{4.28}$$

The 'central difference operator' δ is defined by

$$\delta f(x) = f(x + \tfrac{1}{2}\delta x) - f(x - \tfrac{1}{2}\delta x) = (E^{\frac{1}{2}} - E^{-\frac{1}{2}})f(x)$$

which, expressed as a relation between operators, is

$$\delta = E^{\frac{1}{2}} - E^{-\frac{1}{2}}. \tag{4.29}$$

Another useful operator is the 'averaging operator' μ, defined by

$$\mu f(x) = \tfrac{1}{2}[f(x + \tfrac{1}{2}\delta x) + f(x - \tfrac{1}{2}\delta x)] = \tfrac{1}{2}[E^{\frac{1}{2}}f(x) + E^{-\frac{1}{2}}f(x)],$$

i.e.
$$\mu = \tfrac{1}{2}(E^{\frac{1}{2}} + E^{-\frac{1}{2}}). \tag{4.30}$$

These operators all have their inverses. We have already considered the operator inverse to E. The operator inverse to δ is the 'central sum operator' $\sigma = \delta^{-1}$ defined by

$$\sigma f_n = \sigma f_{n-1} + f_{n-\frac{1}{2}}$$

or
$$\sigma = E^{\frac{1}{2}}/(E - 1).$$

It should be noted that σf, like an indefinite integral, is undetermined to the extent of an arbitrary additive constant. The operator inverse to μ will be considered in § 5.2.

These operators are all linear; that is to say if O is any one of them, and f and F are any two functions, then

$$O(f + F) = Of + OF.$$

The operators E, Δ, D, δ, and ∇ are also commutative; that is, if O_1 and O_2 are two of these operations and f is any function,

$$O_1(O_2 f) = O_2(O_1 f).$$

σ and δ are not necessarily commutative, since $\sigma(\delta f)$ may differ from $\delta(\sigma f)$ by a constant, just as $\int (df/dx)\,dx$ may differ from f by a constant.

Some useful relations may be obtained from (4.23) to (4.30). For example, from (4.29), $\quad \delta^2 = E - 2 + E^{-1}$

(the operational form of $\delta^2 f_0 = f_1 - 2f_0 + f_{-1}$), and from (4.30)

$$\mu^2 = \tfrac{1}{4}(E + 2 + E^{-1}),$$

whence
$$\delta^2 = 4(\mu^2 - 1)$$

or
$$\mu^2 = 1 + \tfrac{1}{4}\delta^2. \tag{4.31}$$

And if in (4.29), (4.30) we substitute for E from (4.25) we obtain the formal relations

$$\delta = 2 \sinh \tfrac{1}{2}(\delta x)D, \tag{4.32}$$

$$\mu = \cosh \tfrac{1}{2}(\delta x)D. \tag{4.33}$$

Also we have

$$(E+1)\delta = E^{\frac{1}{2}}(E^{\frac{1}{2}}+E^{-\frac{1}{2}})(E^{\frac{1}{2}}-E^{-\frac{1}{2}}) = (E^{\frac{1}{2}}+E^{-\frac{1}{2}})(E-1)$$
$$= 2(E-1)\mu. \tag{4.34}$$

Also

$$\delta^n = [E^{-\frac{1}{2}}(E-1)]^n = E^{-\frac{1}{2}n}(E-1)^n,$$

so that

$$\delta^n f_j = (E-1)^n E^{-\frac{1}{2}n} f_j = (E-1)^n f_{j-\frac{1}{2}n};$$

expansion of $(E-1)^n$ by the binomial theorem gives

$$\delta^n f_j = \sum_{k=0}^{n} (-1)^k \frac{n!}{k!(n-k)!} E^{n-k} f_{j-\frac{1}{2}n} = \sum_{k=0}^{n} (-1)^k \frac{n!}{k!(n-k)!} f_{j+\frac{1}{2}n-k}$$

in agreement with (4.8).

We shall make considerable use of relations between operators, such as (4.32) and (4.33), which imply the use of Taylor's series in the form

$$e^{\xi D} f(x) = f(x+\xi) \tag{4.35}$$

without a remainder term. However, in using the formulae we finally obtain by means of these relations, we shall in almost all cases retain only the first few terms, therefore making truncation errors in which the remainder term of the Taylor expansion can be considered as incorporated. In most cases an analysis of the truncation error and its relation to the remainder term in the Taylor expansion can be carried out by the method of § 6.7. But it will be as well to know for what kinds of functions this expansion can be used in the form (4.35).

1. *Polynomials*: it is clearly exact for polynomials since the series terminates.
2. *Exponentials*: if $f(x) = e^{ax}$, then

$$e^{\xi D} e^{ax} = \left(1+\xi D+\frac{1}{2!}\xi^2 D^2+...\right)e^{ax} = \left(1+\xi a+\frac{1}{2!}\xi^2 a^2+...\right)e^{ax}.$$

The series in the bracket converges for all values of ξ and a, and its value is $e^{a\xi}$. Hence

$$e^{\xi D} f(x) = e^{\xi D} e^{ax} = e^{a\xi} e^{ax} = e^{a(x+\xi)} = f(x+\xi),$$

so that we can apply (4.35) without restriction to exponentials in which the exponent is linear in x.

3. *Products of exponentials and polynomials*: we will prove that if

$$e^{\xi D} z(x) = z(x+\xi)$$

then

$$e^{\xi D}[x z(x)] = (x+\xi)z(x+\xi)$$

so that if (4.35) can be applied to a function $z(x)$, then it can be applied to $xz(x)$; and so, by repetition of the argument, it can be applied to $z(x)$ multiplied by any polynomial. We have

$$e^{\xi D}[x z(x)] = \left[1+\xi D+\frac{\xi^2}{2!}D^2+...\right]x z(x)$$

$$= xz+\xi[xDz+z]+\frac{1}{2!}\xi^2[xD^2z+2Dz]+\frac{1}{3!}\xi^3[xD^3z+3D^2z]+...$$

$$= x\left[z+\xi Dz+\frac{1}{2!}\xi^2 D^2 z+\frac{1}{3!}\xi^3 D^3 z+...\right]+\left[\xi z+\xi^2 Dz+\frac{1}{2!}\xi^3 D^2 z+...\right].$$

Since z is assumed to be such that (4.35) is valid, the first square bracket is $xz(x+\xi)$, and the second is $\xi z(x+\xi)$. Hence altogether

$$e^{\xi D}[xz(x)] = (x+\xi)z(x+\xi).$$

Thus (4.35) can be applied to products of exponentials (including circular functions) and polynomials; and, since the operator is linear, it can be extended to sums of products of exponentials and polynomials.

4.7. Examples of the use of finite difference operators

It is convenient, for brevity, to have a single symbol for the operator $(\delta x)D$; this will be written U, that is

$$U = (\delta x)D. \tag{4.36}$$

Then the relations (4.25), (4.32), and (4.33) are

$$E = e^{U}, \qquad \delta = 2\sinh \tfrac{1}{2}U, \qquad \mu = \cosh \tfrac{1}{2}U, \tag{4.37}$$

so that

$$U = 2\sinh^{-1}\tfrac{1}{2}\delta \tag{4.38}$$

$$= [(\sinh^{-1}\tfrac{1}{2}\delta)/\tfrac{1}{2}\delta]\,\delta. \tag{4.39}$$

Since $\delta f = (\delta x)Df + O(\delta x)^3$ for any particular f to which these relations between finite difference operators can be applied, it follows that in expanding these and other relations in powers of δ or U, δ^n or U^n can be regarded as a quantity of order $(\delta x)^n$.

4.71. Derivatives in terms of differences

Taking the nth power of both sides of (4.39) we have

$$U^n = [(\sinh^{-1}\tfrac{1}{2}\delta)/\tfrac{1}{2}\delta]^n\delta^n. \tag{4.40}$$

Since $(\sinh^{-1}z)/z$ is an even function of z, this expresses $U^n = (\delta x)^nD^n$ in *even* powers of δ if n is even, and in *odd* powers of δ if n is odd. The available central differences $\delta^n f_j$ of *even*-order have *integral* values of j, whereas those of odd-order have (integer$+\tfrac{1}{2}$) values of j. Hence this relation can be used to obtain expressions for *even*-order derivatives *at tabular values*, $D^{2m}f_j$, or *odd*-order derivatives *half-way between* tabular values.

An alternative form is

$$U^n = [\mu^{-1}\{(\sinh^{-1}\tfrac{1}{2}\delta)/\tfrac{1}{2}\delta\}^n]\mu\delta^n. \tag{4.41}$$

Since the relation between μ and δ is $\mu^2 = 1+\tfrac{1}{4}\delta^2$, the operator in the square bracket is still an even function of δ, so that for *odd* values of n this expresses $U^n f$ in terms of *odd*-order *mean* differences $\mu\delta^{2m+1}f$, which are available at tabular values; hence this is the useful formula for *odd*-order derivatives at tabular values.

The expansions of (4.40) and (4.41) both for positive and for negative values of n can be carried out by taking the series for $(\sinh^{-1}\frac{1}{2}\delta)/\frac{1}{2}\delta$:

$$(\sinh^{-1}\tfrac{1}{2}\delta)/\tfrac{1}{2}\delta = 1-\tfrac{1}{24}\delta^2+\tfrac{3}{640}\delta^4-\tfrac{5}{7168}\delta^6+\tfrac{35}{294912}\delta^8+O(\delta x)^{10}$$

and raising it to the appropriate power; and in the case of (4.41) multiplying also by the expansion of $\mu^{-1} = (1+\tfrac{1}{4}\delta^2)^{-\frac{1}{2}}$. General expansions for $(U/\delta)^n$ and $[(U/\delta)^n/\mu]$ as far as δ^{10} for any value of n have been given by Bickley;[†] taken to terms in δ^8 that for $(U/\delta)^n$ is

$$\left(\frac{U}{\delta}\right)^n = \left(\frac{\sinh^{-1}\tfrac{1}{2}\delta}{\tfrac{1}{2}\delta}\right)^n$$

$$= 1-\frac{n}{24}\delta^2+\frac{5n^2+22n}{5760}\delta^4-\frac{35n^3+462n^2+1528n}{2903040}\delta^6+$$

$$+\frac{175n^4+4620n^3+40724n^2+119856n}{13934{,}59200}\delta^8+O(\delta x)^{10}. \qquad (4.42)$$

For positive n, the three cases of this formula which we shall need here are the cases $n = 2, 4,$ and 6, namely,

$$(U/\delta)^2 = [1-\tfrac{1}{12}\delta^2+\tfrac{1}{90}\delta^4-\tfrac{1}{560}\delta^6]+O(\delta x)^8, \qquad (4.43)$$

$$(U/\delta)^4 = [1-\tfrac{1}{6}\delta^2+\tfrac{7}{240}\delta^4]+O(\delta x)^6, \qquad (4.44)$$

$$(U/\delta)^6 = [1-\tfrac{1}{4}\delta^2]+O(\delta x)^4. \qquad (4.45)$$

For odd positive powers of (U/δ), the only important case is $n = 1$, for which

$$(U/\mu\delta) = [1-\tfrac{1}{6}\delta^2+\tfrac{1}{30}\delta^4-\tfrac{1}{140}\delta^6+\tfrac{1}{630}\delta^8]+O(\delta x)^{10}. \qquad (4.46)$$

These formulae, which give powers of $U = (\delta x)D$ in terms of δ, are operational forms of formulae for differentiation, since, applied to a function f, they give $D^n f$ in terms of the differences of f. They have, however, other and more important applications as will be seen in the next section and subsequent chapters.

4.72. Negative powers of (U/δ)

Other important relations are some involving negative powers of (U/δ). One way of obtaining these is by use of formula (4.42), or Bickley's corresponding formula for $(U/\delta)^n/\mu$, with negative values of n, for which these formulae are also valid. For example, substitution of $n = -2$ in (4.42) gives

$$(U/\delta)^{-2} = [1+\tfrac{1}{12}\delta^2-\tfrac{1}{240}\delta^4+\tfrac{31}{60480}\delta^6-\tfrac{289}{3628800}\delta^8]+O(\delta x)^{10}. \qquad (4.47)$$

Another procedure is first to express the operator in terms of U, expand as a series in U, and then substitute in terms of δ from formulae (4.43) to (4.46); this only involves the use of formula (4.42) for positive values of n.

† W. G. Bickley, *Journ. Math. and Phys.* **27** (1948), 183.

The main operators which involve inverse powers of U and for which we require expressions in terms of δ are $(\delta/U)^2$, $(\delta/\mu U)$, and $(\mu\delta/U)$. In terms of U they are

$$(\delta/U)^2 = [(\sinh \tfrac{1}{2}U)/\tfrac{1}{2}U]^2 = 2(\cosh U - 1)/U^2, \qquad (4.48)$$

$$(\delta/\mu U) = (\tanh \tfrac{1}{2}U)/\tfrac{1}{2}U, \qquad (4.49)$$

$$(\mu\delta/U) = (\sinh U)/U. \qquad (4.50)$$

Expansion of (4.48) in powers of U gives

$$(\delta/U)^2 = 1 + \frac{2}{4!}U^2 + \frac{2}{6!}U^4 + \frac{2}{8!}U^6 + O(\delta x)^8$$

$$= 1 + \tfrac{1}{12}\delta^2(U/\delta)^2 + \tfrac{1}{360}\delta^4(U/\delta)^4 + \tfrac{1}{20160}\delta^6(U/\delta)^6 + O(\delta x)^8.$$

Substitution from formulae (4.43) to (4.45) then gives, to terms in δ^6,

$$(\delta/U)^2 = 1 + \tfrac{1}{12}\delta^2[1 - \tfrac{1}{12}\delta^2 + \tfrac{1}{90}\delta^4] + \tfrac{1}{360}\delta^4[1 - \tfrac{1}{6}\delta^2] + \tfrac{1}{20160}\delta^6 + O(\delta x)^8$$

$$= [1 + \tfrac{1}{12}\delta^2 - \tfrac{1}{240}\delta^4 + \tfrac{31}{60480}\delta^6] + O(\delta x)^8$$

in agreement with (4.47).

Similarly the following expansions can be obtained:

$$(\delta/\mu U) = [1 - \tfrac{1}{12}\delta^2 + \tfrac{11}{720}\delta^4 - \tfrac{191}{60480}\delta^6 + \tfrac{2497}{3628800}\delta^8] + O(\delta x)^{10}, \qquad (4.51)$$

$$(\mu\delta/U) = [1 + \tfrac{1}{6}\delta^2 - \tfrac{1}{180}\delta^4 + \tfrac{1}{1512}\delta^6 - \tfrac{23}{226800}\delta^8] + O(\delta x)^{10}. \qquad (4.52)$$

The latter of these can alternatively be obtained from the former by multiplying by $\mu^2 = 1 + \tfrac{1}{4}\delta^2$.

4.73. $\delta^2 f$ in terms of f'' and its differences

We will use some of these relations between differential operators and finite difference operators to express $\delta^2 f_0$ in terms of f_0'' and the central differences of f'' at $x = x_0$. A first approximation is

$$\delta^2 f_0 = (\delta x)^2 f_0'' = (\delta x)^2 D^2 f_0 = U^2 f_0;$$

to improve on this we must find an operator $\phi(\delta)$ such that

$$\delta^2 f_0 = \phi(\delta) U^2 f_0. \qquad (4.53)$$

The operator $\phi(\delta)$ required is therefore

$$\phi(\delta) = (\delta/U)^2;$$

its expansion in powers of δ is given by (4.47) above, and substitution in (4.53) gives

$$\delta^2 f_0 = (\delta x)^2[f_0'' + \tfrac{1}{12}\delta^2 f_0'' - \tfrac{1}{240}\delta^4 f_0'' + \tfrac{31}{60480}\delta^6 f_0'' - \tfrac{289}{3628800}\delta^8 f_0''] + O(\delta x)^{12}$$

$$(4.54)$$

(compare formula (4.19) and its derivation in §4.5).

4.74. $\delta f_{\frac{1}{2}}$ symmetrically in terms of f' and its differences at x_0 and x_1

By definition, $\delta f_{\frac{1}{2}} = f_1 - f_0 = (E-1)f_0$, and to a first approximation

$$\delta f_{\frac{1}{2}} = \tfrac{1}{2}(\delta x)(f'_0 + f'_1) = \tfrac{1}{2}(\delta x)(E+1)Df_0 = \tfrac{1}{2}(E+1)Uf_0; \qquad (4.55)$$

we want to obtain a more general relation to which this is the first approximation.

By a formula symmetrical in f' and its derivatives at the two ends of the tabular interval is meant one in which the coefficient a_n of each $\delta^n f'_1$ is the same as that of the corresponding $\delta^n f'_0$, so that these terms together give a contribution $a_n(\delta^n f'_0 + \delta^n f'_1) = a_n \delta^n (E+1)Df_0$, as the terms with $n = 0$ do in the first approximation (4.55). Hence we want a relation of the form

$$\delta f_{\frac{1}{2}} \equiv (E-1)f_0 = \tfrac{1}{2}\phi(\delta)(E+1)Uf_0; \qquad (4.56)$$

to satisfy (4.56), $\phi(\delta)$ must be given by

$$\phi(\delta) = \frac{E-1}{\tfrac{1}{2}(E+1)U}. \qquad (4.57)$$

This can be expressed in terms of U by substituting $E = e^U$; this gives

$$\phi(\delta) = (\tanh \tfrac{1}{2}U)/\tfrac{1}{2}U.$$

Alternatively, it follows from (4.34) that (4.57) can be written

$$\phi(\delta) = \delta/\mu U$$

for which the expansion in powers of δ is given by (4.51). Hence the required formula is

$$f_1 - f_0 = \tfrac{1}{2}(\delta x)[f'_0 + f'_1 - \tfrac{1}{12}(\delta^2 f'_0 + \delta^2 f'_1) + \tfrac{11}{720}(\delta^4 f'_0 + \delta^4 f'_1) -$$
$$- \tfrac{191}{60480}(\delta^6 f'_0 + \delta^6 f'_1)] + O(\delta x)^9. \qquad (4.58)$$

This is an integration formula, for if $f'(x)$ is given as a function of x it enables the change in $f(x)$, that is $\int_{x_0}^{x_1} f'(x)\,dx$, to be evaluated in terms of the values of $f'(x)$ (see Chapter VI).

4.75. $\mu\delta f_0$ in terms of f' and its differences at $x = x_0$

In this case we want to find an operator $\phi(\delta)$ such that

$$\mu\delta f_0 = (\delta x)\phi(\delta)Df_0.$$

The appropriate $\phi(\delta)$ is

$$\phi(\delta) = \mu\delta/U = (\sinh U)/U$$

of which the expansion in powers of δ is given by (4.52). Hence

$$\mu\delta f_0 = \tfrac{1}{2}(f_1 - f_{-1}) = (\delta x)[f_0' + \tfrac{1}{6}\delta^2 f_0' - \tfrac{1}{180}\delta^4 f_0' + \tfrac{1}{1512}\delta^6 f_0' - \tfrac{23}{226800}\delta^8 f_0'] + O(\delta x)^{11}$$

$$(4.59)$$

(compare §4.5, formula (4.21)). This also is an integration formula, relating the change of f in an interval $2\delta x$ of x to the behaviour of its derivative in the neighbourhood of that interval.

V

INTERPOLATION

5.1. Linear and non-linear interpolation

GIVEN a table of values of a function $f(x)$ at a set of tabular values of x, usually, but not necessarily, equally spaced, we may require to determine either the value of $f(x)$ at an intermediate value of x, or the value of x for which $f(x)$ has some specified value. The process for finding a result of this kind is called 'interpolation', and, when it is necessary to distinguish between them, the former is called 'direct' and the latter 'inverse' interpolation. The distinction is not usually significant unless the tabular values of x are equally spaced; this case, however, is much the most usual.

By 'linear interpolation' is meant interpolation using the approximation in which, for $0 < \theta < 1$, we take

$$f(x_0 + \theta \, \delta x) = f_0 + \theta \, \delta f_{\frac{1}{2}}; \qquad (5.1)$$

expressed graphically, this is interpolation along the chord joining the points (x_0, f_0) and (x_1, f_1). This process is valid so long as the tabular values of x are spaced closely enough; we will obtain later (§5.12) a quantitative criterion of what is 'closely enough' in this context. 'Non-linear interpolation' is interpolation in some form which takes account of the departure of the (x, f) curve from the chord between the points corresponding to neighbouring tabular values.

There are two kinds of tables; first, those in which interpolation is required frequently enough to justify the use of intervals of the argument small enough for linear interpolation to be adequate. Secondly, there are those in which interpolation will only be occasional, not frequent enough to justify the calculation and printing at small enough intervals for linear interpolation to be applicable.

In the latter case, non-linear interpolation is necessary. But if non-linear interpolation were generally recognized as a standard process, the bulk of tables could be very greatly reduced. For example, a table of $\sin x$ to five decimals at intervals of $10°$ reads as given on p. 61. We shall see later that the formulae required for carrying out non-linear interpolation in this table are comparatively simple. We shall also see that for linear interpolation we require $|\delta^2 f|$ to be not greater than 2, so that at least 40 times the number of entries are required in order to obtain a table in which linear interpolation can be carried out.

x	$f(x) =$ $\sin x$	δf	$\delta^2 f$	$\delta^3 f$	$\delta^4 f$
0°	0		0		0
		17365		−528	
10°	·17365		− 528		+17
		16837		−511	
20°	·34202		−1039		31
		15798		−480	
30°	·50000		−1519		45
		14279		−435	
40°	·64279		−1954		63
		12325		−372	
50°	·76604		−2326		65
		9999		−307	
60°	·86603		−2633		86
		7366		−221	
70°	·93969		−2854		82
		4512		−139	
80°	·98481		−2993		94
		1519		− 45	
90°	1·00000		−3038		90

The reduction in bulk achieved by the use of a large interval and non-linear interpolation is not important in the case of functions of a single real variable, but becomes important in connexion with functions of two variables (or of a complex variable), or functions of a variable and one or more parameters such as the Bessel functions $J_n(x)$ and the Whittaker functions $W_{k,m}(x)$.

5.11. Linear interpolation

The simplest form of interpolation is linear interpolation, or interpolation by proportional parts, for which the interpolation formula is (5.1) above.

In carrying out linear interpolation on a machine, there is a precaution against mistakes which should always be observed. Suppose first that $\delta f_{\frac{1}{2}}$ is positive. Having cleared the accumulator, set f_0, add it into the accumulator, and clear the multiplier register. Then set $\delta f_{\frac{1}{2}}$, *add it in, and verify that the content of the accumulator is now f_1.* This checks that the right values of f_0 and $\delta f_{\frac{1}{2}}$ have been taken. If θ has m decimals, the accumulator should first be shifted m places right, and f_0 and $\delta f_{\frac{1}{2}}$ then set on the extreme right of the setting levers or keyboard.

For direct interpolation, $\theta \delta f_{\frac{1}{2}}$ is added to f_0; if θ is greater than $\frac{1}{2}$, the addition of $\delta f_{\frac{1}{2}}$ to f_0 to check can be taken as the first step of this multiplication; if θ is less than $\frac{1}{2}$, $\delta f_{\frac{1}{2}}$ should be subtracted from f_1 to restore f_0 before doing the multiplication.

For inverse interpolation, the given value of f is built up in the accumulator, and the fraction θ of the interval length required to give this value of f is read on the multiplier register.

If $\delta f_{\frac{1}{2}}$ is negative, $|\delta f_{\frac{1}{2}}|$ should be set, and operations of addition and subtraction are interchanged; otherwise the procedure is the same.

In some tables, particularly elementary ones, a sequence of function values is given on a single line (for example, $\log 1 \cdot 00$ to $1 \cdot 09$ on a line of a four-figure table of logarithms) with proportional parts of the *mean* first difference at the end of the line. Use of these proportional parts of the mean difference does not usually give the best interpolated value, and should not be used indiscriminately except in contexts in which an error of 2 or 3 units in the last figure is unimportant. The following example is taken from a table of logarithms to five places in which, for $x = 1 \cdot 0$ to $2 \cdot 0$, different sets of proportional parts of mean differences are given for every *five* entries:

x	1·05	1·06	1·07	1·08	1·09	1	2	3 . .	5 . .	. 9
$\log x$	·02119	·02531	·02938	·03342	·03743	40	81	121 . .	202 .	. 364

The last five columns are the proportional parts of the mean difference. Using the actual difference between the first two entries, we get $\log 1 \cdot 055 = 0 \cdot 02325$, whereas using the proportional parts of mean differences we get $0 \cdot 02321$, a difference of four units in the fifth decimal.

For the best linear interpolation, proportional parts should be taken of the actual difference between successive tabular values. Tables of proportional parts for this purpose are given in most good modern books of tables.

If several functions are tabulated in parallel columns, at such an interval that linear interpolation can be used on each of them, then linear interpolation can be used between two columns. For example, a table of $\sin x$ and $\cos x$ against x, in parallel columns, is also a table of $(1 - y^2)^{\frac{1}{2}}$ against y, and can be used as such without reference to the x column at all. Since the values of both functions $f(x)$ and $g(x)$ are subject to rounding error, the possible error in the interpolated value is rather greater than if $f(x)$ were tabulated at exact values of $g(x)$.

5.2. Non-linear interpolation

In considering non-linear interpolation, it will be supposed for the present that the tabular values of the argument are equally spaced. Interpolation with unequally spaced values of the argument will be considered in § 5.7.

5.21. Half-way interpolation

One particular case of non-linear interpolation is so much simpler than the general case, and so useful, that it will be considered separately first. This is interpolation for a value of x half-way between tabular values.

To get a formula for this, we want to express $f(x_0+\frac{1}{2}\delta x)$, which can be expressed as $E^{\frac{1}{2}}f_0$, symmetrically in f_0, f_1 and the differences of f at x_0 and x_1. Now $f(x_0+\frac{1}{2}\delta x) = E^{\frac{1}{2}}f_0$, so we want to find an operator $\phi(\delta)$ such that

$$E^{\frac{1}{2}}f_0 = \phi(\delta)\tfrac{1}{2}(1+E)f_0.$$

This operator is given by

$$\phi(\delta) = 2E^{\frac{1}{2}}/(1+E) = 1/\cosh\tfrac{1}{2}U = 1/(1+\tfrac{1}{4}\delta^2)^{\frac{1}{2}}, \qquad (5.2)$$

so that

$$f_{\frac{1}{2}} = f(x_0+\tfrac{1}{2}\delta x) = (1+\tfrac{1}{4}\delta^2)^{-\frac{1}{2}}[\tfrac{1}{2}(f_0+f_1)]$$

$$= \tfrac{1}{2}[f_0+f_1-\tfrac{1}{8}(\delta^2 f_0+\delta^2 f_1)+\tfrac{3}{128}(\delta^4 f_0+\delta^4 f_1)-$$

$$-\tfrac{5}{1024}(\delta^6 f_0+\delta^6 f_1)]+O(\delta x)^8. \quad (5.3)$$

It will be noted that the operator $\phi(\delta)$ given by (5.2) is the operator inverse to the averaging operator μ. Indeed, the relation (5.3) could be obtained as follows. The definition of the operator μ is $\mu f_{\frac{1}{2}} = \tfrac{1}{2}(f_0+f_1)$, and it follows that the inverse operator μ^{-1} is an operator such that

$$f_{\frac{1}{2}} = \tfrac{1}{2}\mu^{-1}(f_0+f_1). \qquad (5.4)$$

But $f_{\frac{1}{2}} = f(x_0+\tfrac{1}{2}\delta x)$ and $\mu^2 = 1+\tfrac{1}{4}\delta^2$, so that (5.4) is just (5.2) in a different form.

Formula (5.3), perhaps taken to higher orders of differences, is useful in a preliminary breaking down of the interval of a table of a function evaluated at a large interval, before carrying out a subtabulation. The coefficients are easy to calculate and to check if more are required than are given in (5.3). If $(-)^j a_j$ is the coefficient of $(\delta^{2j}f_0+\delta^{2j}f_1)$ in the square bracket in (5.3) then

$$a_{j+1}/a_j = (2j+1)/8(j+1) \qquad (5.5)$$

and the coefficients can most conveniently be calculated by continued multiplication by the successive ratios (5.5). A check is given by the relations $\sum a_j = 2/\sqrt{3} = 1{\cdot}15470$. $\sum 2^j a_j = \sqrt{2} = 1{\cdot}41421$.

It is interesting to examine the result of applying (5.3) to a table of $\cos x$ or $\sin x$ at a large interval such as $60°$ or $90°$. The ratio (5.5) tends to the value $\tfrac{1}{4}$ for large j. Hence provided $|\delta^{2j+2}f/\delta^{2j}f| < 4$ for large j, the infinite series of which (5.3) gives the first few terms formally converges.

Now if $f(x) = B\cos(x+\beta)$, then $\delta^2 f_j = -2(1-\cos\delta x)f_j$, so that if $\delta x = \tfrac{1}{2}\pi$, $|\delta^{2j+2}f/\delta^{2j}f| = 2$. Thus by use of the series (5.3) we can interpolate $\cos x$ and $\sin x$, not only approximately but, by taking enough terms, to any accuracy we require, from the tabular values

x	0	$\tfrac{1}{2}\pi$	π	$\tfrac{3}{2}\pi$	2π
$\cos x$	1	0	-1	0	1
$\sin x$	0	1	0	-1	0

and the condition of periodicity.

It is even possible to interpolate accurately from a table at intervals of $\frac{2}{3}\pi$:

x	0	$\frac{2}{3}\pi$	$\frac{4}{3}\pi$	2π
$\cos x$	1	$-\frac{1}{2}$	$-\frac{1}{2}$	1
$\sin x$	0	$\frac{1}{2}\sqrt{3}$	$-\frac{1}{2}\sqrt{3}$	0

extended by using the condition of periodicity.

5.22. Newton's forward-difference formula

Of the formulae for non-linear interpolation for a general value of the fraction θ of the interval length, the simplest to derive is one in terms of forward differences. Its practical value is, however, limited.

Taylor's series can be written, in terms of operators,

$$f(x_0+\theta\,\delta x) = e^{\theta(\delta x)D}f_0 = E^\theta f_0.$$

Also $E = 1+\Delta$, and expansion of $(1+\Delta)^\theta$ by the binomial theorem gives

$$f(x_0+\theta\,\delta x) = \left[1+\theta\Delta+\frac{1}{2!}\theta(\theta-1)\Delta^2+\ldots\right]f_0$$

$$= f_0+\theta\Delta f_0+\frac{1}{2!}\theta(\theta-1)\,\Delta^2 f_0+\frac{1}{3!}\theta(\theta-1)(\theta-2)\Delta^3 f_0+\ldots \quad (5.6)$$

which is usually known as Newton's formula. It uses values of the differences on an inclined line in a difference table:

It is unsatisfactory if differences beyond the second have to be taken into account, as the differences of a function f depend primarily on the behaviour of the function in the neighbourhood of the value of x on which they are centred, so that the higher-order differences involved in this formula are less and less closely related to the behaviour of f in the interval in which interpolation is being carried out.

Its practical use is restricted to interpolation near the boundaries of a table, and this is rare because unless f or one of its derivatives has a singularity at $x = x_0$, there should usually be little difficulty in extending the table backwards a few intervals from $x = x_0$, whereas if the boundary of the table results from f being infinite at $x = x_0$ (for example $f(x) = \cot x$ at $x = 0$) or undefined for $x < x_0$ (for example $f(x) = x^{\frac{1}{2}}$ at $x = 0$), this situation is usually associated with an infinite derivative $f'(x_0)$, in which case the Taylor series expansion on which Newton's formula is based is invalid.

There are various other interpolation formulae, which can all be derived from Newton's by substitution for the forward differences $\Delta^n f_0$ in terms of differences more representative of the behaviour $f(x)$ in the interval through which the interpolation is being carried out. It is difficult, however, to obtain the form of the general term by such a derivation, and it is better to derive these other interpolation formulae independently. Of the various formulae Comrie writes[†] 'only three are found in good modern practice, namely those associated with the names of Bessel and Everett, each of which is a simple transformation of the other, and that of Lagrange'. The present treatment will be restricted to these three.

From Newton's (or Bessel's) formula it is possible to deduce the conditions in which linear interpolation gives a sufficiently accurate result. The greatest numerical value of the coefficient of the second difference in formula (5.6) is $\frac{1}{8}$. It is best to keep the contribution from this term to the interpolated value less than $0\cdot 3$ in the last figure; if it were greater it should be included as it might affect the rounding off of the final result. Hence linear interpolation should not be used if second differences are greater than 2 unless errors up to 2 units in the last place of the interpolated value can be tolerated.

Occasionally the contribution from the second differences to the interpolated value is negligible when those from higher orders of differences are not; an example is provided by the function $x(x^2-1)(x^2-4)$ tabulated at unit intervals of x and interpolated between $x = 0$ and 1. To avoid this situation it is only necessary to see that not only the second differences used in the interpolation formula, but also a number of neighbouring values, are not greater than 2 in the last figure.

5.3. Some expansions

For the purpose of deriving interpolation formulae in central differences,[‡] we shall require some expansions, namely those of $\sinh \beta U$, $(\cosh \beta U)/\cosh \frac{1}{2}U$, and $(\sinh \beta U)/\sinh U$ in terms of $\delta = 2\sinh \frac{1}{2}U$, for non-integral β. These could be written down from the similar expressions for circular functions of a numerical variable;[§] but their derivations will be given here for completeness.

For the purposes of this section, let u stand for an ordinary numerical variable, and let
$$z = 2\sinh \tfrac{1}{2}u \quad \text{and} \quad y = \cosh \beta u. \tag{5.7}$$

[†] *Chambers's 6-Figure Tables*, vol. 2 (1949), Introduction, p. xxvii.

[‡] The treatment of this and the following section follows that of J. G. L. Michel, *Journ. Inst. of Actuaries*, **72** (1946), 470.

[§] e.g. T. J. I'A. Bromwich, *Theory of Infinite Series* (Macmillan, 2nd ed. 1926) § 68.

Consider first the expansion of y as a power series in z. We shall obtain this by forming the differential equation for y in terms of z as independent variable, then differentiating n times and putting $z = 0$; this will give recurrence relations for the derivatives $d^n y / dz^n$ at $z = 0$, from which their values, and so the required series, can be written down.

Since $y = \cosh \beta u$, it satisfies the equation

$$\frac{d^2 y}{du^2} = \beta^2 y, \tag{5.8}$$

and since $z = 2 \sinh \tfrac{1}{2} u$, it follows that

$$\frac{dz}{du} = \cosh \tfrac{1}{2} u, \tag{5.9}$$

so that
$$\frac{d^2 y}{du^2} = (\cosh \tfrac{1}{2} u) \frac{d}{dz} \left[(\cosh \tfrac{1}{2} u) \frac{dy}{dz} \right].$$

On differentiating this out, substituting for $\sinh \tfrac{1}{2} u$ from (5.7) and for du/dz from (5.9), we obtain

$$(1 + \tfrac{1}{4} z^2) \frac{d^2 y}{dz^2} + \tfrac{1}{4} z \frac{dy}{dz} = \beta^2 y, \tag{5.10}$$

and then, on differentiating n times with respect to z and putting $z = 0$,

$$y^{(n+2)}(0) = (\beta^2 - \tfrac{1}{4} n^2) y^{(n)}(0). \tag{5.11}$$

Also, for small u, $z = u + O(u^3)$, and so

$$y = 1 + O(u^2) = 1 + O(z^2)$$

and hence $y(0) = 1$, $y'(0) = 0$. Hence, from (5.11), for the odd derivatives

$$y^{(2n+1)}(0) = 0$$

and for the even derivatives

$$y''(0) = \beta^2, \qquad y^{iv}(0) = \beta^2(\beta^2 - 1), \qquad y^{vi}(0) = \beta^2(\beta^2 - 1)(\beta^2 - 4)\ldots,$$

and in general, in terms of the functions ψ_m introduced in § 4.41,

$$y^{(2n)}(0) = \beta \psi_{2n-1}(\beta). \tag{5.12}$$

Hence
$$y = \cosh \beta u = 1 + \beta \sum_n \psi_{2n+1}(\beta) z^{2n+2}/(2n+2)!.$$

Differentiation with respect to z then gives

$$\beta(\sinh \beta u) \frac{du}{dz} = \beta z \sum_{n,} \psi_{2n+1}(\beta) z^{2n}/(2n+1)!.$$

But from (5.9)

$$z \, dz/du = (2 \sinh \tfrac{1}{2} u) \cosh \tfrac{1}{2} u = \sinh u;$$

hence

$$\frac{\sinh \beta u}{\sinh u} = \sum_n \psi_{2n+1}(\beta) z^{2n}/(2n+1)! \qquad (5.13)$$

$$= \beta \left[1 + \frac{1}{3!}(\beta^2-1)z^2 + \frac{1}{5!}(\beta^2-1)(\beta^2-4)z^4 + ... \right]. \qquad (5.14)$$

To obtain corresponding expressions for $\sinh \beta u$ and $\cosh \beta u/\cosh \tfrac{1}{2}u$, take $z = 2\sinh \tfrac{1}{2}u$ as before, and $y = \sinh \beta u$. This also satisfies equation (5.8), and the above argument applies as far as the recurrence relation (5.11). Now, however, $y = \beta z + O(z^3)$ for small z, so that $y(0) = 0$, $y'(0) = \beta$. Hence $y^{(2n)}(0) = 0$, and

$$y'(0) = \beta, \qquad y'''(0) = \beta(\beta^2-\tfrac{1}{4}), \qquad y^v(0) = \beta(\beta^2-\tfrac{1}{4})(\beta^2-\tfrac{9}{4}), \qquad ...,$$

and in general, in terms of the functions ψ_m of § 4.41 (p. 41),

$$y^{(2n+1)}(0) = \beta\psi_{2n}(\beta)$$

(compare (5.12) for the expansion of $\cosh \beta u$). Hence

$$y = \sinh \beta u = \beta \sum_n \psi_{2n}(\beta) z^{2n+1}/(2n+1)! \qquad (5.15)$$

$$= \beta \left[z + \frac{1}{3!}\left(\beta^2-\frac{1}{4}\right)z^3 + \frac{1}{5!}\left(\beta^2-\frac{1}{4}\right)\left(\beta^2-\frac{9}{4}\right)z^5 + ... \right]. \qquad (5.16)$$

The expansion of $(\cosh \beta u)/(\cosh \tfrac{1}{2}u)$ can be obtained by differentiating (5.15) with respect to z. On the left-hand side this gives $\beta(\cosh \beta u)(du/dz)$. But from (5.9) this is just $\beta(\cosh \beta u)/(\cosh \tfrac{1}{2}u)$. Hence

$$\frac{\cosh \beta u}{\cosh \tfrac{1}{2}u} = \sum_n \psi_{2n}(\beta) z^{2n}/(2n)! = 1 + \frac{1}{2!}\left(\beta^2-\frac{1}{4}\right)z^2 + \frac{1}{4!}\left(\beta^2-\frac{1}{4}\right)\left(\beta^2-\frac{9}{4}\right)z^4 + ... \qquad (5.17)$$

5.4. Everett's interpolation formula

The simplest central-difference interpolation formula to obtain is that known as Everett's. This expresses the interpolated value of f in terms of the values of f and of its *even*-order differences only, at the beginning and end of the interval in which the interpolation is being carried out; that is, it is of the form

$$f(x_0+\theta\,\delta x) = (1-\theta)f_0 + \theta f_1 + E_0^{\mathrm{ii}}(\theta)\,\delta^2 f_0 + E_1^{\mathrm{ii}}(\theta)\,\delta^2 f_1 + \\ + E_0^{\mathrm{iv}}(\theta)\,\delta^4 f_0 + E_1^{\mathrm{iv}}(\theta)\,\delta^4 f_1 + ... \qquad (5.18)$$

The coefficients in this interpolation formula are usually known as 'Everett interpolation coefficients'; they are functions of the fraction θ of the interval length δx for which the interpolation is being carried out.

To obtain a formula of this kind we must find operators $\phi_0(\delta)$, $\phi_1(\delta)$ which involve only even powers of δ and which are such that

$$f(x_0+\theta\,\delta x) = \phi_0(\delta)f_0 + \phi_1(\delta)f_1. \qquad (5.19)$$

Now $f(x_0+\theta\,\delta x) = e^{\theta U}f_0$, and $f_1 = e^U f_0$, so (5.19), expressed as a relation between operators, becomes

$$e^{\theta U} = \phi_0(\delta) + \phi_1(\delta)e^U.$$

Since $\phi_0(\delta)$, $\phi_1(\delta)$ are to be even functions of δ, and so of U, it follows that they do not change on replacing U by $-U$; hence

$$e^{-\theta U} = \phi_0(\delta) + \phi_1(\delta) e^{-U},$$

and solution for $\phi_0(\delta)$, $\phi_1(\delta)$ then gives

$$\phi_1(\delta) = (e^{\theta U} - e^{-\theta U})/(e^U - e^{-U}) = \sinh \theta U / \sinh U$$

$$\phi_0(\delta) = \sinh(1-\theta)U/\sinh U = \sinh \bar{\theta} U / \sinh U,$$

where, for convenience later, $\bar{\theta}$ has been written for $(1-\theta)$.

We require expressions for these operators in terms of δ. These could be obtained by expanding in powers of U and then substituting for U in terms of δ from formulae (4.43) to (4.45); but the form of the general term is most easily obtained by the formal substitution of U for u, δ for z, and θ or $\bar{\theta} = 1-\theta$ for β in (5.13) or (5.14). This, followed by substitution of the results into (5.19), gives

$$f(x_0 + \theta \, \delta x) = \sum_n \frac{1}{(2n+1)!} [\psi_{2n+1}(1-\theta) \, \delta^{2n} f_0 + \psi_{2n+1}(\theta) \, \delta^{2n} f_1] \qquad (5.20)$$

$$= \bar{\theta} \left[f_0 + \frac{1}{3!}(\bar{\theta}^2 - 1)\delta^2 f_0 + \frac{1}{5!}(\bar{\theta}^2 - 1)(\bar{\theta}^2 - 4)\delta^4 f_0 + \cdots \right] +$$

$$+ \theta \left[f_1 + \frac{1}{3!}(\theta^2 - 1)\delta^2 f_1 + \frac{1}{5!}(\theta^2 - 1)(\theta^2 - 4)\delta^4 f_1 + \cdots \right] \qquad (5.21)$$

which is Everett's interpolation formula.

Comparison of (5.20) with (5.18) gives the following general expressions for the coefficients in (5.18):

$$\left. \begin{array}{l} E_0^{2n}(\theta) = \psi_{2n+1}(1-\theta)/(2n+1)! \\ E_1^{2n}(\theta) = \psi_{2n+1}(\theta)/(2n+1)! \end{array} \right\} . \qquad (5.22)$$

5.41. Bessel's interpolation formula

Bessel's interpolation formula expresses the interpolated value $f(x_0 + \theta \, \delta x)$ in terms of mean differences of even-order $\mu \delta^{2n} f_{\frac{1}{2}}$ and odd-order differences $\delta^{2n+1} f_{\frac{1}{2}}$, centred on the middle of the interval in which interpolation is being carried out. For practical work it is most convenient to have the contribution from the even-order differences expressed in terms of the sum $(\delta^{2n} f_0 + \delta^{2n} f_1)$ of the values at the beginning and end of the interval. Thus this formula is of the general form†

$$f(x_0 + \theta \, \delta x) = \tfrac{1}{2}(f_0 + f_1) + (\theta - \tfrac{1}{2}) \, \delta f_{\frac{1}{2}} + B^{\mathrm{ii}}(\theta)(\delta^2 f_0 + \delta^2 f_1) +$$

$$+ B^{\mathrm{iii}}(\theta) \, \delta^3 f_{\frac{1}{2}} + B^{\mathrm{iv}}(\theta)(\delta^4 f_0 + \delta^4 f_1) + B^{\mathrm{v}}(\theta) \, \delta^5 f_{\frac{1}{2}} + \cdots . \qquad (5.23)$$

† In this formula, $B^{\mathrm{ii}}(\theta)$ is written for the coefficient of $(\delta^2 f_0 + \delta^2 f_1)$, not for the coefficient of $\mu \delta^2 f_{\frac{1}{2}}$, and similarly for the higher even orders of differences. This usage follows that adopted by Comrie (*Chambers's 6-Figure Tables*, 1949, vol. 2). In some earlier work and tabulation of coefficients in Bessel's formulae B'' or B^{ii} has been used for the coefficient of $\mu \delta^2 f_{\frac{1}{2}}$.

The coefficients $B^n(\theta)$ of successive orders of differences in this formula are called 'Bessel interpolation coefficients', or simply 'Bessel coefficients' when there is no danger of confusion with the other meaning of this term. The first two terms give the value $f_0 + \theta \,\delta f_{\frac{1}{2}}$ obtained by linear interpolation, expressed in a form consistent with the other terms of the series.

A formula of this kind can be derived quite easily from Everett's formula (5.18). Consider the pairs of terms involving $\delta^{2n} f_0$ and $\delta^{2n} f_1$ in Everett's formula. These can be written

$$E_0^{2n}(\theta)\,\delta^{2n} f_0 + E_1^{2n}(\theta)\,\delta^{2n} f_1$$
$$= \tfrac{1}{2}[E_0^{2n}(\theta) + E_1^{2n}(\theta)](\delta^{2n} f_0 + \delta^{2n} f_1) + \tfrac{1}{2}[E_1^{2n}(\theta) - E_0^{2n}(\theta)]\,\delta^3 f_{\frac{1}{2}},$$

which is of the form of the contributions from $\delta^{2n} f$ and $\delta^{2n+1} f$ in Bessel's formula. Comparison with (5.23) and use of the formulae (5.22) for the Everett coefficients gives

$$B^{2n}(\theta) = \tfrac{1}{2}[E_0^{2n}(\theta) + E_1^{2n}(\theta)]$$
$$= \frac{1}{2}\frac{1}{(2n+1)!}[\psi_{2n+1}(1-\theta) + \psi_{2n+1}(\theta)]$$

and

$$B^{2n+1}(\theta) = \tfrac{1}{2}[E_1^{2n}(\theta) - E_0^{2n}(\theta)] = \frac{1}{2}\frac{1}{(2n+1)!}[\psi_{2n+1}(\theta) - \psi_{2n+1}(1-\theta)];$$

and on substitution from (4.13), (4.14) these become

$$\left.\begin{aligned}
B^{2n}(\theta) &= \frac{1}{2}\frac{1}{(2n)!}\,\psi_{2n}(\theta - \tfrac{1}{2}) \\
B^{2n+1}(\theta) &= \frac{1}{(2n+1)!}\,(\theta - \tfrac{1}{2})\psi_{2n}(\theta - \tfrac{1}{2})
\end{aligned}\right\} \tag{5.24}$$

The first few functions $B^m(\theta)$ are

$$B^{ii}(\theta) = \theta(\theta-1)/2.2! \qquad B^{iii}(\theta) = \theta(\theta-\tfrac{1}{2})(\theta-1)/3!$$
$$B^{iv}(\theta) = (\theta+1)\theta(\theta-1)(\theta-2)/2.4!$$
$$B^{v}(\theta) = (\theta+1)\theta(\theta-\tfrac{1}{2})(\theta-1)(\theta-2)/5!$$

Bessel's formula can alternatively be derived directly without using Everett's formula; the following is a summary of this derivation.

Expressed in terms of operators, formula (5.23) can be written

$$E^\theta f_0 = \phi_1(\delta)(E+1)f_0 + \phi_2(\delta)E^{\frac{1}{2}}f_0$$

where $\phi_1(\delta)$ is an even function of δ and $\phi_2(\delta)$ an odd function. Thus the operators $\phi_1(\delta)$ and $\phi_2(\delta)$ must satisfy

$$E^{\theta-\frac{1}{2}} = \phi_1(\delta)(E^{\frac{1}{2}} + E^{-\frac{1}{2}}) + \phi_2(\delta),$$

that is

$$e^{(\theta-\frac{1}{2})U} = \phi_1(\delta).(2\cosh\tfrac{1}{2}U) + \phi_2(\delta).$$

But $e^{(\theta-\frac{1}{2})U} = \cosh(\theta-\frac{1}{2})U + \sinh(\theta-\frac{1}{2})U,$

of which the first term is an even function of U and so of δ, and the second is an odd function. Hence we obtain a formula of the kind sought by taking

$$\phi_1(\delta) = \cosh(\theta-\tfrac{1}{2})U/2\cosh\tfrac{1}{2}U, \qquad \phi_2(\delta) = \sinh(\theta-\tfrac{1}{2})U.$$

The expansions of these in powers of $\delta = 2\sinh\tfrac{1}{2}U$ can be written down from (5.16), (5.17) by making the formal substitutions of U for u, δ for z, and $(\theta-\tfrac{1}{2})$ for β.

5.42. Use of Bessel's and Everett's formulae

Bessel's formula to second differences, namely,

$$f(x_0+\theta\,\delta x) = f_0 + \theta\,\delta f_{\frac{1}{2}} + B^{ii}(\theta)(\delta^2 f_0 + \delta^2 f_1), \qquad (5.25)$$

or to third differences, with second differences modified as explained below, is generally the most useful formula for non-linear interpolation, unless so large a number of figures is required, or the spacing δx is so large, that fourth and perhaps higher-order differences have to be taken into account. Then Everett's formula is probably more convenient, especially when using tables in which only differences of even order are tabulated.

The coefficient $B^{ii}(\theta)$ is always negative. A critical table to four decimals is given in Comrie and Milne-Thompson's *Standard 4-Figure Tables* and one to five decimals in *Interpolation and Allied Tables*, where $B^{iii}(\theta)$ is also tabulated; $B^{ii}(\theta)$ and $B^{iii}(\theta)$ are also tabulated in *Chambers's 6-Figure Tables*, vol. 2 (1949). For other tables of coefficients in this (and other) interpolation formulae, reference should be made to the *Index of Mathematical Tables*.

In Bessel's interpolation formula, the coefficients of the odd-order differences are all zero at $\theta = \tfrac{1}{2}$ as well as at $\theta = 0$ and 1; this is an advantage over most other interpolation formulae which involve all orders of differences. The greatest value of $|B^{iii}(\theta)|$ is about $0\cdot008$, so the contribution from $\delta^3 f$ to the interpolated value is less than $0\cdot5$ in the least significant figure if $|\delta^3 f|$ is less than 60.

Further, the contribution from the second and fourth differences together is
$$B^{ii}(\theta)[(\delta^2 f_0 + \delta^2 f_1) + \tfrac{1}{12}(\theta+1)(\theta-2)(\delta^4 f_0 + \delta^4 f_1)]$$

and $-\tfrac{1}{12}(\theta+1)(\theta-2)$ does not vary greatly over the range of θ, from 0 to 1, over which this formula will be used; its maximum value is $0\cdot1875$ at $\theta = \tfrac{1}{2}$ and it is greater than $0\cdot180$ over half this range of θ; its smallest value is $0\cdot1667$ at $\theta = 0$ and 1, where $B^{ii}(\theta)$, by which it is multiplied, is zero. Hence a good approximation to the contribution from $\delta^4 f$ to the interpolated value can be made by subtracting a *constant* multiple of $\delta^4 f$ from each $\delta^2 f$, and applying Bessel's formula, correct to second or third differences only, with the second differences so modified. If we write

$$\delta_m^2 f_j = \delta^2 f_j - C\,\delta^4 f_j \tag{5.26}$$

and use $B^{ii}(\theta)(\delta_m^2 f_0 + \delta_m^2 f_1)$ in such a formula, the residual contribution from $\delta^4 f$ is

$$\tfrac{1}{2}\theta(\theta-1)[C+\tfrac{1}{12}(\theta+1)(\theta-2)]\mu\delta^4 f_{\frac{1}{2}}. \tag{5.27}$$

The best value of C is that which makes the extreme values of the coefficient here equal and opposite, and is $C = 0 \cdot 184$; the greatest value of the coefficient of $\delta^4 f$ in (5.27) is then $0 \cdot 00045$, whereas the greatest value of $|B^{iv}(\theta)|$ is $0 \cdot 0117$. The residual contribution from $\delta^4 f$ is less than $0 \cdot 5$ in the least significant figure if $\delta^4 f$ is less than 1100.

Quantities $\delta_m^2 f_j$ given by (5.26) with $C = 0 \cdot 184$ are called 'modified second differences' and this inclusion of a constant multiple of the fourth differences in modified second differences is called 'throwback' of the fourth differences to the second. It is due to L. J. Comrie, and is a valuable device for simplifying practical interpolation, particularly inverse interpolation and subtabulation.

In Everett's formula E_0^{2n}, the coefficient of $\delta^{2n} f_0$ is the same function of $(1-\theta)$ as E_1^{2n} is of θ, so that in tables of interpolation coefficients the number of separate functions which have be to tabulated for Everett's formula is only about half as many as for formulae involving all orders of differences. Also in tables of the function f to be interpolated, only even-order differences need be given. Tables of Everett coefficients are given in *Interpolation and Allied Tables* and in *Chambers's 6-Figure Tables*, vol. 2 (1949).

The 'throwback' can be used with Everett's formula as with Bessel's. The contribution from $\delta^2 f_1$ and $\delta^4 f_1$ together in Everett's formula is

$$\tfrac{1}{6}\theta(\theta^2-1)[\delta^2 f_1 + \tfrac{1}{20}(\theta^2-4)\,\delta^4 f_1];$$

the coefficient $-\tfrac{1}{20}(\theta^2-4)$ varies from $0 \cdot 15$ to $0 \cdot 20$ over the range $\theta = 0$ to 1, and is multiplied by a zero factor at both ends of the range. If the same modified second differences are used, namely,

$$\delta_m^2 f = \delta^2 f - 0 \cdot 184\,\delta^4 f,$$

the residual contribution from $\delta^4 f_1$ is

$$\tfrac{1}{6}\theta(\theta^2-1)[0 \cdot 184 + \tfrac{1}{20}(\theta^2-4)]\,\delta^4 f_1;$$

the greatest value of this coefficient is about $0 \cdot 0008$, so that this contribution is less than $0 \cdot 3$ in the last figure if $\delta^4 f_1$ is less than about 400. Similarly for the contribution from $\delta^4 f_0$.

If fourth differences are too large to be treated by means of the throw-back, Everett's formula can be taken as far as the $\delta^4 f$ terms, and the sixth differences thrown back to the fourth differences.† If eighth differences are appreciable, very effective use can be made of a joint throwback of the sixth and eighth differences to the second and fourth differences.†

5.43. Practical details in non-linear interpolation

In using Bessel's or Everett's formulae, values of the coefficients can either be calculated as required or taken from tables. In the latter case the interpolation will have to be done in two stages if the number of decimals in θ is greater than that in the argument of the tables of interpolation coefficients. One method of dealing with this situation is to carry out a subsidiary interpolation in the tables of interpolation coefficients themselves. But it is generally better to carry out a small subtabulation of the function $f(x)$ using only tabular values of the interpolation coefficients. For example, if $f(x)$ is tabulated at intervals $\delta x = 0 \cdot 1$ and its value is wanted for $x = 0 \cdot 854377$, and available tables of the interpolation coefficients have the argument θ at intervals $\delta \theta = 0 \cdot 001$, the values of $f(x)$ for $x = 0 \cdot 8541(\cdot 0001)0 \cdot 8545$ can be obtained without interpolation in the tables of the interpolation coefficients, and interpolation in this small table of $f(x)$ will then give the result required; linear interpolation will often be adequate at this stage.

In carrying out a non-linear interpolation, it is advisable to carry one guarding figure to avoid accumulation of rounding errors from the various contributions to the interpolated value. For a similar reason, a guarding figure should be kept in the subtabulation mentioned in the previous paragraph. Also it is advisable to retain contributions greater than $0 \cdot 2$ in the least significant digit from the higher orders of differences.

On this basis:

In Bessel's formula, with throwback of fourth differences to second:

$$\delta^3 f \text{ can be neglected if less than } 15$$

$$\delta^4 f \text{ can be neglected if less than } 500.$$

In Everett's formula, with throwback of fourth differences to second:

$$\delta^4 f \text{ can be neglected if less than } 250.$$

† For these and other developments of the idea of the throwback, see *Chambers's 6-Figure Tables*, vol. 2 (1949), p. 533.

Examples:

(a) Given the following values, to find $f(\tfrac{2}{3})$:

x	$f(x)$	δf	$\delta^2 f$	$\delta^3 f$	$(\delta^2 f_0 + \delta^2 f_1)$
0·60	1·66667				
		−5377			
·62	·61290		337		
		−5040		−32	
·64	·56250		305		
		−4735		−26	
·66	·51515		279		
		−4456		−25	+533
·68	·47059		254		
		−4202		−20	
·70	·42857		234		
		−3968			
0·72	1·38889				

Here $(\delta x) = 0.02$, $x = \tfrac{2}{3} = 0.66 + \tfrac{1}{3}(\delta x)$, $\theta = \tfrac{1}{3}$. The contribution from the third difference is just worth taking into account, but the fourth-difference contribution is negligible, even without using the throwback. The value of $B^{ii}(\theta)$ is $\tfrac{1}{2}\theta(\theta-1) = -\tfrac{1}{18}$, and that of $B^{iii}(\theta)$ is $\tfrac{1}{6}\theta(\theta-1)(\theta-\tfrac{1}{2}) = +\tfrac{1}{162}$. Hence we have

$$
\begin{aligned}
f_0 &= 1.51515 \\
\theta\,\delta f_{\tfrac{1}{2}} &= -0.01485_3 \\
B^{ii}(\theta)[\delta^2 f_0 + \delta^2 f_1] &= -0.00029_6 \\
B^{iii}(\theta)\delta^3 f_{\tfrac{1}{2}} &= \underline{-0.00000_2} \\
&\ \ 1.49999_9,
\end{aligned}
$$

or rounded off, 1·50000.

The guarding figure is written here as a suffix; this is a convenient convention.
Notes: (i) The point of expressing the second-difference contribution in the form $B^{ii}(\theta).(\delta^2 f_0 + \delta^2 f_1)$, rather than $\{2B^{ii}(\theta)\}\mu\delta^2 f_{\tfrac{1}{2}}$, is clear from this example. If the quantity $\delta^2 f_0 + \delta^2 f_1$ is odd, then in dividing by 2 to obtain $\mu\delta^2 f_{\tfrac{1}{2}}$ we would either have to round off or keep an extra figure, and this is avoided by incorporating the division by 2 in the factor $B^{ii}(\theta) = \tfrac{1}{2}\theta(\theta-1)$ by which this quantity is multiplied.

(ii) The function $f(x)$ here is $1/x$, the tabular values being rounded off to five decimals, so that the correct value of $f(\tfrac{2}{3})$ is 1·5 exactly.

(b) Given the following values, to find $f(\tfrac{2}{3})$:

x	$f(x)$	δf	$\delta^2 f$	$\delta^3 f$	$\delta^4 f$	$-0.184\delta^4 f$	$\delta^2_m f$	$\delta^2_m f_0 + \delta^2_m f_1$
0·50	2·00000							
		−18182						
·55	1·81818		3031					
		−15151		−701				
·60	·66667		2330		203	--37	2293	
		−12821		−498				
·65	·53846		1832		131	−24	1808	
		−10989		−367				3256
·70	·42857		1465		93	−17	1448	
		− 9524		−274				
·75	·33333		1191		63	−12	1179	
		− 8333		−211				
·80	·25000		980					
		− 7353						
0·85	1·17647							

Here $(\delta x) = 0\cdot 05$, $x = \frac{2}{3} = 0\cdot 65 + \frac{1}{3}(\delta x)$, so $\theta = \frac{1}{3}, \bar{\theta} = \frac{2}{3}$.

(i) By Bessel's formula

$$B^{ii}(\theta) = \tfrac{1}{2}\theta(\theta - 1) = -\tfrac{1}{18}$$
$$B^{iii}(\theta) - \tfrac{1}{6}\theta(\theta - 1)(\theta - \tfrac{1}{2}) = +\tfrac{1}{162}$$

$$
\begin{aligned}
f_0 &= 1\cdot 53846\\
\theta\,\delta f_{\frac{1}{2}} &= -0\cdot 03663_0\\
B^{ii}(\theta)(\delta_m^2 f_0 + \delta_m^2 f_1) &= -0\cdot 00180_9\\
B^{iii}(\theta)\delta^3 f_{\frac{1}{2}} &= -0\cdot 00002_3\\
\hline
&1\cdot 49999_8
\end{aligned}
$$

(ii) By Everett's formula

$$E_0^{ii}(\theta) = -\tfrac{1}{6}\bar{\theta}(1 - \bar{\theta}^2) = -\tfrac{5}{81}$$
$$E_1^{ii}(\theta) = -\tfrac{1}{6}\theta(1 - \theta^2) = -\tfrac{4}{81}$$

$$
\begin{aligned}
f_0 &= 1\cdot 53846\\
\theta\,\delta f_{\frac{1}{2}} &= -0\cdot 03663_0\\
E_0^{ii}(\theta)\,\delta_m^2 f_0 &= -0\cdot 00111_6\\
E_1^{ii}(\theta)\,\delta_m^2 f_1 &= -0\cdot 00071_5\\
\hline
&1\cdot 49999_9
\end{aligned}
$$

Rounded off to five decimals = $1\cdot 50000$ Rounded off to five decimals

$$= 1\cdot 50000$$

In this example modified second differences have been used, and the residual contributions from fourth differences are negligible. If modified second differences had not been used, it would have been necessary to include the fourth difference terms in each case.

(iii) By preliminary subtabulation:

θ	·30	·32	·34	·36
$E_0^{ii}(\theta) = \tfrac{1}{6}\bar{\theta}(1 - \bar{\theta}^2)$	·05950	·06093	·06208	·06298
$E_1^{ii}(\theta) = \tfrac{1}{6}\theta(1 - \theta^2)$	·04550	·04787	·05012	·05222
x	·665	·666	·667	·668
f_0	$1\cdot 53846$	$1\cdot 53846$	$1\cdot 53846$	$1\cdot 53846$
$\theta\,\delta f_{\frac{1}{2}}$	-3296_7	-3516_5	-3736_3	-3956_0
$\tfrac{1}{6}\bar{\theta}(1 - \bar{\theta}^2)\delta_m^2 f_0$	-107_6	-110_2	-112_2	-113_9
$\tfrac{1}{6}\theta(1 - \theta^2)\delta_m^2 f_1$	-65_9	-69_3	-72_6	-75_6
f	$1\cdot 50375_8$	$1\cdot 50150_0$	$1\cdot 49924_9$	$1\cdot 49700_5$

Differences at the smaller interval $\begin{cases} -225_8 & -225_1 & -224_4 \\ 0_7 & 0_7 & \end{cases}$

Linear interpolation between the subtabulated values is now adequate; $\theta = \frac{2}{3}$, so

$$f(\tfrac{2}{3}) = 1\cdot 50150_0 - \tfrac{2}{3}(225_1)$$
$$= 1\cdot 50000 \text{ on rounding off to five decimals.}$$

Note: Since the interval length has been reduced by a factor 50, second differences are reduced by a factor 2500 from those of the original table, so their values would be expected to be about 0_8 in the fifth decimal, and are certainly negligible for interpolation purposes. It is then only necessary to calculate two values of f (for example those for $x = 0\cdot 666$ and $0\cdot 667$); but four values have been calculated to give a partial check. A thorough check of an isolated interpolation is difficult to achieve, but a good check is provided by carrying out the interpolation between two sets of values of the original function at different intervals.

5.5. Lagrange's formula

The interpolation formulae so far given have expressed the interpolated value of $f(x)$ in terms of contributions from its various orders of differences. An alternative type of formula expresses the interpolated value of $f(x)$ as a sum of multiples of the values of the function f itself, with coefficients which are functions of the fraction θ of the interval length for which the interpolation is required, thus:

$$f(x_0 + \theta\,\delta x) = \sum_j L_j(\theta)f_j. \tag{5.28}$$

An interpolation formula of this type is called a 'Lagrange interpolation formula', and the coefficients $L_j(\theta)$ are known as 'Lagrange interpolation coefficients'. There are several formulae of this type, with different numbers of terms taken in the sum in (5.28), and correspondingly with different sets of coefficients.

A formula using n function values is usually known as an 'n-point' formula; n is usually taken as even, and an equal number of points taken on each side of the interval in which interpolation is to be carried out. Such formulae can be obtained by expressing the finite differences in Bessel's or Everett's formula in terms of function values by formula (4.8) and collecting terms involving the same function value. But they are more conveniently obtained as special cases of a formula, which will be derived in § 5.7, for interpolation of a function given at unequal intervals of the argument. An n-point formula is based on the approximation to f by a polynomial of degree $(n-1)$ through n successive values of the function, interpolation being carried out by evaluating this polynomial at the value of x for which the interpolation is required. For even values of n, use of such a formula is equivalent to the use of Bessel's formula to $(n-1)$th differences or of Everett's to $(n-2)$th differences, without throwback.

Tables of Lagrange coefficients for 4-point and 6-point interpolation, for $\theta = 0(0\cdot01)1\cdot00$, are given in *Chambers's 6-Figure Tables*; for other tabulations the *Index of Mathematical Tables* should be consulted.

The advantage of Lagrangian coefficients formulae, if it is an advantage, is that they can be used directly on tables in which no differences are given. On the other hand, they have several disadvantages, as pointed out by Comrie:†

(i) They provide no check that the function values used in them have been taken correctly, whereas the differences used in a difference formula also provide a check on the function values used;

(ii) A single calculation of an interpolated value provides no indication whether the degree of the polynomial used is inadequate, adequate, or excessive;

† *Chambers's 6-Figure Tables*, vol. 2 (1949), Introduction, p. xxix.

(iii) At least one of the coefficients $L_j(\theta)$ is greater than 0·5; if therefore an interpolation is required for a value of θ which is not a
tabular value in the table of Lagrangian interpolation coefficients,
interpolation in these tables is required to the same number of
significant figures as that required for the interpolation of f itself;

(iv) Use of Lagrangian formulae does not lend itself to an easy process
for inverse interpolation.

To these may be added:

(v) They do not provide the facilities for improving the accuracy of
interpolation without complicating the formulae, such as are
provided by interpolation formulae in terms of differences by
use of the 'throwback'. The Lagrangian formulae are based on
the approximation to the function to be interpolated by a polynomial of the nth degree through $(n+1)$ points. But consider
the significance of the use of the throwback from fourth to second
differences and subsequent use of Everett's formulae to second
differences. The fact that this modification of the second differences improves the accuracy of the interpolation (and moreover
by a factor of about 10, not only by a small amount) means that
for interpolation between f_0 and f_1 the best cubic is *not* the cubic
through f_{-1}, f_0, f_1, f_2 which is the one used in the four-point
Lagrange formula.

Certainly there is a formula of Lagrangian type corresponding
to the Everett formula to second differences, used with modified
second differences; but this is no simpler than a six-point Lagrangian formula based on the use of a quintic polynomial. The
corresponding formula using differences is Everett's to fourth
differences, and if in this the joint throwback of sixth and eighth
differences to second and fourth is used, a very substantial
improvement in the accuracy, compared with that of a six-point
Lagrangian interpolation, is achieved.

Comrie's comment† is that he 'has to admit that his experience has
not made him partial to blind Lagrangian interpolation, except when
special circumstances point very definitely to it'.

5.51. Special interpolation methods for particular functions

For some particular functions, special interpolation methods may be
more convenient than the use of the Bessel or Everett formulae. For

† *Chambers's 6-Figure Tables*, vol. 2 (1949), Introduction, p. xxx.

example, for the exponential function it may be most convenient to use the addition formula

$$e^{x+y} = e^x e^y$$

and carry out interpolation by a multiplication or succession of multiplications. If, for example, e^x is tabulated at intervals of $0{\cdot}01$ in x, an auxiliary table for $x = 0(0{\cdot}0001)0{\cdot}01$ would enable values to be obtained for four-decimal values of x in the range of the main table by a single multiplication; alternatively a set of auxiliary tables for $x = [0(0{\cdot}1)1] \times 10^{-n}$ for n from 2 to 5, say, would enable values of e^x for six-decimal values of x to be obtained with not more than four multiplications.

If the function y to be interpolated satisfies a simple differential equation such as $y'' = xy$, formulae for successive derivatives of y, obtained by successive differentiation of the differential equation, may be simple enough to be used for the numerical evaluation of these derivatives. Then Taylor's series can be used for interpolation between tabular values, $f(x_0 + \theta \delta x)$ being calculated from as many terms of the series

$$f(x_0 + \theta \delta x) = f_0 + \theta(\delta x)f_0' + \frac{1}{2!}\theta^2(\delta x)^2 f_0'' + \frac{1}{3!}\theta^3(\delta x)^3 f_0''' + \cdots$$

as are appreciable. A good check is provided by evaluation of the alternative expansion, in terms of f and its derivatives at $x = x_1$, namely:

$$f(x_0 + \theta x) = f(x_1 - \bar{\theta}\delta x) \qquad (\text{where } \bar{\theta} = 1 - \theta)$$

$$= f_1 - \bar{\theta}(\delta x)f_1' + \frac{1}{2!}\bar{\theta}^2(\delta x)^2 f_1'' - \frac{1}{3!}\bar{\theta}^3(\delta x)^3 f_1''' + \cdots.$$

The convenient quantities to tabulate for interpolation purposes are not the derivatives $f^{(k)}$ but the quantities $[(\delta x)^k/k!]f^{(k)}$, sometimes called 'reduced derivatives'. This method of interpolation is particularly convenient in the case of functions which have been evaluated by integration of the appropriate differential equation by the Taylor series method (§ 7.4), since the reduced derivatives are evaluated in the course of this calculation, and so are available for interpolation purposes without any further work. An example is provided by the tables[†] of the function usually written $\mathrm{Bi}(x)$, which is one solution of the equation $y'' = xy$.

5.6. Subtabulation

Subtabulation is a special case of interpolation, of which the purpose is to take a function $f(x)$ at tabular interval δx and construct from it a table at a smaller tabular interval $q\,\delta x$; in practice q is usually $\frac{1}{2}$, $\frac{1}{5}$, or $\frac{1}{10}$.

† *British Association Mathematical Tables*, Part-volume B, *The Airy Integral* (1946).

The values of the function at the large interval (δx), between which interpolation is carried out, are called 'pivotal values' of $f(x)$.

It is a valuable process when the direct calculation of $f(x)$ is difficult or long, for example by summing a series of a large number of terms, or evaluation of a definite integral in which the integrand is a function of x. In such cases we want to restrict the number of values of x for which $f(x)$ is calculated directly, and derive from them a table at a smaller interval, probably one in which second differences at most have to be included in interpolation, and possibly one in which linear interpolation is adequate. There is no purpose in subtabulation if linear interpolation *is* already adequate; the purpose of subtabulation is to break down the tabular interval when linear interpolation is certainly not adequate; so it is essentially concerned with non-linear interpolation.

Since $\delta^n f$ is of order $(\delta x)^n$, the higher-order differences are very much reduced by even a moderate degree of subtabulation. For example, subtabulation to fifths reduces fourth differences by a factor of over 500 and sixth differences by a factor of over 15,000.

In subtabulation, a systematic set of results is required, instead of an isolated result as is more usual in an interpolation process. This suggests that a systematic procedure should be used for obtaining the results.

We could interpolate a sequence of values of the function itself and check the differences; alternatively we could construct the sequence of second (or higher) order differences of the function at the smaller interval and build up from these, using the facilities for building up a function from its differences (the 'National' machine, for example, if available). The latter process has the advantages that (i) most of the work is done with small numbers, and (ii) a good overall check is provided by the reproduction of the pivotal values in the course of the summation of the differences of the function at the smaller interval. The former does not check that the correct pivotal values have been taken, and the use of incorrect pivotal values may not be apparent in the differences of the subtabulated function; these differences check against random errors, but the effect of an incorrect pivotal value is a systematic error, and may not be indicated by differences. This is illustrated by the following example.

Consider the subtabulation to tenths of $\sin x$ from a table at intervals of $10°$. Use of an incorrect value at $x = 50°$ ($0·76624$ for $0·76604$) might give a set of subtabulated values as follows:

x	'sin x'			x	'sin x'		
30°	0·50000			50°	0·76624		−23
31	1504	1504	−16	51	7734	1110	−24
32	2992	1488	−16	52	8820	1086	−25
33	4464	1472	−17	53	0·79881	1061	−25
34	5919	1455	−17	54	0·80917	1036	−26
35	7357	1438	−18	55	1927	1010	−24
36	0·58777	1420	−18	56	2913	986	−25
37	0·60179	1402	−17	57	3874	961	−26
38	1564	1385	−18	58	4809	935	−25
39	2931	1367	−19	59	5719	910	−26
40	0·64279	1348	−19	60	0·86603	884	−26
41	5608	1329	−20	61	7461	858	−26
42	6917	1309	−20	62	8293	832	−26
43	8206	1289	−20	63	9099	806	−26
44	0·69475	1269	−21	64	0·89879	780	−28
45	0·70723	1248	−22	65	0·90631	752	−28
46	1949	1226	−23	66	1355	724	−29
47	3152	1203	−22	67	2050	695	−27
48	4333	1181	−23	68	2718	668	−28
49	5491	1158	−25	69	3358	640	−29
50	0·76624	1133	−23	70	0·93969	611	

Here the pivotal values are underlined; that at $x = 50°$ is in error by 20 units in the fifth decimal, the others are correct to five decimals. The differences of the subtabulated values are no more irregular than would be expected as the result of rounding errors, and certainly contain no suggestion of an error of 20 units.

Certainly such an error in a pivotal value ought to be detected by differencing the pivotal values before beginning the subtabulation. But if a Lagrangian formula were used for carrying out the subtabulation, this step might be omitted since the differences of the pivotal values would not be used in the subtabulation process; if they were to be obtained to check the pivotal values, it would be better to use them in the subtabulation also. The point of this example, however, is to show that differencing the subtabulated values does not *by itself* provide an adequate check of the subtabulation process.

5.61. End-figure method for subtabulation

Comrie† has given a convenient process for subtabulation, in which only the *last digit* of each interpolated value is evaluated by the use of a suitable interpolation formula, and the complete values are then built up from their differences. From the last digits in the interpolated function values, only the last digits in the differences can be obtained directly;

† L. J. Comrie, *Monthly Notices, R.A.S.*, **88** (1928), 506; *Interpolation and Allied Tables*, incorporated in *Nautical Almanac*, 1931.

but in subtabulation at a fraction q of the interval between the pivotal values, the nth differences of the subtabulated values are approximately q^n times those of the pivotal values, and for some value of n these nth differences of the subtabulated values will vary slowly enough for their last digits to establish the values of the differences themselves. Suppose for example that, for the pivotal values, $\delta^2 f_j = 610$ and $\delta^2 f_{j+1} = 505$, and subtabulation is to fifths ($q = \frac{1}{5}$). Then the second differences of the subtabulated values will be approximately $\frac{1}{25}$ of those of the pivotal values, that is (allowing for possible effects of rounding errors) from about 25 at the beginning of this interval to 19 at the end. Hence if the last digits of the second differences of the interpolated values are

$$5, 3, 3, 1, 0,$$

these second differences can with confidence be given the values

$$25, 23, 23, 21, 20,$$

and the function can then be evaluated by summation from these values (see § 4.46). If any mistake is made, it is shown up by the pivotal values not being reproduced in the summation.

The process can be illustrated in a simple case by example (b) of § 5.43 (see p. 74). If in that example the values of $f(0\cdot665)$ and $f(0\cdot666)$ had been evaluated in full, but only the last digits of $f(0\cdot667)$ and $f(0\cdot668)$ had been determined, the results (rounded off to five decimals) would have been:

x	0·665	0·666	0·667	0·668
$f(x)$	1·50376	1·50150	5	0
Differences at the smaller interval	−226	−..5	−..5	

where the dots represent digits so far undetermined. But, as mentioned on p. 74, the second differences of f at the smaller interval are about 0_8 so each of the first differences whose last digit is 5 must be −225. The values of $f(x)$ at $x = 0\cdot667$ and $0\cdot668$ could then be built up from these differences.

The following is a more extensive example, in which it is necessary to go to second differences before writing down the values of a set of differences from their last digits, and which also illustrates some further points of procedure.

Example: Given the following table:

x	$f(x)$			
0·310	2·96671			
		8476		
0·305	3·05147		340	
		8816		20
0·300	3·13963		360	
		9176		21
0·295	3·23139		381	
		9557		22
0·290	3·32696		403	
		9960		26
0·285	3·42656		429	
		10389		
0·280	3·53045			

to subtabulate to fifths (i.e. at intervals 0·001 in x) from $x = 0·300$ to $x = 0·290$.

(*Note*: for this function it is convenient to take differences in the direction of x decreasing, as in this table; then, apart from effects of rounding errors, they are all positive.)

Everett's formula to second differences (unmodified) is adequate in this case; the Everett coefficients for the points of subtabulation are:

θ	0	$\frac{1}{5}$	$\frac{2}{5}$	$\frac{3}{5}$	$\frac{4}{5}$	1
$E_0^{II}(\theta)$	0	$-·048$	$-·064$	$-·056$	$-·032$	0
$E_1^{II}(\theta)$	0	$-·032$	$-·056$	$-·064$	$-·048$	0

The second differences of the pivotal values over the range specified for the subtabulation are from 360 to 403, so for subtabulation to fifths the second differences of the subtabulated values will be from about 14 to 16. Thus it is only necessary to difference the end digits to second differences in order to be sure of the values to be used in building up the function values. Since this building up is to be done from second differences, we will need two function values from which to start, namely the pivotal value $f(0·300)$ and the value $f(0·299)$. For the latter, Everett's formula gives:

$$
\begin{array}{ll}
f(0·300) & 3·13963 \\
+\frac{1}{5}\delta f(0·2995) & 1835_2 \\
+ E_0^{II}(\frac{1}{5})\delta^2 f(0·300) & -17_3 \\
+ E_1^{II}(\frac{1}{5})\delta^2 f(0·295) & -12_2 \\
\hline
f(0·299) & = 3·15768_7, \text{ or, rounded off, } 3·15769.
\end{array}
$$

Only the rounded value is needed subsequently; guarding figures are kept in the contributions to it, but can be discarded in the interpolated value itself. Guarding figures, written as suffixes, will similarly be kept in the contributions to the other subtabulated values.

For the interval $x = 0·300$ to $0·299$, the last two digits of δf for the pivotal values are 76, so the first differences of the linear contributions $f_0 + \theta \delta f_{\frac{1}{2}}$ to the interpolated values in this interval end with 5_2. The end figure of $f(0·300)$ is 3, and successive additions of 5_2 give for the end figures of $f(0·300)$ to $f(0·295)$ inclusive the values

$$3_0, \quad 8_2, \quad 3_4, \quad 8_6, \quad 3_8, \quad 9_0$$

G

of which the last is the end figure of the pivotal value $f(0\cdot295)$; this provides a check on the additions. For the next interval the first difference of the pivotal values ends with 57, so the first differences of the linear contributions to the interpolated values end with 1_4, and for $f(0\cdot295)$ to $f(0\cdot290)$ inclusive are

$$9_0, \quad 0_4, \quad 1_8, \quad 3_2, \quad 4_6, \quad 6_0;$$

the comparison of the last of these with the pivotal value $f(0\cdot290)$ again furnishes a check.

The complete calculation can be arranged in tabular form as follows (δ is used for the central-difference operator at the smaller intervals):

x	$\delta^2 f_0$	$\delta^2 f_1$	$\tfrac{1}{5}\delta f$	(a)	(b)	(c)	(d)	f	δf	$\delta^2 f$	$\delta^2 f$	δf	f
								\multicolumn{3}{c}{*Last figure of*}			
$0\cdot300$ ⎫				3_0			$= 3_0$	3					$3\cdot13963$
									6			1806	
299				8_2	-17_3	-12_2	$= 8_7$	9		4	14		5769
									0			1820	
298				3_4	-23_0	-21_3	$= 9_1$	9		5	15		7589
	360	381	5_2						5			1835	
297				8_6	-20_2	-24_4	$= 4_0$	4		5	15		19424
									0			1850	
296				3_8	-11_5	-18_3	$= 4_0$	4		5	15		$3\cdot21274$
									5			1865	
295 ⎭				9_0			$= 9_0$	9		5	15		3139
									0			1880	
294 ⎫				0_4	-18_3	-13_0	$= 9_1$	9		6	16		5019
									6			1896	
293				1_8	-24_4	-22_7	$= 4_7$	5		5	15		6915
									1			1911	
292 ⎬	381	403	1_4	3_2	-21_3	-26_0	$= 5_9$	6		6	16		28826
									7			1927	
291				4_6	-12_2	-19_5	$= 2_9$	3		6	16		$3\cdot30753$
									3			1943	
$0\cdot290$ ⎭				6_0			$= 6_0$	6					$3\cdot32696$

(a) Linear contribution $f_0 + \theta\delta f_{\frac{1}{2}}$, end figure and guarding figure only.

(b), (c): $E_0^{11}(\theta)\delta^2 f_0$ and $E_1^{11}(\theta)\delta^2 f_1$.

(d) Sum of (a), (b), (c), end figure and guarding figure only.

The column headed $\tfrac{1}{5}\delta f$ gives the last figure and guarding figure, as required for building up the linear contributions to the interpolated values in column (a). Columns (b) and (c) give the second-difference contributions to the interpolated values; these are here given in full as this makes the work easier to follow; however only the last full digit and a guarding figure are necessary. The sums of entries (a), (b), (c) with guarding figures are given in column (d) to illustrate the procedure, but only the rounded values of the last digit, as given in the next column, are required for the subsequent work. These rounded values are then differenced to second differences, and from the result we have already had, that the values of $\delta^2 f$ are about 14 to 16, the complete values can now be written down from their last digits. Then from $f(0\cdot300)$, $f(0\cdot299)$ and these second differences, the values of f can be built up. A thorough check is provided by the reproduction of all the pivotal values.

Notes: (i) In this example, $f(x)$ is the function $[(1/x)^{\gamma}-1]/\gamma$ with $\gamma = 1\cdot 4$. The pivotal values were calculated from this defining formula; for the intermediate values subtabulation is a much quicker and easier process than evaluation of this formula.

(ii) It is not necessary to carry out the full evaluation of $f(0\cdot 299)$ by interpolation. The value of $\delta f(0\cdot 2995)$ is approximately $\frac{1}{10}[f(0\cdot 305)-f(0\cdot 295)]$ which is 1799—rather larger since $\delta^2 f$ is positive—and its last digit is 6, which indicates the value 1806 with some certainty. But even if a wrong value were taken, this would be shown by the pivotal value $f(0\cdot 295)$ not being reproduced; and from the amount of the discrepancy, the corrections to be made can easily be determined. For example, if $\delta f(0\cdot 2995)$ were taken as 1796 instead of 1806, each of the first five first differences would be in error by -10, so the discrepancy between the value of $f(0\cdot 295)$ obtained by building up and the pivotal values would be -50; this would indicate that each of these first differences must be increased by 10. (This correction process is not available if the subtabulated function values are built up from differences of higher order than the second.)

If the second differences of the subtabulated values vary too rapidly for their last figures to be a certain indication of their complete values, a corresponding process involving building up from third or fourth differences can be used. Alternatively, the process could be carried out with the last *two* digits in each subtabulated value instead of with the last digit only.

Another method of subtabulation, also suggested by Comrie,[†] involves the direct calculation of second or fourth differences of the subtabulated values from formulae relating differences at interval $q\delta x$ to differences at interval δx. The subtabulated values are then built up from their differences.

5.7. Interpolation of a function given at unequal intervals of the argument

For the interpolation of a function given at unequal intervals of the argument, the interpolation formula usually used is that of Lagrange. This is based on the use of an nth degree polynomial which takes the given function values at $(n+1)$ values of x. Such a formula is called an $(n+1)$-point formula. An even number of points (odd value of n) gives an equal number on either side of the value of x for which the interpolation is to be carried out.

If the function values are $f_0, f_1,..., f_n$ at $x = x_0, x_1,..., x_n$, not necessarily equally spaced, the polynomial of lowest degree which takes these values is

$$F = \left(\frac{x-x_1}{x_0-x_1}\frac{x-x_2}{x_0-x_2}...\frac{x-x_n}{x_0-x_n}\right)f_0 + \left(\frac{x-x_0}{x_1-x_0}\frac{x-x_2}{x_1-x_2}...\frac{x-x_n}{x_1-x_n}\right)f_1 + \cdots$$
$$(5.31)$$

† L. J. Comrie, *Journ. Roy. Stat. Soc.*, Supplement **3** (1936), 87.

this polynomial is of course not the function f itself, unless f is a polynomial of degree n or lower; it is the polynomial which coincides with f at $x = x_0, x_1,..., x_n$. Interpolation is done by evaluating this polynomial for the intermediate value of x.

If f is a polynomial of degree n or less, then $F = f$ and the interpolation formula (5.31) is closely related to the expansion in partial fractions of $f/(x-x_0)(x-x_1)... (x-x_n)$. For if $g(x) = 0$ has roots $x = x_0, x_1,... x_n$, all distinct, the expansion of $f(x)/g(x)$ in partial fractions is

$$\frac{f(x)}{g(x)} = \sum_j \frac{f(x_j)}{g'(x_j)(x-x_j)}$$

and this, applied to $g(x) = (x-x_0)(x-x_1)...(x-x_n)$, is

$$\frac{f}{(x-x_0)(x-x_1)...(x-x_n)} = \frac{f_0}{(x_0-x_1)(x_0-x_2)...(x_0-x_n)} \frac{1}{x-x_0} + ...$$

which is just another form of formula (5.31).

Lagrange's interpolation formula (5.31) is not restricted to functions given at unequal intervals of the argument. Its application when the intervals of x are equal has already been mentioned in §§ 5.5 and 5.6, and its disadvantages in that context pointed out. For functions not tabulated at equal intervals, however, some form of it may be the only method available. It is then important to systematize the work of evaluating the polynomial, since if it is not done in a systematic way it is easy to make a mistake, and adequate checking is at best difficult. One scheme of working, in which the coefficients of the various values of f_j in formula (5.31) are first calculated and checked and are then used to form the sum (5.31), has been given by Comrie;[†] an important feature is the check of the coefficients which is provided. In another type of method, suggested by Aitken,[‡] the result is obtained by a sequence of steps each of which is similar to a linear interpolation; this is considered in § 5.71. Another way of arranging the work is considered in § 5.72.

5.71. Evaluation of Lagrange's interpolation formula by a sequence of linear cross-means

Linear interpolation or extrapolation of $f(x)$ from the values f_a, f_b, of f at $x = x_a, x_b$ respectively, gives

$$f(x) = \frac{(x_b-x)f_a+(x-x_a)f_b}{x_b-x_a}. \qquad (5.32)$$

† L. J. Comrie, *Chambers's 6-Figure Tables*, vol. 2 (1949), Introduction, p. xxxi.
‡ A. C. Aitken, *Proc. Edin. Math. Soc.*, ser. 2, **3** (1932), 56.

Aitken calls this quantity the 'linear cross-mean' between f_a and f_b; let it be written $f_{a,b}(x)$. Linear interpolation between the values $f_{a,b}(x)$ and $f_{b,c}(x)$, regarded as values of an auxiliary function at $x = x_a$ and $x = x_c$ respectively, gives

$$f(x) = \frac{(x_c - x)f_{a,b}(x) + (x - x_a)f_{b,c}(x)}{x_c - x_a}.$$

Let this be written $f_{a,b,c}(x)$. It can be verified that this is the value of $f(x)$ given by a three-term Lagrange interpolation formula using the values of f at $x = x_a, x_b$, and x_c.

In general, let $f_{a,b,c\ldots j,k,l}(x)$ be a set of numbers obtained by successive use of the linear cross-mean formula

$$f_{a,b,c\ldots i,j,k}(x) = \frac{(x_k - x)f_{a,b,c\ldots i,j}(x) + (x - x_a)f_{b,c\ldots i,j,k}(x)}{x_k - x_a}. \tag{5.33}$$

(n suffixes)

Then it can be proved by induction that $f_{a,b,c\cdots i,j,k}(x)$ is the value of $f(x)$ given by an n-point Lagrangian interpolation formula using the values of f at $x = x_a, x_b, \ldots, x_j, x_k$, which need not be in monotonic sequence.

The process suggested by Aitken consists of forming the linear cross-means $f_{0,1}(x), f_{0,2}(x), f_{0,3}(x), \ldots$ and in general $f_{0,j}(x)$, then using these to form $f_{0,1,2}(x), f_{0,1,3}(x), \ldots$ and in general $f_{0,1,j}(x)$, then $f_{0,1,2,3}(x), f_{0,1,2,4}(x), \ldots, f_{0,1,2,j}(x)$ and so on. A graphical representation of the formation of the first set of linear cross-means $f_{0,j}(x)$ is shown in Fig. 7. An alternative order of procedure[†] consists of forming first $f_{0,1}(x), f_{1,2}(x), \ldots$ and in general $f_{j,j+1}(x)$, then $f_{0,1,2}(x), f_{1,2,3}(x), \ldots, f_{j,j+1,j+2}(x)$ and so on. The formation of the first set of linear cross-means $f_{j,j+1}(x)$ in this procedure is shown in Fig. 8.

In using the latter procedure, the work can be arranged as follows:

x	$x - x_j$	f_j	$f_{j,j+1}(x)$	$f_{j,j+1,j+2}(x)$	$f_{j,j+1,j+2,j+3}(x)$
x_0	$x - x_0$	f_0			
			$f_{0,1}(x)$		
x_1	$\boxed{x - x_1}$	f_1		$f_{0,1,2}(x)$	
			$f_{1,2}(x)$		$f_{0,1,2,3}(x)$
x_2	$x - x_2$	f_2		$\boxed{f_{1,2,3}(x)}$	
			$f_{2,3}(x)$		$f_{1,2,3,4}(x)$
x_3	$x - x_3$	f_3		$\boxed{f_{2,3,4}(x)}$	
			$f_{3,4}(x)$		
x_4	$\boxed{x - x_4}$	f_4			

This layout is similar to that of a difference table, though the entries are not differences. The entries used in forming $f_{1,2,3,4}(x)$ are enclosed in

---

† E. H. Neville, *Journ. Indian Math. Soc.* **20** (1934), 87. This paper includes an extension of the procedure to use known values of derivatives of $f(x)$.

'boxes', and the way in which they are selected is shown by the lines joining them to the entry $f_{1,2,3,4}(x)$.

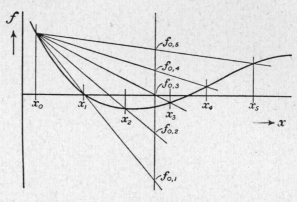

Fig. 7.

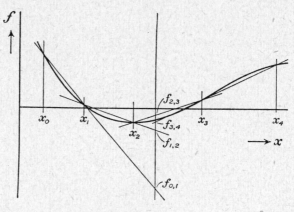

Fig. 8.

This process has the advantages

   (i) successive calculations are all repetitions of this simple process of forming linear cross-means;
  (ii) the results provide their own criterion of when the process has been carried far enough;
 (iii) common leading figures in two of the linear cross-means can be suppressed in taking higher cross-means.

The process can be used on functions tabulated at equal intervals of the argument, but takes no advantage of this uniform tabulation.

5.72. Divided differences

For the treatment of polynomials at unequal intervals of the argument, it is sometimes convenient to use what are called 'divided differences'. If $x_0, x_1, ...$, and in general x_j, are the values of x at which the function is tabulated (not necessarily in monotonic sequence), the first-order divided differences are

$$\left. f(x_0, x_1) = \frac{f(x_1) - f(x_0)}{x_1 - x_0}, \qquad f(x_1, x_2) = \frac{f(x_2) - f(x_1)}{x_2 - x_1}, \atop ..., \qquad f(x_j, x_{j+1}) = \frac{f(x_{j+1}) - f(x_j)}{x_{j+1} - x_j} \right\} \quad (5.34)$$

The second-order divided differences are

$$f(x_0, x_1, x_2) = \frac{f(x_1, x_2) - f(x_0, x_1)}{x_2 - x_0},$$

$$. \quad . \quad . \quad . \quad . \quad . \quad . \quad .$$

$$f(x_j, x_{j+1}, x_{j+2}) = \frac{f(x_{j+1}, x_{j+2}) - f(x_j, x_{j+1})}{x_{j+2} - x_j}$$

and in general, the nth order divided differences are

$$f(x_j, x_{j+1}, ..., x_{j+n}) = \frac{f(x_{j+1}, x_{j+2}, ..., x_{j+n}) - f(x_j, x_{j+1}, ..., x_{j+n-1})}{x_{j+n} - x_j}.$$

$$(5.35)$$

For a function tabulated at equal intervals (δx) of x, the divided differences become the quantities $\delta^n f / n! (\delta x)^n$. The main property of divided differences for practical purposes is that the nth order divided differences of a polynomial of the nth degree are constant.

Another application of divided differences is in the derivation of interpolation formulae. Such formulae for equally spaced arguments can be derived from an interpolation formula in terms of divided differences which is equivalent to Lagrange's interpolation formula; but this derivation does not take advantage of the equal spacing of the arguments until a later stage, and also does not exhibit the relation between the coefficients in interpolation formulae such as those of Bessel and Everett and the coefficients in the expansions considered in § 5.3. The derivation of these formulae by the use of finite-difference operators seems preferable.

To show that the nth order differences of a polynomial of the nth degree are constant, consider first some properties of divided differences. The relations (5.35) defining the successive orders of divided differences are all linear in the function values f_j, hence any divided difference is a linear combination of a set of function values with coefficients which are functions of the x_j's only. It can easily be proved by induction that if $j \leqslant k \leqslant j+n$, the coefficient of f_k in $f(x_j, x_{j+1},...,x_{j+n})$ is

$$1\Big/\prod_{i=j}^{j+n}{}' (x_k-x_i)$$

the dash in Π' indicating that the factor with $i = k$ is omitted from the product; if k is outside the range j to $j+n$, the coefficient of f_k is zero. The value of this coefficient is unaltered by a change in the order of the factors, and it follows that for any function $f(x)$ the value of a divided difference $f(x_j, x_{j+1},...,x_{j+n})$ depends only on the values of x_j involved, and not on the order in which they are taken.

Now consider the function $f(x) = x^n$. The first-order divided differences are given by

$$\frac{f(x_{j+1})-f(x_j)}{x_{j+1}-x_j} = x_{j+1}^{n-1}+x_j x_{j+1}^{n-2}+...+x_j^{n-2}x_{j+1}+x_j^{n-1},$$

a homogeneous polynomial of degree $(n-1)$ in x_j, x_{j+1}. Similarly $f(x_j, x_{j+1}, x_{j+2})$ is a homogeneous polynomial of degree $(n-2)$; and by induction it can be shown that $f(x_j, x_{j+1},...,x_{j+m})$ is a polynomial of degree $n-m$. For consider the difference

$$f(x_{j+1},...,x_{j+k}, x_{j+k+1})-f(x_j, x_{j+1},...,x_{j+k}). \qquad (5.36)$$

Since divided differences are independent of the order in which the values of x_j are taken, this difference is

$$f(x_{j+k+1}, x_{j+1},...,x_{j+k})-f(x_j, x_{j+1},...,x_{j+k}),$$

and this is zero if $x_{j+k+1} = x_j$. Hence if the kth order divided difference $f(x_j, x_{j+1},...,x_{j+k})$ is a polynomial in $x_j,...,x_{j+k}$, the difference (5.36) contains $(x_{j+k+1}-x_j)$ as a factor, and the divided difference $f(x_j, x_{j+1},..., x_{j+k}, x_{j+k+1})$ is a polynomial of degree one lower than $f(x_j, x_{j+1},...,x_{j+k})$. Now for $f(x) = x^n$, $f(x_j, x_{j+1})$ is a polynomial of degree $(n-1)$, so $f(x_j, x_{j+1}, x_{j+2})$ is a polynomial of degree $(n-2)$, and so on. In particular $f(x_j, x_{j+1},...,x_{j+n})$ is a polynomial of degree zero, that is a constant; it is therefore independent of the values of $x_j,...,x_{j+n}$, and has the same value as if these were equally spaced, namely, 1.

For a polynomial of the nth degree with leading term $a_0 x^n$, the nth order divided differences of all terms but the leading term are zero, so the nth order divided differences of this polynomial are constant and of value a_0.

The result that for a polynomial of degree n, the nth order divided differences are constant, can be used to verify whether a set of $(n+m)$ values of f can be fitted by a polynomial of the nth degree. It can also be used to determine values of this polynomial for other values of x, and so to carry out interpolation.

The latter calculation can be done by a process of building up from nth order divided differences, rather in the way in which a polynomial of the nth order can be built up, at equal intervals in x, from its nth differences (§ 4.42). Further, it is possible to determine derivatives of this polynomial, as follows.

If $x_{j+1} = x_j + \epsilon$, then $f(x_j, x_{j+1}) = f'(x_j) + O(\epsilon)$, and in the limit $\epsilon \to 0$, $f(x_j, x_j) = f'(x_j)$. Although $f(x_j, x_j)$ cannot be evaluated directly from the values of f and the definition (5.34) of divided differences, it can be built up from *higher* orders of divided differences and so determined in this way. Similarly

$$f(x_j, x_j, x_j) = \frac{1}{2!} f''(x_j)$$

and in general

$$\underbrace{f(x_j, x_j, ..., x_j)}_{n+1 \text{ arguments}} = \frac{1}{n!} f^{(n)}(x_j).$$

Example: To show that the following values of $f(x)$ are consistent with $f(x)$ being a cubic in x, and to find $f(6), f'(6), f''(6)$ for this cubic:

x	-1	0	2	3	7	10
f	-11	1	1	1	141	561

The working can be arranged as follows:

x	f	1st order	2nd order	3rd order
-1	-11			
		$12/1 = 12$		
0	1		$-12/3 = -4$	
		$0/2 = 0$		$4/4 = 1$
2	1		$0/3 = 0$	
		$0/1 = 0$		$7/7 = 1$
3	1		$35/5 = 7$	
		$140/4 = 35$		$8/8 = 1$
7	141		$105/7 = 15$	
		$420/3 = 140$		$3/3 = 1$
10	561		$-18/-1 = 18$	
		$-448/-4 = 122$		$-1/-1 = 1$
6	73		$-68/-4 = 17$	
		54		$-4/-4 = 1$
6			13	
6				

The working above the inclined line is concerned with showing that the third-order divided differences are constant, as is necessary for a cubic; that below the line is concerned with the evaluation of this cubic and its derivatives at $x = 6$. The arrows indicate the sequence in which the numbers in the lower part are obtained.

In the first part, the divided differences of successively *higher* orders are calculated directly from the definition; for example:

$$f(-1,0) = \frac{1-(-11)}{0-(-1)} = 12; \qquad f(0,2) = \frac{1-1}{2-0} = 0;$$

$$f(-1,0,2) = \frac{0-12}{2-(-1)} = \frac{-12}{3} = -4.$$

In the second part, the divided differences of successively *lower* orders are built up
from those of higher orders. The value 6 of x for which $f(x)$ is wanted is written
as the next value of x in the table. The value of $f(3,7,10,6)$ must be the constant
value 1 for this cubic, that is

$$\frac{f(7,10,6)-f(3,7,10)}{6-3} = 1$$

so that $\qquad\qquad\qquad\qquad f(7,10,6)-f(3,7,10) = 3.$

This value is added to $f(3,7,10) = 15$ to give $f(7,10,6) = 18$. Then

$$f(7,10,6) = \frac{f(10,6)-f(7,10)}{6-7} = \frac{f(10,6)-f(7,10)}{-1}$$

so that $\qquad\qquad\qquad\qquad f(10,6)-f(7,10) = -18$

and this is added to $f(7,10) = 140$, to give $f(10,6) = 122$. Finally

$$f(10,6) = \frac{f(6)-f(10)}{6-10} = \frac{f(6)-f(10)}{-4}$$

so that $f(6)-f(10) = -488$, which added to $f(10)$ gives $f(6) = 73$.

This value of $f(6)$ can be checked by taking it, with the values of $f(3), f(7)$, and
$f(10)$, as given values of the cubic, and using them to obtain $f(2)$ in a similar way;
the value obtained should reproduce the value which was used in forming the
divided difference table used in the evaluation of $f(6)$.

To obtain $f'(6)$ we put a second value of 6 for x, and repeat the process as far as
the first-order divided difference only, and for $\frac{1}{2}f''(6)$ we put $x = 6$ again and repeat
the process as far as the second-order divided differences. The result gives the
cubic in powers of $(x-6)$; in this case

$$f = f(6)+f'(6)(x-6)+\tfrac{1}{2}f''(6)(x-6)^2+\tfrac{1}{6}f'''(6)(x-6)^3$$
$$= 73+54(x-6)+13(x-6)^2+(x-6)^3,$$

and the evaluation of this for the values of x for which the function values are
originally given checks the whole calculation.

5.8. Inverse interpolation

The problem of inverse interpolation is this: given a table of $f(x)$ as
a function of x, to find the value of x for which $f(x)$ has a specified value.
If the table is not at equal intervals in x, there is no distinction between
direct and inverse interpolation; the following applies to tables at equal
intervals in x, as is the case in almost all tables.

The table can be regarded as one of x at *unequal* intervals of $f(x)$, and
a method of interpolation of functions given at unequal intervals of

the argument (§ 5.7) can be used for inverse interpolation. This process takes no advantage of the equal intervals in x, and needs care in use; an example of how *not* to use it is given below (§ 5.81).

Bessel's formula to third differences, using modified second differences, is

$$f_\theta = f(x_0 + \theta\,\delta x) = f_0 + \theta\,\delta f_{\frac{1}{2}} + B^{ii}(\theta)(\delta_m^2 f_0 + \delta_m^2 f_1) + B^{iii}(\theta)\delta^3 f_{\frac{1}{2}};$$

in inverse interpolation, $f(x_0 + \theta\,\delta x)$ is given and this equation is to be solved for θ. If the third-difference contribution can be neglected, it is a quadratic for θ, and could be solved as such, using the conventional formula, but this is a laborious and unsuitable method for practical work; it has been said that 'nobody but a mathematician would do it that way'.

One method is to determine θ roughly by means of a graph or a few trial direct interpolations, and then make a small subtabulation in the neighbourhood of the rough value of θ, at such an interval that linear interpolation can be used for the final step. This method may be found the best for occasional isolated inverse interpolations, and in the neighbourhood of turning values of $f(x)$.

Another method is to write Bessel's formula in the form

$$\theta = [f_\theta - f_0 - B^{ii}(\theta)(\delta_m^2 f_0 + \delta_m^2 f_1) - B^{iii}(\theta)\,\delta^3 f_{\frac{1}{2}}]/\delta f_{\frac{1}{2}} \qquad (5.37)$$

and use an iterative method, improved if required by the process of 'exponential extrapolation' (see §§ 3.4 (a) and 9.32). If second differences are modified by the use of the throwback from fourth differences, as indicated in formula (5.37), this can be used provided fourth differences are less than 500. If they are greater than this, it would be best to proceed by means of some preliminary subtabulation, for values of θ in the neighbourhood of that given by (5.37).

The accuracy to which θ can be determined depends on the number of figures in $\delta f_{\frac{1}{2}}$ and in assessing this accuracy it must be remembered that the last digit of $\delta f_{\frac{1}{2}}$ may be affected by rounding errors to the extent of ± 1. Thus a value of $\delta f_{\frac{1}{2}}$ of about 200 is necessary to establish a second decimal in θ.

Example: Given the following table, find $\sin^{-1} 0\cdot 4$ in degrees and decimals.

x	$f(x) = \sin x$		$\delta^2 f$		$\delta^4 f$	$-0\cdot 184\delta^4 f$	$\delta_m^2 f$
0	0		0		0	0	0
		17365		-528			
10°	0·17365		-528		17	-3	-531
		16837		-511			
20°	·34202		-1039		31	-6	-1045
		15798		-480			
30°	·50000		-1519		45	-8	-1527
		14279		-435			
40°	·64279		-1954				
		12325					
50°	0·76604						

For interpolation in the interval $x = 20°$ to $30°$, we have

$$f_0 = \quad 34202$$
$$\delta f_{\frac{1}{2}} = \quad 15798$$
$$\delta_m^2 f_0 + \delta_m^2 f_1 = \ -2572$$
$$\delta^3 f_{\frac{1}{2}} = - \ 480$$

in terms of the fifth decimal as unit. We want θ for $f = 0.4, f - f_0 = 5798$ in terms of the fifth decimal. Hence, substituting in (5.37),

$$\theta = [5798 + 2572 B^{\mathrm{ii}}(\theta) + 480 B^{\mathrm{iii}}(\theta)]/15798$$
$$= 0.3670_1 + 0.1628 B^{\mathrm{ii}}(\theta) + 0.0304 B^{\mathrm{iii}}(\theta). \qquad (5.38)$$

A nominal fifth decimal is kept here in $(f - f_0)/\delta f_{\frac{1}{2}}$, but not in the other terms since the quantities $B^{\mathrm{ii}}(\theta)$, $B^{\mathrm{iii}}(\theta)$ by which they are multiplied are less than $\frac{1}{10}$.

The first term in (5.38) is the value of θ which would be obtained by linear interpolation. Taking it as a first approximation to θ, the iterative process is as follows:

θ	r.h.s. of (5.38)
·367	$\cdot3670_1 + (0 \cdot 1628)(-0 \cdot 05808) + (0 \cdot 0304)(+0 \cdot 0051)$
	$= \cdot3670_1 - \cdot0094_6 + \cdot0001_5 = \cdot3577_0$
·3577	$\cdot3670_1 + (0 \cdot 1628)(-0 \cdot 05744) + (0 \cdot 0304)(+0 \cdot 0054)$
	$= \cdot3670_1 - \cdot0093_5 + \cdot0001_6 = \cdot3578_2$

The change in the value of the right-hand side of (5.38) is only about $\frac{1}{80}$ of the change in the value of θ, so the value 0.3578_2 would not be changed by more than 1 in the fifth decimal (due to rounding errors) if the right-hand side were evaluated for the better approximation $\theta = 0.3578_2$. The number of figures in $\delta f_{\frac{1}{2}}$ is not enough to determine the fifth decimal in θ to several units. According to the purpose for which the value of $\sin^{-1} 0.4$ was wanted, it could be rounded off to four decimals, or the fifth retained as a guarding figure; if the latter course is taken it would be advisable to write it as a suffix, as a reminder that it is subject to an uncertainty of several units. Thus the result would be written $\sin^{-1} 0.4 = 23.578_2°$.

For the worker who is fortunate enough to have the use of two machines simultaneously a convenient way of carrying out this successive approximation has been devised by Comrie.[†]

Care is necessary when carrying out inverse interpolation near a stationary value of the tabulated function. In such cases it is advisable to carry out a preliminary subtabulation so that in formula (5.37) $(\delta^2 f_0 + \delta^2 f_1)$ is not greater than $\frac{1}{2} \delta f_{\frac{1}{2}}$, before carrying out the interpolation.

5.81. How not to do inverse interpolation

The following example illustrates the dangers of trying to carry out inverse interpolation by using a Lagrange interpolation formula for x in terms of $f(x)$.[‡]

[†] See *Chambers's 6-Figure Tables*, vol. 2 (1949), Introduction, p. xxix.

[‡] The warning provided by this example seems necessary, as this method has been recommended without qualification in a book on finite differences, and, moreover, in a context very similar to this example.

Example: Given the following table

$$x = 0 \quad 1 \quad 2 \quad 3 \quad 4$$
$$y = 0 \quad 1 \quad 8 \quad 27 \quad 64$$

find x for $y = 20$.

The five-point Lagrangian formula for x in terms of y is

$$x = y\left[\frac{(y-8)(y-27)(y-64)}{1.(-7)(-26)(-63)}.1 + \frac{(y-1)(y-27)(y-64)}{8.7.(-19)(-56)}.2 + \right.$$
$$\left. + \frac{(y-1)(y-8)(y-64)}{27.26.19.(-37)}.3 + \frac{(y-1)(y-8)(y-27)}{64.63.56.37}.4\right] \quad (5.39)$$

and evaluation of this for $y = 20$ gives $x = -1\cdot316$, instead of the correct value $(20)^{\frac{1}{3}} = 2\cdot71442$. The result is not appreciably improved if one takes a six-point formula by including the value $x = 5$, $y = 125$ so that there are three points on each side of the value for which the interpolation is carried out; and a better result ($x = +2\cdot923$) is obtained if a three-point formula involving only the values $x = 1$, 2, and 3, is used in preference to the five-point formula.

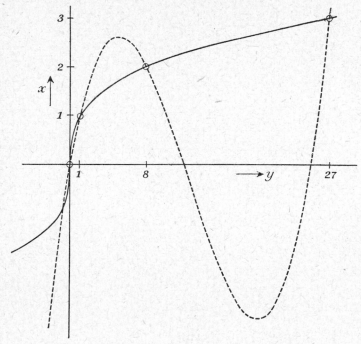

FIG. 9.

The reason for this discrepancy is that $x = y^{\frac{1}{3}}$ cannot be represented adequately by a polynomial in y over the range in question, whereas Lagrange's interpolation formula is based on a polynomial approximation to the function being interpolated. Fig. 9 shows a comparison between $x = y^{\frac{1}{3}}$ (full curve) and the quartic polynomial (5.39) by which the Lagrangian interpolation is carried out (broken curve).

If this method is used for doing inverse interpolation, it is advisable to check the resulting value of x by doing a direct interpolation in the table of $f(x)$ for that value of x, and to verify that this reproduces the value of $f(x)$.

5.9. Truncation errors in interpolation formulae

Except for polynomials of degree not greater than n, an interpolation formula to nth differences, or an $(n+1)$-point Lagrangian interpolation formula, is only an approximation. All the formulae for direct interpolation which we have considered express the interpolated value $f(x)$ of a function as a linear combination of tabular values $f(x_j)$, or, to put it another way, as the result of some linear operation on the function specified by these tabular values. A general method for finding a formal expression for the truncation error in such a formula has been given by W. E. Milne, and is considered in the next chapter (§ 6.7).

The method of inverse interpolation considered in § 5.8 is *not* linear in f, and is not covered by Milne's treatment.

VI

INTEGRATION (QUADRATURE) AND DIFFERENTIATION

6.1. Definite and indefinite integrals, and the integration of differential equations

THERE are two kinds of situation in which we may want to carry out numerical integration. One is the integration of a *given* function of the independent variable; this is sometimes called quadrature.† The other is the integration of a differential equation, which can be regarded as the evaluation of an integral in which the integrand at each value of x depends on the value of the integral at that value of x. This is represented formally by writing the solution of the equation $dy/dx = f(x, y)$ as

$$y = \int f(x, y)\, dx. \tag{6.1}$$

From the point of view of carrying out the integration by numerical (or mechanical) means, the only difference between quadrature and the integration of an ordinary differential equation is that in the former case the integrand in (6.1) is independent of y, and so is known as a function of the variable of integration over the whole range of x before the integration is started, whereas in the latter case the integrand at any value of x is not known until the integration has been taken as far as that value of x. The present chapter is concerned with the integration and differentiation of *given* functions of x. The integration of differential equations is considered in Chapter VII.

In integration of a given function of x, the results required may be of two kinds, a definite integral $\int_a^b f(x)\, dx$ between a single specified pair of limits a, b, or an indefinite integral $\int_a^x f(\xi)\, d\xi$ as a function of its upper limit. The latter is much the more important, and will be considered first. Usually when results of this kind are wanted, they are wanted at the same values of x as those at which $f(x)$ is tabulated, though occasionally results at twice this interval will be adequate.

---

† It is also sometimes called 'mechanical quadrature'; but this term is misleading since there is nothing more mechanical about the process than there is about any other numerical calculation.

6.2. Integration formula in terms of integrand and its differences

The relation between the first differences of a function and its first derivative and the differences of this derivative has already been obtained in § 4.74, where it has been pointed out that such a relation is an integration formula. We have

$$f_1 - f_0 = \int_{x_0}^{x_1} f' dx;$$

substituting this in (4.58) and replacing f' by f we have

$$\int_{x_0}^{x_1} f \, dx = \tfrac{1}{2}(\delta x)[f_0 + f_1 - \tfrac{1}{12}(\delta^2 f_0 + \delta^2 f_1) +$$
$$+ \tfrac{11}{720}(\delta^4 f_0 + \delta^4 f_1) - \tfrac{191}{60480}(\delta^6 f_0 + \delta^6 f_1)] + O(\delta x)^9. \quad (6.2)$$

This could be obtained directly by the use of finite-difference and differential operators, without reference to § 4.74, as follows. Expressed in terms of operators, $\int_{x_0}^{x_1} f \, dx$ is $(E-1)D^{-1}f_0$, and we want to express this in the form $\tfrac{1}{2}(\delta x)\phi(\delta)(E+1)f_0$. Hence

$$\tfrac{1}{2}(\delta x)\phi(\delta)(E+1) = (E-1)D^{-1}$$

or
$$\phi(\delta) = \frac{E-1}{E+1} \frac{2}{U} = \frac{\tanh \tfrac{1}{2}U}{\tfrac{1}{2}U}$$

and the algebraical work of expanding $\phi(\delta)$ in powers of δ then proceeds as in § 4.74.

An alternative derivation is by integration of Bessel's or Everett's interpolation formula with respect to θ, for

$$\int_{x_0}^{x_1} f \, dx = (\delta x) \int_{\theta=0}^{1} f(x_0 + \theta \delta x) \, d\theta. \quad (6.3)$$

In Bessel's formula, the coefficients of the odd order differences are odd functions of $(\theta - \tfrac{1}{2})$, so they give zero on integration. The integrals of the coefficients of the even-order differences in Bessel's formula give the coefficients in (6.2).

The ratio of the coefficients of $\delta^4 f$ in (6.2) to that of $\delta^2 f$ is $-\tfrac{11}{60} = -0\cdot1833$, which is very close to the value $-0\cdot184$ used in modifying second differences in interpolation by means of the throwback; this is not surprising in view of the close relation just mentioned between the interpolation and integration formulae. However, unless modified second differences have to be calculated anyway for interpolation purposes, use of them in the integration formula is no simpler than calculating the fourth-difference contribution as it stands.

In using the integration formula (6.2) it is advisable to add the contributions in the square bracket *first* and finally multiply the whole by *one half* (δx), rather than dividing each separate contribution by two before adding; this halves the possible rounding error without requiring that any additional figures should be kept.

For reference later, an alternative form of formula (6.2) should be noted. From the relation (4.34) between the operators μ and δ it follows that $(E+1)\delta^{2n} = 2(E-1)\mu\delta^{2n-1}$. So each pair of terms $(\delta^{2n}f_0+\delta^{2n}f_1)$ can be written $2(\mu\delta^{2n-1}f_1-\mu\delta^{2n-1}f_0)$ and formula (6.2) can be written alternatively

$$\int_{x_0}^{x_1} f\,dx = (\delta x)[\tfrac{1}{2}(f_0+f_1)-\tfrac{1}{12}(\mu\delta f_1-\mu\delta f_0)+\tfrac{11}{720}(\mu\delta^3 f_1-\mu\delta^3 f_0)-$$
$$-\tfrac{191}{60480}(\mu\delta^5 f_1-\mu\delta^5 f_0)]+O(\delta x)^9. \quad (6.4)$$

This is not as convenient as (6.2) for integration through a single interval, but may be more convenient for integration over a number of intervals.

6.21. An alternative derivation

Formula (6.2) and other integration formulae can be obtained by a rather different approach as follows. The simplest integration formula, often known as the 'trapezium rule' or the 'trapezoidal formula', is

$$\int_{x_0}^{x_1} f\,dx = \tfrac{1}{2}(\delta x)(f_0+f_1). \quad (6.5)$$

For a more accurate formula, let us write

$$\int_{x_0}^{x_1} f\,dx = \tfrac{1}{2}(\delta x)[f_0+f_1+C_1]; \quad (6.6)$$

$\tfrac{1}{2}(\delta x)C_1$ can be regarded as a correction to the result obtained by the trapezium rule.

Now $\int_{x_0}^{x_1} f\,dx = (E-1)D^{-1}f_0$ and $(f_0+f_1) = (E+1)f_0$

so that C_1 is given in terms of operators by

$$C_1 = \left[\frac{2(E-1)}{U}-(E+1)\right]f_0. \quad (6.7)$$

Different integration formulae are given by different ways of expressing C_1.

If we want to express C_1 in terms of the *sum* of contributions from the beginning and end of the interval, we write it as the result of an operation on $(E+1)f_0$, thus:

$$C_1 = \left[\frac{2(E-1)}{U(E+1)}-1\right](E+1)f_0 = \left(\frac{\tanh\tfrac{1}{2}U}{\tfrac{1}{2}U}-1\right)(f_1+f_0), \quad (6.8)$$

and expansion of the operator here in powers of δ gives formula (6.2).

It is also possible to expand it in powers of U and so obtain an integration formula in terms of higher derivatives of f, but this is of little practical value as these high derivatives are seldom available.

If we want to express C_1 in terms of the *difference* between contributions from the beginning and end of the interval, we write it as a result of an operation on $(E-1)f_0$. One way of doing this is to use in formula (6.8) the relation (4.34), namely $(E+1)\delta = 2(E-1)\mu$. This gives

$$C_1 = \frac{2}{\delta^2}\left[\frac{\tanh\frac{1}{2}U}{\frac{1}{2}U}-1\right](\mu\delta f_1 - \mu\delta f_0);$$

and expansion of $(\tanh\frac{1}{2}U)/\frac{1}{2}U$ in powers of δ then gives (6.4).

6.22. Integration formula in terms of the integrand and the differences of its derivative

Another way of writing C_1 as a difference between contributions from the beginning and end of the interval is

$$C_1 = \frac{1}{D}\left[\frac{2}{U}-\frac{E+1}{E-1}\right](E-1)Df_0 = \frac{\delta x}{U}\left[\frac{2}{U}-\frac{E+1}{E-1}\right](f'_1-f'_0). \quad (6.9)$$

This form for C_1, in terms of the derivative f' of the integrand and its differences, is convenient as the operator here is an even function of U and so of δ.

From formula (4.34), $(E+1)/(E-1) = 2\mu/\delta$, so formula (6.9) for C_1 can be written

$$C_1 = -(2/\delta^2)(\delta x)[(\mu\delta/U)-(\delta^2/U^2)](f'_1-f'_0). \quad (6.10)$$

The expansions for $(\mu\delta/U)$ and (δ^2/U^2) in terms of δ are given by (4.52) and (4.47) respectively; substitution in (6.10) gives

$$C_1 = -\tfrac{1}{6}(\delta x)[1-\tfrac{1}{60}\delta^2+\tfrac{1}{560}\delta^4-\tfrac{79}{302400}\delta^6](f'_1-f'_0)+O(\delta x)^9,$$

so that

$$\int_{x_0}^{x_1} f(x)\,dx = \tfrac{1}{2}(\delta x)[(f_0+f_1)-\tfrac{1}{6}(\delta x)\{(f'_1-f'_0)-\tfrac{1}{60}(\delta^2 f'_1-\delta^2 f'_0)+ \\ +\tfrac{1}{560}(\delta^4 f'_1-\delta^4 f'_0)-\tfrac{79}{302400}(\delta^6 f'_1-\delta^6 f'_0)\}]+O(\delta x)^{10}. \quad (6.11)$$

An advantage of this formula is the small coefficient ($\tfrac{1}{6}\cdot\tfrac{1}{60} = \tfrac{1}{360}$) of the term of order $(\delta x)^4$ in the square bracket, compared with that ($\tfrac{11}{720}$) of the corresponding term in (6.2). Further, the term of order $(\delta x)^2$ in the square bracket only involves values of quantities at the beginning and end of the interval of integration, whereas the corresponding term in (6.2) involves the values of f_2 and f_{-1} outside that interval. We shall see later that both these advantages are important in the integration of differential equations.

6.23. Integration formula in terms of integrand and its derivatives

Expansion of the operator in (6.9) in terms of U instead of in terms of δ will give an integration formula in terms of the integrand and its derivatives. This is known as the Euler–Maclaurin formula.

In terms of U, (6.9) becomes

$$C_1 = -\{2(\delta x)/U^2\}[\tfrac{1}{2}U \coth \tfrac{1}{2}U - 1](f_1' - f_0'). \qquad (6.12)$$

Now the expansion of $\tfrac{1}{2}z \cot \tfrac{1}{2}z$ in powers of z is†

$$\tfrac{1}{2}z \cot \tfrac{1}{2}z = 1 - \frac{1}{2!}B_1 z^2 - \frac{1}{4!}B_2 z^4 - \frac{1}{6!}B_3 z^6 - ..., \qquad (6.13)$$

the coefficients B_n being the Bernoulli numbers; the values of the first few are

$$B_1 = \tfrac{1}{6}, \qquad B_2 = \tfrac{1}{30}, \qquad B_3 = \tfrac{1}{42}, \qquad B_4 = \tfrac{1}{30}, \qquad B_5 = \tfrac{5}{6}.$$

The corresponding expansion of $\tfrac{1}{2}y \coth \tfrac{1}{2}y$ is given by putting $z = iy$ in (6.13), so the required expansion of $(2/U^2)[\tfrac{1}{2}U \coth \tfrac{1}{2}U - 1]$ is

$$(2/U^2)[\tfrac{1}{2}\coth \tfrac{1}{2}U - 1] = B_1 - \frac{2}{4!}B_2 U^2 + \frac{2}{6!}B_3 U^4 - \frac{2}{8!}B_4 U^6 + O(\delta x)^8$$

$$= \tfrac{1}{6}[1 - \tfrac{1}{60}U^2 + \tfrac{1}{2520}U^4 - \tfrac{1}{10080}U^6] + O(\delta x)^8. \qquad (6.14)$$

Substitution in (6.12) then gives an expression for C_1, and substitution of this in (6.6) gives the Euler–Maclaurin integration formula

$$\int_{x_0}^{x_1} f(x)\, dx = \tfrac{1}{2}(\delta x)[f_0 + f_1 - \tfrac{1}{6}(\delta x)\{(f_1' - f_0') - \tfrac{1}{60}(\delta x)^2(f_1''' - f_0''') +$$

$$+ \tfrac{1}{2520}(\delta x)^4(f_1^{v} - f_0^{v}) - \tfrac{1}{10080}(\delta x)^6(f_1^{vii} - f_0^{vii})\}] + O(\delta x)^9. \qquad (6.15)$$

This formula is of limited practical value, since values of the higher derivatives of the integrand will not generally be available. They may, however, be available in two cases; first, when the integrand is given by a sufficiently simple analytical formula, and secondly, when f satisfies a sufficiently simple differential equation. The analytical formula or differential equation must be such that it can be differentiated several times without leading to expressions too complicated for practical numerical evaluation.

6.3. Integration over more than one interval

If it is adequate to obtain the values of the integral at intervals greater than those at which the integrand is given, other integration

---

† E. T. Whittaker and G. N. Watson, *Modern Analysis* (C.U.P. 1927), § 7.2. The notation for the Bernoulli numbers used here follows that of Whittaker and Watson

formulae are available. For integration over $2k$ successive intervals (δx) we have

$$\int_{x_{-k}}^{x_k} f(x)\, dx = (E^k - E^{-k})D^{-1}f_0 = 2(\sinh kU)D^{-1}f_0.$$

A first approximation is $2k(\delta x)f_0$, so we try to obtain a $\phi(\delta)$ such that

$$\int_{x_{-k}}^{x_k} f(x)\, dx = 2k(\delta x)\phi(\delta)f_0.$$

The operator $\phi(\delta)$ required is therefore given by

$$2k(\delta x)\,\phi(\delta) = 2(\sinh kU)/D$$

or
$$\phi(\delta) = (\sinh kU)/kU. \qquad (6.16)$$

In particular, for $k = 1$ (integration over two intervals),

$$\phi(\delta) = (\sinh U)/U.$$

The expansion of this operator in powers of δ has already been considered in § 4.75; substitution from formula (4.52) gives

$$\int_{x_{-1}}^{x_1} f(x)\, dx = 2(\delta x)[f_0 + \tfrac{1}{6}\delta^2 f_0 - \tfrac{1}{180}\delta^4 f_0 + \tfrac{1}{1512}\delta^6 f_0] + O(\delta x)^9. \qquad (6.17)$$

The first two terms give the finite-difference form of the integration formula usually called 'Simpson's rule'. This can be seen by expressing $\delta^2 f_0$ in terms of function values; then the first two terms in (6.17) give

$$\int_{x_{-1}}^{x_1} f(x)\, dx = 2(\delta x)[f_0 + \tfrac{1}{6}(f_1 - 2f_0 + f_{-1})] = \tfrac{1}{3}(\delta x)[f_1 + 4f_0 + f_{-1}],$$
$$(6.18)$$

the usual form of Simpson's rule.

Another important formula of this kind is related to the result of putting $k = 3$ in (6.16). For $k = 3$,

$$\phi(\delta) = (\sinh 3U)/3U = 1 + \tfrac{1}{2}U^2 + \tfrac{27}{40}U^4 - \tfrac{81}{560}U^6 + O(\delta x)^8$$
$$= [1 + \tfrac{3}{2}\delta^2 + \tfrac{11}{20}\delta^4 + \tfrac{41}{840}\delta^6] + O(\delta x)^8.$$

If now we replace the coefficient $\tfrac{41}{840}$ by $\tfrac{42}{840} = \tfrac{1}{20}$ we obtain a formula certainly not correct to sixth differences of the integrand but in which almost the whole of the contribution from the sixth difference is included, namely

$$\int_{x_{-3}}^{x_3} f(x)\, dx = \tfrac{3}{10}(\delta x)[20f_0 + 30\,\delta^2 f_0 + 11\,\delta^4 f_0 + \delta^6 f_0] - \tfrac{1}{140}(\delta x)\,\delta^6 f_0 + O(\delta x)^9,$$

or, in terms of function values, taking only the terms in the square brackets,

$$\int\limits_{x-3}^{x_3} f(x)\, dx = \tfrac{3}{10}(\delta x)[f_3 + 5f_2 + f_1 + 6f_0 + f_{-1} + 5f_{-2} + f_{-3}]. \tag{6.19}$$

This is known as 'Weddle's rule'.

Another procedure for evaluating an integral over a number of equal intervals is to express it as the sum of a number of trapezium-rule contributions and a correction.

The approximation to $\int\limits_{x_0}^{x_n} f(x)\, dx$ as the sum of a number of trapezium-rule contributions over intervals δx is

$$\tfrac{1}{2}(\delta x)(f_0 + 2f_1 + 2f_2 + \ldots + 2f_{n-1} + f_n)$$
$$= \tfrac{1}{2}(\delta x)(1 + E)(1 + E + E^2 + \ldots + E^{n-1})f_0$$
$$= \tfrac{1}{2}(\delta x)[(E+1)(E^n-1)/(E-1)]f_0.$$

The integral itself is $(E^n - 1)D^{-1}f_0$; let us write it as the sum of the trapezium-rule contributions, plus a correction $\tfrac{1}{2}(\delta x)C_n$; that is,

$$(E^n - 1)D^{-1}f_0 = \int\limits_{x_0}^{x_n} f(x)\, dx = \tfrac{1}{2}(\delta x)\left[\frac{E+1}{E-1}(E^n - 1)f_0 + C_n\right].$$

Then
$$C_n = \left(\frac{2}{U} - \frac{E+1}{E-1}\right)(E^n - 1)f_0 = \left(\frac{2}{U} - \frac{E+1}{E-1}\right)(f_n - f_0),$$

so that C_n is related to $(f_n - f_0)$ in just the same way as C_1 is to $(f_1 - f_0)$ (see § 6.21). Thus we can write down three integration formulae directly from the results of §§ 6.2 to 6.23.

In terms of the integrand f and its differences:

$$\int\limits_{x_0}^{x_n} f(x)\, dx = (\delta x)[\tfrac{1}{2}(f_0 + 2f_1 + 2f_2 + \ldots + 2f_{n-1} + f_n) - \tfrac{1}{12}(\mu\delta f_n - \mu\delta f_0) +$$
$$+ \tfrac{11}{720}(\mu\delta^3 f_n - \mu\delta^3 f_0) - \tfrac{191}{60480}(\mu\delta^5 f_n - \mu\delta^5 f_0)]. \tag{6.20}$$

In terms of the integrand, its first derivative, and the differences of this first derivative:

$$\int\limits_{x_0}^{x_n} f(x)\, dx = \tfrac{1}{2}(\delta x)[f_0 + 2f_1 + 2f_2 + \ldots + 2f_{n-1} + f_n -$$
$$- \tfrac{1}{6}(\delta x)\{(f'_n - f'_0) - \tfrac{1}{60}(\delta^2 f'_n - \delta^2 f'_0) + \tfrac{1}{560}(\delta^4 f'_n - \delta^4 f'_0) - \ldots\}]. \tag{6.21}$$

In terms of the integrand and its derivatives (Euler–Maclaurin formula):

$$\int_{x_0}^{x_n} f(x)\,dx = \tfrac{1}{2}(\delta x)[f_0+2f_1+2f_2+\ldots+2f_{n-1}+f_n-$$
$$-\tfrac{1}{6}(\delta x)\{(f'_n-f'_0)-\tfrac{1}{60}(\delta x)^2(f'''_n-f'''_0)+\tfrac{1}{2520}(\delta x)^4(f^v_n-f^v_0)-\ldots\}]. \quad (6.22)$$

The last is of limited practical use as a formula for numerical integration for reasons already mentioned in § 6.23. It is, however, useful for numerical work in another context (see § 11.12).

6.4. Evaluation of an integral as a function of its upper limit

The evaluation of an integral as a function of the upper limit can be carried out by successive addition of the contributions from a sequence of intervals (δx) covering the relevant range of x. Let us for brevity write $F(x)$ for $\int_a^x f(\xi)\,d\xi$. Then if, for example, the integration formula (6.2) is used, these contributions are

$$\delta F_{j+\frac{1}{2}} = \int_{x_j}^{x_{j+1}} f(x)\,dx = \tfrac{1}{2}(\delta x)s_{j+\frac{1}{2}}, \quad (6.23)$$

where $s_{j+\frac{1}{2}} = (f_j+f_{j+1})-\tfrac{1}{12}(\delta^2 f_j+\delta^2 f_{j+1})+\tfrac{11}{720}(\delta^4 f_j+\delta^4 f_{j+1})-\ldots; \quad (6.24)$

and $\int_{x_0}^{x_n} f(x)\,dx$ is the sum of n such contributions. The summation of these contributions can be expressed by use of the central-sum operator σ, the inverse of δ (see § 4.6); operating on both sides of (6.23) with σ we have

$$F_j-F_0 = \tfrac{1}{2}(\delta x)[(\sigma s)_j-(\sigma s)_0]. \quad (6.25)$$

If values of the integrand are available at half the interval δx at which the values of the integral are required, a convenient alternative formula for $s_{j+\frac{1}{2}}$, based on (6.17), is

$$\tfrac{1}{2}s_{j+\frac{1}{2}} = f_{j+\frac{1}{2}}+\tfrac{1}{6}\delta^2 f_{j+\frac{1}{2}}-\tfrac{1}{180}\delta^4 f_{j+\frac{1}{2}}+\tfrac{1}{1512}\delta^6 f_{j+\frac{1}{2}}-\ldots, \quad (6.26)$$

where δ indicates the central-difference operator for intervals $\tfrac{1}{2}\delta x$.

In summing contributions of the form (6.23), there will be an accumulation of rounding errors from the corrections to the trapezium rule for the successive intervals. This accumulation can be made unimportant by the use of a guarding figure in the contributions (6.23).

However the calculation of the integral is done, it must be checked. The details of the checking procedure depend on the method used to evaluate the integral; the following procedure, given as an example, refers to a calculation carried out by evaluating the successive contributions (6.23) and adding them. It is then advisable to carry out one check on the values of $s_{j+\frac{1}{2}}$ and another on the evaluation of the integral from them; the intermediate check of the values of $s_{j+\frac{1}{2}}$ will avoid the possibility of a large number of values of the integral having to be corrected if one of the values of $s_{j+\frac{1}{2}}$ is in error.

Operating on both sides of (6.24) with δ^2 we have

$$\delta^2 s_{j+\frac{1}{2}} = (\delta^2 f_0 + \delta^2 f_1) - \tfrac{1}{12}(\delta^4 f_0 + \delta^4 f_1) + \tfrac{11}{720}(\delta^6 f_0 + \delta^6 f_1) - \ldots \qquad (6.27)$$

A comparison of the values of $\delta^2 s$ calculated (i) from successive values of s by the method of § 4.45, and (ii) from formula (6.27), provides a good check on s values, and a clear indication of the location of mistakes, if any. When this check has been made and mistakes, if any, corrected, and only then, the values of $s_{j+\frac{1}{2}}$ should be summed, and the values of the integral F calculated from (6.25); the multiplication by $\tfrac{1}{2}(\delta x)$ should follow the summation, otherwise it may be necessary to keep an extra figure to avoid rounding errors.

This summation and multiplication by $\tfrac{1}{2}(\delta x)$ can be checked as follows. From (6.23) we have $\qquad \delta^3 F_{j+\frac{1}{2}} = \tfrac{1}{2}(\delta x)\,\delta^2 s_{j+\frac{1}{2}}, \qquad\qquad\qquad (6.28)$

and values of $\delta^2 s$ are already available as they have been used in the process of checking the values of s. The values of the integral F can be checked by comparing the values of $\delta^3 F$ obtained (i) as $\delta(\delta^2 F)$ from the values of F, the second differences being evaluated by the method of § 4.45 and *then* differenced once more, and (ii) from formula (6.28).

Various alternative checking procedures of this kind can be devised, for example by taking the fourth differences of both sides of (6.24) to give a check of the values of s. Another kind of check is an overall check by one of the methods considered in § 6.5; but this is less useful, since although it will indicate the presence of a mistake it will not usually locate it.

Example: To evaluate $\int_0^{} e^{x^2}\,dx$ to five decimals at intervals $0\cdot1$ in x.

The first seven intervals of the calculation are given on p. 105, in which each column, rather than each row, refers to a single value of x. The values of s are calculated from formulae (6.24), the contributions from the sixth differences being just appreciable; the second differences of these values of s are in the line below the values of s themselves, and the sums of the right-hand side of formula (6.27) occur four lines lower down. The discrepancies ($+60$, -121, $+61$) between these two sets of values at $x = 0\cdot35, 0\cdot45$, and $0\cdot55$ clearly indicate a mistake, probably of 60 units in the last figure, at $x = 0\cdot45$, and this is easily traced to the value of $-\tfrac{1}{12}(\delta^2 f_j + \delta^2 f_{j+1})$ for the interval $0\cdot4$ to $0\cdot5$, which should read -583_0, so that $s(0\cdot45) = 2\cdot45180$.

The differences $\delta^2 s$ affected by this correction should be recalculated and the comparison with formula (6.27) verified to make sure that the correction itself has been rightly made. In actual working the corrected values could be written in place of the erroneous values, but in this example they have been written separately to display both the incorrect and correct values. The successive values of s are then summed, and the sums multiplied by $\frac{1}{2}(\delta x)$ and rounded off. Finally, this summation and multiplication is checked by comparing $\delta(\delta^2 F)$ with $\frac{1}{2}(\delta x)\delta^2 s$.

Notes: (i) In the check comparisons between the values of $\delta^2 s$ calculated by the two ways, and in the similar comparisons for $\delta^3 F$, discrepancies of a unit can be expected as the result of accumulated rounding errors, but discrepancies in successive values should usually be in opposite directions.

(ii) The contribution of $\delta^6 f$ to $\delta^2 s$ may be appreciable, although its contribution to s itself is negligible, and similarly for other orders of differences.

(iii) In this case f is an even function of x, hence each difference of even order is an even function of x, so the even-order differences at $x = 0$ can be calculated from the formula
$$\delta^{2n+2}f(0) = 2[\delta^{2n}f(\delta x) - \delta^{2n}f(0)].$$

To obtain the second and higher differences at $x = 0.8$, the values of $f(x)$ up to $f(1.1)$ have been used, though to save space they are not given explicitly.

(iv) Each value of f is subject to a rounding error of up to $\frac{1}{2}$ in the last figure, so each value of s is subject to a rounding error of up to 1. If these rounding errors were randomly distributed, the 'probable error' (in the technical sense of the term as used in the theory of errors) of the sum of N values of s would be approximately $\frac{1}{4}N^{\frac{1}{2}}$, so that of the result would be about $\frac{1}{4}N^{\frac{1}{2}}(\delta x)$ in the last significant figure of the values of the integrand. In the present case, with $N = 8$, this is rather less than 1 in the sixth decimal in the integral. In making estimates of this kind, it must be remembered that errors up to 2 or 3 times the 'probable error' are not unlikely.

(v) Another method of calculating this integral, more convenient for large values of x, is given in the example in § 7.3.

(vi) The checks indicated verify the calculation from the values of the integrand f but they do not check these values themselves. The differences of the values of the integrand form a check against gross errors, but do not check the last digit with certainty. An overall check on the whole calculation, including the values of the integrand, is provided by doing an integration by one of the methods of § 6.5 using another set of values of the integrand, say in this case by integrating from $x = 0$ to 0.8 using ten steps of length 0.08, or by using a Gauss integration formula (see § 6.57).

6.41. Change of interval length in an integration

It may sometimes be required to change the interval length (δx) in the course of an integration. Where the third and higher derivatives of the integrand are large, it is advisable to take small intervals, not only in order that the corrections to the trapezium rule should not be too large, but in order that the behaviour of the integrand should be adequately defined by those of its values which are used in the integration formula. It may happen that the values of the third and higher derivatives vary considerably over the range of integration. If in such

	$-0{\cdot}1$	0	$+0{\cdot}1$	$0{\cdot}2$	$0{\cdot}3$	$0{\cdot}4$	$0{\cdot}5$	$0{\cdot}6$	$0{\cdot}7$	$0{\cdot}8$
x										
$f = e^{x^2}$	1·01005	1·00000	1·01005	1·04081	1·09417	1·17351	1·28403	1·43333	1·63232	1·89648
$\delta^2 f$		2010	2071	2260	2598	3118	3878	4969	6517	8727
$\delta^4 f$		122	128	149	182	240	331	457	662	957
$\delta^6 f$		12	15	12	25	33	35	79	90	170
$f_j + f_{j+1}$		2·01005	2·05086	2·13498	2·26768	2·45754	2·71736	3·06565	3·52880	
$-\frac{1}{12}(\delta^2 f_j + \delta^2 f_{j+1})$		-340_1	-360_9	-404_8	-476_3	-523_0	-737_2	-957_2	-1270_3	
$+\frac{11}{720}(\delta^4 f_j + \delta^4 f_{j+1})$		$+3_8$	$+4_2$	$+5_1$	$+6_4$	$+8_7$	$+12_0$	$+17_1$	$+24_8$	
$-\frac{191}{60480}(\delta^6 f_j + \delta^6 f_{j+1})$		-0_1	-0_1	-0_1	-0_2	-0_2	-0_4	-0_5	-0_8	
sum $= s_{j+\frac12}$		2·00669	2·04729	2·13098	2·26298	2·45240	2·71010	3·05624	3·51634	
$\delta^2 s$		4060	4309	4831	5742	6828	8844	11396		
$\delta^2 f_j + \delta^2 f_{j+1}$		4081	4331	4858	5716	6996	8847	11486		
$-\frac{1}{12}(\delta^4 f_j + \delta^4 f_{j+1})$		-20_8	-23_1	-27_6	-35_2	-47_6	-65_7	-93_2		
$+\frac{11}{720}(\delta^6 f_j + \delta^6 f_{j+1})$		$+0_4$	$+0_4$	$+0_6$	$+0_9$	$+1_0$	$+1_7$	$+2_6$		
sum		4061	4308	4831	5682	6949	8783	11395		
corrected s		2·00669	2·04729	2·13098	2·26298	2·45180	2·71010	3·05624	3·51634	
$\delta^2 s$		4060	4309	4831	5682	6948	8784	11396		
σs		0·00000	2·00669	4·05398	6·18496	8·44794	10·89974	13·60984	16·66608	20·18242
$\frac{1}{2}\delta x\,\sigma s = \int_0^x f\,dx = F$		0·00000	0·10033	0·20270	0·30925	0·42240	0·54499	0·68049	0·83330	1·00912
$\delta^2 F$		0	204	418	660	944	1291	1731	2301	
$\delta(\delta^2 F)$		204	214	242	284	347	440	570		
$\frac{1}{2}(\delta x)\delta^2 s$		203_0	214_4	241_5	284_1	347_4	439_2	569_8		

a case the interval length (δx) which is necessary when these derivatives are large were used over the whole range, this would involve an unnecessary amount of work in the region in which they are small. So a change of interval length, or several such changes, may be required in the course of the integration.

When such a change is made, there should *always* be an overlap between the ranges of x for which the different sizes of interval are used. This is a potent check against mistakes, which are particularly likely to be made at points like this at which a systematic procedure is interrupted. It provides a check not only against random mistakes but against some forms of systematic mistakes as well; if, for example, the term $-\frac{1}{12}(\delta^2 f_j + \delta^2 f_{j+1})$ in (6.24) had been taken systematically with the wrong sign, this would be shown up by a discrepancy between the integration carried out with two different interval lengths.

In practice, the convenient intervals are 1, 2, and 5 times a power (positive or negative) of 10; an increase of interval length from 2.10^q to 5.10^q involves some interpolation, but this is all of the simplest 'halfway' interpolation (see §5.21) and should give no trouble.

6.42. Integration in the neighbourhood of a singularity of the integrand

A point at which f or any of its derivatives becomes infinite will be called a 'singularity' of f.

In deriving the integration formulae of the previous sections, it has been assumed that the integrand $f(x)$ is expansible in a Taylor series through each interval δx. This is not the case if there is a singularity at any point (including end-points) of the interval, and the approximations used are likely to be bad in the neighbourhood of a singularity even if it does not lie in the interval through which the integration is being taken. Examples are:

(i) $\displaystyle\int_1 \frac{e^{-ax}}{(x^2-1)^{\frac{1}{2}}}\, dx$ (integrand infinite at $x = 1$);

(ii) $\displaystyle\int_0 x^{\frac{1}{2}} \sin x\, dx$ (second derivative of integrand infinite at $x = 0$).

A singularity can often be removed by a change of independent variable; for example, the substitution $x = \cosh u$ makes

$$\int_1 \frac{e^{-ax}}{(x^2-1)^{\frac{1}{2}}}\, dx = \int_0 e^{-a\cosh u}\, du,$$

and usually such a change of independent variable will also give results in a more satisfactory form for interpolation. But if the results are required in terms of x, and in a context in which no interpolation will be carried out on them, it may sometimes be better to obtain them directly in such a form.

A singularity can sometimes be removed by the following process. We subtract from the integrand f a function g which can be integrated formally and has a singularity of the same kind as f, evaluate the analytical formula for $\int g\,dx$, and evaluate $\int (f-g)\,dx$ by numerical integration. This may be called 'subtracting out the singularity'.

This is satisfactory if the singularity is a pole of order n, but otherwise it may not be possible to remove the singularity in this way, though it may be made less severe. For example, we can write

$$\int_1 \frac{e^{-ax}}{(x^2-1)^{\frac{1}{2}}}\,dx = e^{-a}\int_1 \frac{dx}{(x^2-1)^{\frac{1}{2}}} + \int_1 \frac{e^{-ax}-e^{-a}}{(x^2-1)^{\frac{1}{2}}}\,dx.$$

The integrand in the integral on the left is infinite at $x=1$, whereas that in the second integral on the right is finite, though its derivative is infinite.

An alternative, and often more effective, treatment is as follows. Write the integral $\int f(x)\,dx = g(x)\,h(x)$, where g is a chosen function for which dg/dx has a singularity of the same kind as that of f. This leads to a differential equation for $h(x)$ for which, however, numerical integration may be quite practicable. This may be called 'dividing out the singularity'.

Consider, for example, integrals of the form

$$\int_0 x^p f(x)\,dx,$$

where $f(x)$ is regular at $x=0$ and $f(0)\neq 0$, and p is greater than -1 and is not an integer. For this case the appropriate function $g(x)$ is $x^{p+1}/(p+1)$, so we write

$$\int_0 x^p f(x)\,dx = \frac{1}{p+1}x^{p+1}h(x) \tag{6.29}$$

and on differentiation obtain

$$x\frac{dh}{dx} = (p+1)(f-h). \tag{6.30}$$

On differentiating k times and putting $x=0$, this gives

$$kh^{(k)}(0) = (p+1)[f^{(k)}(0)-h^{(k)}(0)],$$

so that

$$h^{(k)}(0) = \frac{p+1}{p+1+k}f^{(k)}(0). \tag{6.31}$$

In particular

$$h(0) = f(0)$$

$$h'(0) = \frac{p+1}{p+2} f'(0) \left.\right\rbrace . \tag{6.32}$$

$$h''(0) = \frac{p+1}{p+3} f''(0)$$

These serve as starting values for a numerical integration of equation (6.30).

Numerical integration of equation (6.30) is also useful as a means of evaluating integrals of the form $\int x^p f(x)\, dx$ for values of the lower limit in the neighbourhood of zero when p is negative and $|p| > 1$.

6.43. Integration when the integrand increases 'exponentially'

A similar device of writing an integral in the form

$$\int f(x)\, dx = g(x)\, h(x),$$

choosing a convenient function $g(x)$, and solving numerically the resulting differential equation for $h(x)$ can often be applied when the integrand increases rapidly with x, particularly when $\log f(x)$ increases more rapidly than linearly in x. This process then consists of dividing out the singularity at infinity. One good choice of $g(x)$ is the leading term in the asympotic behaviour of $f(x)$; this makes $h \to 1$ as $x \to \infty$. For example, $\int_0^{} e^{x^2}\, dx$ behaves asymptotically like $e^{x^2}/2x$, so we may write

$$\int_0^{} e^{x^2}\, dx = (e^{x^2}/2x) h(x) \tag{6.33}$$

then

$$\frac{dh}{dx} + 2x \left[\left(1 - \frac{1}{2x^2} \right) h - 1 \right] = 0. \tag{6.34}$$

This, however, is clearly not convenient for small x, and in order to obtain an equation applicable to the whole range of x we may be content to divide out the main part of the singularity at infinity by writing

$$\int_0^{} e^{x^2}\, dx = e^{x^2} h,$$

then

$$\frac{dh}{dx} + 2xh = 1, \tag{6.35}$$

a simpler equation than (6.34), and one which there is no difficulty in integrating numerically from $x = 0$ (see the example in § 7.3).

6.44. Twofold integration

By a many-fold integration of a function $f(x)$ is meant a result obtained by repeated integration with respect to the *same* independent variable, as distinct from a double integral which is obtained by one integration with respect to each of two independent variables. That is, a twofold integral of a function f is a function F such that

$$\frac{d^2F}{dx^2} = f(x).$$

It is sometimes convenient to be able to obtain such a twofold integral directly without going through the intermediate stage of evaluating $\int f\,dx$. This can be done by using formula (4.54), which for this case becomes

$$\delta^2 F_0 = (\delta x)^2 [f_0 + \tfrac{1}{12}\delta^2 f_0 - \tfrac{1}{240}\delta^4 f_0 + \tfrac{31}{60480}\delta^6 f_0] + O(\delta x)^{10}. \qquad (6.36)$$

The twofold summation of the second differences $\delta^2 F$ to give the function values F can be done either directly by the method of §4.46 or by obtaining the first differences as an intermediate step and then summing these.

Effects of rounding errors may build up somewhat rapidly in this twofold summation, and it is advisable to carry some guarding figures. The twofold integration could be carried out by two single integrations, one from F'' to F' and the other from F' to F. Suppose that in an integration carried out by this method, n decimals would have been kept in F'. Then in a twofold integration carried out by a method not involving the calculation of F', the number of decimals kept in δF (or in F if δF is not calculated) should be enough to give n decimals in $\delta F/\delta x$.

6.5. Integrals between fixed limits

An integral between fixed limits can be evaluated by any of the formulae of §6.3 or §6.4, the difference being that the value of the integral is only wanted for a single value of the upper limit.

Example: To evaluate $\int_0^{0.8} e^{x^2}\,dx$ using formula (6.21).

In this case $f'(x) = 2xe^{+x^2}$ is an odd function of x, hence all even-order differences of $f'(x)$ at $x = 0$ are zero, and their contribution to formula (6.21) is zero. For the even-order differences at $x = 0.8$ we have the following values:

x	$f'(x) = 2xe^{x^2}$	$\delta^2 f'$	$\delta^4 f'$	$\delta^6 f'$
0·5	1·2840			
·6	1·7200	1292		
·7	2·2852	1840	238	
·8	3·0344	2626	374	50
·9	4·0462	3786	560	
1·0	5·4366	5506		
1·1	7·3776			

At $x = 0.8$
$$f' = 3{\cdot}0344$$
$$-\tfrac{1}{60}\delta^2 f' = -\ 43_8$$
$$+\tfrac{1}{560}\delta^4 f' = +\ \ \ 0_7$$
$$\text{Sum} = 3{\cdot}0301$$

The values of $f(x)$ are given in the example in § 6.4 (p. 105); using them we have

$$2 \sum_{j=1}^{7} f(j \, \delta x) = 17 \cdot 33644$$

$$f(0) + f(0 \cdot 8) = 2 \cdot 89648$$

and, from the values of f' above,

$$-\tfrac{1}{6}(\delta x)(f' - \tfrac{1}{60}\delta^2 f' + \tfrac{1}{560}\delta^4 f') = -\cdot 05050$$

$$\overline{20 \cdot 18242}$$

Hence $\qquad \displaystyle\int_{0}^{0 \cdot 8} e^{x^2} \, dx = \tfrac{1}{2}(0 \cdot 1) 20 \cdot 18242 = 1 \cdot 00912_1.$

The tolerance on this result, due to the accumulation of rounding errors of the function values used, is a few units in the sixth decimal.

Some other forms which are only appropriate to an integral between fixed limits are considered in the following sections. In particular, there is the possibility of using values of the integrand $f(x)$ not spaced at equal intervals in x if there is any advantage in doing so (§ 6.57). If the integrand is specified by a table at equal intervals in x, then an integration formula which makes use of this feature is usually the more convenient; the interpolation necessary to give its values for use in an integration formula using unequally spaced values of x would usually outweigh the advantages of such a formula. But if it is specified by a formula which can equally well be evaluated for any value of x, then use of values of x at unequal intervals may become practicable.

6.51. Gregory's formula

The integration formula (6.20) expresses the correction C_n to the sum of a set of trapezium rule contributions in terms of central differences at the beginning and end of the range of integration. If the only available values of the integrand are those from f_0 to f_n, the ends of the range of integration, then only forward differences from the beginning and backward differences from the end of the range are available, and a formula in terms of these differences is needed. This is

$$\int_{x_0}^{x_n} f(x) \, dx = (\delta x)[\tfrac{1}{2}(f_0 + 2f_1 + 2f_2 + \dots + 2f_{n-1} + f_n) +$$

$$+ (\tfrac{1}{12}\Delta - \tfrac{1}{24}\Delta^2 + \tfrac{19}{720}\Delta^3 - \dots)f_0 - (\tfrac{1}{12}\nabla + \tfrac{1}{24}\nabla^2 + \tfrac{19}{720}\nabla^3 + \dots)f_n] \quad (6.37)$$

and is known as *Gregory's formula*.

Its practical use is limited, because usually the reason for the limitation on the range over which a function is defined is the occurrence of a singularity, as at $x = \pm 1$ in $\displaystyle\int_{-1}^{1} e^{-x^2}(1 - x^2)^{-\frac{1}{2}} \, dx$, in which case the extension of the integration formula up to those points is invalid. In most other cases, values of the integrand outside the range of integration, and therefore the central differences required in formula (6.20), are available, and then this formula should *always* be used in preference to Gregory's formula.

6.52. Integral in terms of function values

By expressing the differences in formula (6.20), (6.21), or (6.37) in terms of function values, we obtain a set of formulae expressing the integral as a sum of multiples of the values of the integrand and, in the case of formula (6.25), its derivatives. Such a formula is sometimes called a 'Lagrange-type' integration formula, by analogy with the form of Lagrange's interpolation formula.

For example, if in (6.20) we substitute

$$\mu\delta f_0 = \tfrac{1}{2}(f_1 - f_{-1}), \qquad \mu\delta f_n = \tfrac{1}{2}(f_{n+1} - f_{n-1})$$

and neglect terms beyond these, we obtain

$$\int_{x_0}^{x_n} f(x)\,dx = (\delta x)[-\tfrac{1}{24}f_{-1} + \tfrac{1}{2}f_0 + \tfrac{25}{24}f_1 + f_2 + \dots + f_{n-2} + \tfrac{25}{24}f_{n-1} + \tfrac{1}{2}f_n - \tfrac{1}{24}f_{n+1}].$$

$$(6.38)$$

Coefficients in a number of formulae of this type, differing in the order of differences to which they are correct and in the number of function values outside the range x_0 to x_n used, are given in *Chambers's 6-Figure Tables*.†

The writer's own preference is for formulae in terms of differences, such as (6.17), as it is much easier to see which differences have to be taken into account, and inclusion of an extra one does not mean altering the whole formula.

6.53. Use of Simpson's or Weddle's rules

The $\delta^2 f$ terms in the integration formula (6.23) can be taken into account by using Simpson's rule for the intervals (δx) taken in pairs, instead of by using the term $(\mu\delta f_n - \mu\delta f_0)$ in (6.20). There is no great advantage in this procedure, except the smaller coefficient of the $\delta^4 f$ term, and it has certain mild disadvantages. It is equivalent to calculating a correction to the trapezoidal formula for *each* pair of intervals in the integration, which is unnecessary when only a single value of an integral between fixed limits is required, and it involves a substantial amount of work in calculating a correction which may vanish identically, as, for example, in $\int_0^\infty e^{-x^2}\,dx$. It also gives different weights to alternate function values, and requires that the total number of intervals required to cover the range of x should be even. Use of Weddle's rule has similar disadvantages, of which the fact that the number of intervals has to be a multiple of 6 may be more serious.

6.54. The integral $\int_0^\infty e^{-x^2}\,dx$

If all odd derivatives of $f(x)$ are zero at one of the limits of $\int_a^b f(x)\,dx$, then the total contribution from that end of the range of integration to the correction to the trapezium rule formula is zero. And if all the odd derivatives are zero at both ends of the range, it would appear from the Euler–Maclaurin formula that the expression for the integral as the sum of a number of trapezoidal contributions is exact, whatever interval length (δx) is used in the integration.

An example is provided by the integral $\int_0^\infty e^{-x^2}\,dx$. Since the integrand $f(x)$ is an

† Vol. 2, p. 549.

even function of x, every odd derivative is zero at $x = 0$; also all derivatives are zero at $x = \infty$. Hence the Euler–Maclaurin formula appears to give

$$\int_0^\infty e^{-x^2}\,dx = (\delta x)\left[\tfrac{1}{2} + \sum_{j=1}^\infty e^{-j^2(\delta x)^2}\right] \qquad (6.39)$$

exactly, for any value of (δx). If both sides of (6.39) are evaluated for different values of (δx), the results are as follows:

$$\int_0^\infty e^{-x^2}\,dx = \tfrac{1}{2}\pi^{\frac{1}{2}} = 0{\cdot}88622\ 69254\ 5 \text{ to eleven decimals}$$

(δx)	$(\delta x)\left[\tfrac{1}{2} + \sum_{j=1}^\infty e^{-j^2(\delta x)^2}\right]$
0·5	0·88622 69254 5 to eleven decimals
0·6	69254 8
0·7	69285
0·8	0·88622 72808
0·9	23 598
1·0	32 0
1·1	0·88674

Thus the relation (6.39) is nearly true for values of δx which are quite considerable. Why it is not exact is that the Euler–Maclaurin formula is only asymptotic. We saw in § 4.6 that the finite difference operators, and Taylor's series in the form $E = e^U$, could be used freely on functions which were the products of polynomials and exponentials of *linear* functions of x; e^{-x^2} is not of this form, and an examination of the error term is necessary before the Euler–Maclaurin formula is applied to it with (δx) so large that the approximation to the integrand in each interval by a sum of products of polynomials and exponentials becomes dubious. Such an examination has been carried out by Goodwin.[†]

The point might seem of formal rather than practical interest, since anyone with experience of numerical work, faced with the values of e^{-x^2} at intervals of, say, $\delta x = 1$, namely:

x	$f = e^{-x^2}$	δf	$\delta^2 f$	$\delta^3 f$	$\delta^4 f$
0	1		−12642		−30934
		−6321		−15467	
1	0·3679		+2825		+15956
		−3496		+ 489	
2	0·0183		3314		− 3622
		− 182		− 3133	
3	0·0001		181		+ 2953
		− 1		− 180	
4	0·0000		1		179
				− 1	
5	0·0000				1

would say that these function values alone did not define the integrand well enough to justify evaluating the integral to more than two significant figures at most; it is hardly necessary actually to form the difference table to reach this conclusion. Of all the functions which take these tabular values, there is presumably at least one for which the Euler–Maclaurin formula happens to give the right value of the integral; that e^{-x^2} so nearly has this property seems to a certain extent accidental.

† E. T. Goodwin, *Proc. Camb. Phil. Soc.* **45** (1949), 241.

However, the fact that it has this property raises the question whether the use of relatively large intervals (δx) in the evaluation of other integrals of the form $\int_0^\infty e^{-x^2} f(x)\, dx$ may also give results of useful accuracy. This also has been examined by Goodwin.†

6.55. Evaluation of a definite integral when the integrand has a singularity

In evaluating an integral $\int f(x)\, dx$ of which the integrand has a singularity, the singularity can often be removed by a change of independent variable. If the integral is required as a function of the upper limit, we may want to avoid this in order to obtain directly, without further interpolation, values of the integral at equally spaced values of x. But this does not apply to an integral between fixed limits, and in this context the only reason for avoiding a change of variable is that a certain amount of interpolation may be required in order to obtain the values of the integrand at equal spacings in the new variable.

There is, of course, no need to use the new independent variable over the whole range. For example, to evaluate $\int_0^1 [f(x)/(1-x)^{\frac{1}{2}}]\, dx$ we might use the substitution $x = 1-y^2$ over the whole range of x, and so evaluate the integral as

$$\int_0^1 \frac{f(x)\, dx}{(1-x)^{\frac{1}{2}}} = 2 \int_0^1 f(1-y^2)\, dy$$

or we might divide the range of x into two parts, one from $x = 0$ to ξ and the other from $x = \xi$ to 1 and only make the substitution in the second part, thus evaluating the integral in the form

$$\int_0^1 \frac{f(x)}{(1-x)^{\frac{1}{2}}}\, dx = \int_0^\xi \frac{f(x)}{(1-x)^{\frac{1}{2}}}\, dx + 2 \int_0^{\sqrt{(1-\xi)}} f(1-y^2)\, dy.$$

In this case ξ should be chosen so that $1-\xi$ is a perfect square. For example $\xi = 0.64$ might be taken; this would enable intervals of 0.04 or 0.08 in x to be used in the first integral and intervals of 0.1 in y in the second.

6.56. Definite integrals which are functions of a parameter

An important class of integrals between fixed limits comprises those which define a function of a parameter which occurs in the integrand, such as

$$\int_{-1}^1 \frac{e^{-xu}}{(1-u^2)^{\frac{1}{2}}}\, du \quad \text{or generally} \quad g(x) = \int_a^b f(x, u)\, du. \tag{6.40}$$

† E. T. Goodwin, *Proc. Camb. Phil. Soc.* **45** (1949), 241.

Such an integral can be evaluated by quadrature for each value of x, and this may be the only way of evaluating it. But another method of treatment may be much easier and less laborious if it is possible at all. This consists of finding a differential equation which the integral (6.40) satisfies, and solving this differential equation by a numerical process (see Chapter VII). The amount of work required to obtain a single value of the integral is then very much less than that required to carry out the evaluation by quadrature, and probably evaluation by quadrature will only be carried out for two or three values of x, to give initial values for the integration and to provide an overall check. It is not always possible to obtain such a differential equation, but many integrals of this kind of which the values are actually wanted in various contexts do satisfy differential equations. In such cases, the differential equations can often be obtained by one or two differentiations with respect to x and an integration by parts with respect to u.

Consider, for example, the function

$$f(x) = \int_0^\infty [e^{-u^2}/(u+x)] \, du$$

which has been studied by Goodwin and Staton.† The range of integration here is infinite, but for $x > 0$ the integrand is of such a form that differentiation with respect to x is justified. One differentiation gives

$$f'(x) = -\int_0^\infty e^{-u^2}/(u+x)^2 \, du$$

and integration by parts with respect to u then gives

$$f'(x) = \int_0^\infty e^{-u^2} \frac{d}{du}[1/(u+x)] \, du$$

$$= [e^{-u^2}/(u+x)]_{u=0}^\infty + \int_0^\infty 2u[e^{-u^2}/(u+x)] \, du$$

$$= -(1/x) + 2\left[\int_0^\infty e^{-u^2} \, du - x \int_0^\infty \{e^{-u^2}/(u+x)\} \, du\right]$$

$$= -(1/x) + \pi^{\frac{1}{2}} - 2xf(x),$$

so that this function $f(x)$ satisfies the differential equation

$$f' + 2xf = \pi^{\frac{1}{2}} - (1/x). \tag{6.41}$$

Evaluation of $f(x)$ by quadrature for one value of x, say $x = 1$, could be used to give a value from which the numerical integration of equation (6.41) could be started, though Goodwin and Staton actually used a series expansion to obtain such a value.

† *Quart. J. Mech. and Applied Math.* **1** (1948), 319.

6.57. Use of unequal intervals of the independent variables

As already mentioned, in evaluating integrals between fixed limits there is no need to use values of the integrand at equal intervals in x, and there may be advantages in using formulae in terms of some other set of values. An integration formula using a finite number of values of the integrand can be regarded as giving a weighted mean of these values:

$$\int_a^b f(x)\, dx = (b-a)\left[\sum_n w_n f(x_n)\right], \qquad (6.42)$$

where the w_n's are the weights to be assigned to the values of the integrand at the points x_n. Given any m values of x_n, not necessarily equally spaced, values of w_n can be obtained which will make such a formula correct for any polynomial of degree up to $(m-1)$. And it is possible to put a condition on the w_n's (such as that they should all be equal) and determine the corresponding x_n's such that this formula should be exact for polynomials of degree up to $(m-1)$. But if no condition is imposed on either the x_n's or the w_n's, then these can be determined so that a formula (6.42) with m terms in the sum will be exact for any polynomial of degree $(2m-1)$. Such a formula is known as an m-point Gaussian integration formula.

For work on numerical evaluation of integrals of given functions the practical value of such a formula is limited by two things; first, the necessity for interpolating the values of the integrand at the required values of x_n, and, secondly, the difficulty of checking both these values, which are at unequal intervals in x, and the evaluation of the integral. Further, no formula which is based on a polynomial approximation can be appropriate to an infinite range of integration.

On the other hand, use of such a formula may be very valuable in simplifying problems in more than one variable. It can be used, for example, to simplify integro-differential equations involving integrals of the type $\int_{\theta=0}^{\pi} f(r,\theta)\sin\theta\, d\theta$. If such an integral is replaced by a sum $\sum_j w(\theta_j)f(r,\theta_j)$, the solution of the equation in which the integral occurs can be reduced to the solution of a finite number of equations for the functions $f(r,\theta_j)$, each of which is a function of the single variable r only. In making such a replacement it is clearly desirable to obtain as good an approximation as possible with a small number of terms, and this is given by taking the values of θ_j and the weights $w(\theta_j)$ to be those of a Gauss formula.

The values of $\qquad \xi_j = (x_j - a)/(b - a)$

and of the weights w_j for values of m from 1 to 5 can be found in Whittaker and Robinson's *Calculus of Observations*.†

For $m = 5$ they are‡

$$\xi_1 = 1 - \xi_5 = 0{\cdot}046910 \qquad w_1 = w_5 = 0{\cdot}118464$$
$$\xi_2 = 1 - \xi_4 = 0{\cdot}230765 \qquad w_2 = w_4 = 0{\cdot}239314$$
$$\xi_3 = 0{\cdot}5 \qquad\qquad\qquad w_3 = 0{\cdot}284444$$

Example: To evaluate $\int_0^{0{\cdot}8} e^{+x^2}\, dx$ by a five-point Gauss formula. The values of x_j, the integrand values, and weights are as follows:

j	x_j	$f_j = \exp x_j^2$	w_j
1	·037528	1·001409	·118464
2	·184612	1·034669	·239314
3	·400000	1·173511	·284444
4	·615388	1·460388	·239314
5	·762472	1·788475	·118464

$$\sum w_j f_j = 1{\cdot}261401 \qquad (b-a) = 0{\cdot}8$$
$$(b-a) \sum w_j f_j = 1{\cdot}009121$$

Note: This value of the integral agrees with those calculated in §§ 6.4 and 6.5.

6.6. Numerical differentiation

We have already seen that a table of values does not define a function uniquely. Still less does it establish whether the function tabulated is differentiable everywhere, or even anywhere, within the range of the table; two functions may be indistinguishable, to any specified degree of numerical accuracy, for every value of x (not only for the tabular values), yet one may be differentiable everywhere and the other nowhere. And still less does a table establish whether a function is differentiable two or more times. These considerations alone suggest that numerical differentiation of a function specified by a table may be a dubious process.

Further, the entries in a table are affected in an irregular way by rounding errors, and differentiation exaggerates irregularities whereas integration smooths them. In differentiation we are concerned with a limit process carried out on the quantity $[f(x+\delta x) - f(x)]/(\delta x)$, and as δx becomes smaller, irregularities in the values of f become *more* prominent in the result; whereas in integration we are concerned with a limit process carried out on the quantity $\sum f \delta x$ and the effect of an irregularity in any one value of f becomes *less* prominent as δx becomes

† See § 80.
‡ The values are rounded off so as to have the sum 1·000,000.

smaller. This is illustrated by Fig. 10, which shows the graph of the function

$$y = \frac{1}{2} \frac{\sin 10\pi x}{10\pi x} e^{-100x^2}$$

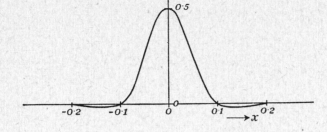

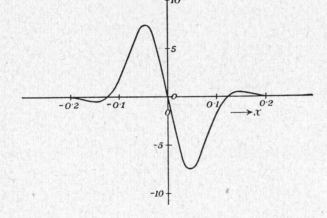

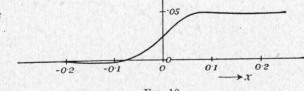

FIG. 10.

which might represent approximately an irregularity produced by a rounding error at $x = 0$ in a table at intervals of $0\cdot1$ in x, and the derivative and integral of this function.

For such reasons, the differentiation of a function specified only by a table of values, or determined experimentally and so subject to errors of observation, is a notoriously unsatisfactory process, particularly if higher derivatives than the first are required. It is a process to be avoided if possible, unless the context in which the results are required is such that the limited accuracy attainable by the numerical process is certainly adequate. In general, values of the second and higher derivatives obtained from such data should be regarded with caution if not scepticism.

In some cases it may be possible to evaluate derivatives by some process other than numerical differentiation. If, for example, a function y is known to satisfy a first-order differential equation, values of y' can be obtained by substituting the values of y into the differential equation. And if y satisfies a differential equation of higher order, it is usually better to obtain y' by numerical solution of the equation as an equation for y', taking y as a given function of x, than to try to obtain y' directly from the values of y by a differentiation formula.

6.61. Differentiation formulae

To obtain a first-order derivative there are two useful formulae, one giving the values of the derivative f' at the values x_j of x at which the function is tabulated, and the other giving f' at $x_{j+\frac{1}{2}}$. The former has already been obtained in § 4.71, and is (see formula (4.46))

$$(\delta x)f'_0 = \mu\delta f_0 - \tfrac{1}{6}\mu\delta^3 f_0 + \tfrac{1}{30}\mu\delta^5 f_0 - \tfrac{1}{140}\mu\delta^7 f_0 + O(\delta x)^9$$

$$= \tfrac{1}{2}[(f_1 - f_{-1}) - \tfrac{1}{6}(\delta^2 f_1 - \delta^2 f_{-1}) + \tfrac{1}{30}(\delta^4 f_1 - \delta^4 f_{-1}) - \tfrac{1}{140}(\delta^6 f_1 - \delta^6 f_{-1})] + O(\delta x)^9.$$

$$(6.43)$$

The other can be obtained either by differentiating Bessel's interpolation formula with respect to θ and then putting $\theta = \frac{1}{2}$, or by using finite-difference operators as follows. We want to find a $\phi(\delta)$ such that

$$(\delta x)f'_{\frac{1}{2}} = \phi(\delta)\,\delta f_{\frac{1}{2}}.$$

Hence

$$\phi(\delta) = U/\delta = (\sinh^{-1}\tfrac{1}{2}\delta)/\tfrac{1}{2}\delta = 1 - \tfrac{1}{24}\delta^2 + \tfrac{3}{640}\delta^4 - \tfrac{5}{7168}\delta^6 + O(\delta x)^8$$

on putting $n = 1$ in (4.42). Hence

$$(\delta x)f'_{\frac{1}{2}} = \delta f_{\frac{1}{2}} - \tfrac{1}{24}\delta^3 f_{\frac{1}{2}} + \tfrac{3}{640}\delta^5 f_{\frac{1}{2}} - \tfrac{5}{7168}\delta^7 f_{\frac{1}{2}} + O(\delta x)^9. \tag{6.44}$$

This formula is much preferable to (6.43) on account of the more rapid decrease of the coefficients of the higher orders of differences. If, however, values of f'_j are required, there is no advantage in using (6.44) followed by 'half-way' interpolation between the values of $f'_{j+\frac{1}{2}}$ by use of formula (5.3), since these two processes together just give formula (6.43).

For a second-order derivative, the appropriate formula is (4.43), namely

$$(\delta x)^2 f''_0 = \delta^2 f_0 - \tfrac{1}{12}\delta^4 f_0 + \tfrac{1}{90}\delta^6 f_0 - \tfrac{1}{560}\delta^8 f_0 + O(\delta x)^{10}. \tag{6.45}$$

In carrying out the calculations, the interval (δx) taken *should not be too small*, since the smaller it is taken, the smaller the number of significant figures in $\delta f_{\frac{1}{2}}$ and so in f' (and similarly for a second derivative). Rather, δx should be taken as large as is convenient, subject to the truncation error of the differentiation formula used being negligible.

It will often be advisable either to smooth the values of f before differentiation, or to smooth the values of f' or f'' obtained (for a smoothing process see § 11.4). Let us write f'_s for the smoothed values which form an approximation to f'. To ensure that no systematic errors are introduced in the smoothing process, the values of f'_s should be integrated, and compared with the original values of f. If the quantities $f - \int f'_s \, dx$, which are called the 'residuals', show any significant systematic variation with x, a process of differentiation should be carried out on these residuals.

Example: The function tabulated below as $Y(x)$ is the solution of the equation $y'' = 1 + xy$ with $y(0) = y'(0) = 0$, and the function $z(x)$ is the solution of $z'' = xz$ with $z(0) = 0$, $z'(0) = 1$; to find $y'(0)$ and $y(2)$ for the solution of $y'' = 1 + xy$ for which $y(0) = 0$, $y'(0) = 2$.

x	$Y(x)$	$\delta^2 Y$	$\delta^4 Y$	$\delta^6 Y$	$z(x)$
1·6	1·56205				
1·7	1·83254	4125			
1·8	2·14428	4873	154		2·80444
1·9	2·50475	5775	188	7	3·17749
2·0	2·92297	6865	229	7	3·61107
2·1	3·40984	8184	277	18	4·11708
2·2	3·97855	9780	343		4·70978
2·3	4·64506	11719			
2·4	5·42876				

$$z'(2·0) = 4·67626$$

Two standard solutions of the equation $y'' = xy$ have been tabulated.[†] They are written $\text{Ai}(x)$ and $\text{Bi}(x)$, and the function $z(x)$ of this example is related to them by

$$z(x) = [\text{Bi}(x) - 3^{\frac{1}{2}}\text{Ai}(x)]/2 . 3^{\frac{1}{2}}\beta,$$

where β is a constant given in the Introduction to the Tables (p. B. 17; the value of $2 . 3^{\frac{1}{2}}\beta$ is 0·896577; this function $z(x)$ is that written $y_2(x)$ in that Introduction). The values of $z(x)$ and $z'(x)$ here tabulated have been calculated from this formula; only the value of $z(2·0)$ is required to give the results sought, but neighbouring values are given for use in a check.

The general solution of $y'' = 1 + xy$ with $y = 0$ at $x = 0$ is

$$y = Y + cz,$$

where c is an arbitrary constant; for the solution with $y'(2·0) = 0$,

$$c = -Y'(2·0)/z'(2·0),$$

† *British Association Mathematical Tables*, Part-volume B (1946), *The Airy Integral*.

so we need to determine $Y'(2\cdot0)$. From the tabulated results and formula (6.43)

$$0\cdot2Y'(2\cdot0) = 0\cdot90509 - \tfrac{1}{6}(2409) + \tfrac{1}{30}(89) - \tfrac{1}{140}(11)$$

$$= 0\cdot90509 - 401_5 + 3_0 - 0_1 = 0\cdot90110_4,$$

while $0\cdot2z'(2\cdot0) = 0\cdot935252$, so $c = -(0\cdot90110_4)/(0\cdot935252) = -0\cdot96348_2$.

With this value of c we have

x	Y	$-cz$		y	$\delta^2 y$	$\delta^4 y$
1·8	2·14428	$-2\cdot70203$	=	$-0\cdot55775$		
1·9	2·50475	$-3\cdot06145$	=	$-0\cdot55670$	$-\ 58$	
2·0	2·92297	$-3\cdot47920$	=	$-0\cdot55623$	-113	-1
2·1	3·40984	$-3\cdot96673$	=	$-0\cdot55689$	-169	
2·2	3·97855	$-4\cdot53779$	=	$-0\cdot55924$		

and for this function y, $f(2\cdot1) - f(1\cdot9) = -\cdot00019$ and $\delta^2 f(2\cdot1) - \delta^2 f(1\cdot9) = -111$, so

$$0\cdot2y'(2\cdot0) = -\cdot00019 - \tfrac{1}{6}(-111) + \tfrac{1}{30}(-1)$$

$$= -\cdot00019 + 18_5 = -\cdot00000_5,$$

which is within the tolerance for rounding errors. This provides a check of the work.

Notes: (i) The value of $y(2\cdot0)$ is not determined correctly to a unit in the last figure; the value $c = -0\cdot96347_5$ gives $0\cdot2y'(2\cdot0) = +\cdot00000_5$, which is equally within the tolerance for rounding errors, and $y(2\cdot0) = -0\cdot55621$.

(ii) The value of $y'(0)$ for this solution is just $y'(0) = c$.

(iii) The value of $Y'(2\cdot0)$, is not determined with certainty to several units in the fifth decimal, since $y(2\cdot1) - y(1\cdot9)$ is subject to rounding errors up to 1 in the fifth decimal and is multiplied by $1/2(\delta x) = 5$. A more accurate value of $Y'(2\cdot0)$ could be obtained by using $\delta x = 0\cdot2$, but the contribution to $2(\delta x)Y'$ from the higher orders of differences would be considerably greater; that from $\delta^6 Y$, for example, would be greater by a factor of over 100.

6.62. Graphical differentiation

The residuals $f - \int f'_s\, dx$ of a numerical differentiation over a range of x will usually be numbers of one or two digits only, so can easily be plotted to the accuracy to which they are known. In such a case, a graphical method of carrying out the differentiation is adequate. The best way of doing this is to plot on *good* squared paper (see § 2.5) the values of the function to be differentiated, and through each plotted point draw a vertical line to indicate the range of uncertainty, due to rounding error or other causes, of that value. Then draw the smoothest curve passing each plotted point within the indicated tolerance. The latitude in drawing such a curve will give an indication of the reliability of the values of the derivative.

The best way of finding the gradient of such a curve, or of one representing a set of results of some experiment or observations, is as follows. Take a flat piece of polished sheet metal (aluminium or stainless steel is satisfactory), or surface-aluminized glass, mounted in such a way that it can be placed on a piece of paper with its surface accurately perpendicular to the paper and extending right down to the paper. Set this so as to intersect the curve at the point at which the gradient is wanted (see Fig. 11), and rotate it until there is no discontinuity in direction between the curve and its reflection in the mirror. With care, this setting can be made with considerable accuracy, probably greater than that to which the curve can be drawn. The gradient of the curve can then be determined directly from the intersections of the plane of the mirror with the grid lines of the paper in which the curve is plotted.

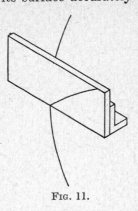

Fig. 11.

6.7. Errors of interpolation and integration formulae

W. E. Milne† has given a convenient general method for obtaining formally exact expressions for the truncation errors of formulae for interpolation, integration, etc.

We have derived and expressed such formulae as results of linear operations on the function to be interpolated, integrated, or differentiated. If we take one of these formulae to a finite number of terms, then the remainder after n terms can also be expressed as the result of a linear operation on this function. For example, if we take formula (6.11) as far as the terms in f', the remainder, which is the truncation error of the formula in this form, is

$$\int_{x_0}^{x_1} f\,dx - \tfrac{1}{2}(\delta x)[(f_0+f_1) - \tfrac{1}{6}(\delta x)(f'_1 - f'_0)]$$

$$= (\delta x)\left[\frac{1}{U}(E-1) - \tfrac{1}{2}(E+1) + \tfrac{1}{12}(E-1)U\right]f_0, \quad (6.46)$$

which is the result of a linear operation R on f. Milne calls an operator R 'of degree n' when $Rx^m = 0$ for $m \leqslant n$, $Rx^{n+1} \neq 0$, and writes R_n for an operator of degree n. The purpose is to obtain an expression for $R_n f$ for any function f. It is assumed that R_n does not involve higher powers of U than U^{n-1}.

R may contain some shift operators E so that Rf_0 may depend on values of f or its derivatives for values of x other than x_0. Let x_m be the least and x_M the greatest of these; and let a be a value of x less than x_m. Also let us write $\phi_n(z)$ for the function

$$\phi_n(z) = z^n \quad \text{for } z \geqslant 0, \qquad \phi_n(z) = 0 \quad \text{for } z < 0. \qquad (6.47)$$

† *Numerical Calculus* (Univ. of Princeton Press, 1949), §§ 30, 31.

One form of Taylor's series to $n+1$ terms with a remainder is

$$f(x) = f(a) + (x-a)f'(a) + \frac{1}{2!}(x-a)^2 f''(a) + \ldots +$$

$$+ \frac{1}{n!}(x-a)^n f^{(n)}(a) + \frac{1}{n!}\int_a^x f^{(n+1)}(\xi)(x-\xi)^n \, d\xi; \quad (6.48)$$

this form can be obtained by repeated integration by parts, using

$$m\int_a^x f^{(m)}(\xi)(x-\xi)^{m-1} \, d\xi = (x-a)^m f^{(m)}(a) + \int_a^x f^{(m+1)}(\xi)(x-\xi)^m \, d\xi.$$

The last term in (6.48) can be written

$$\frac{1}{n!}\int_a^\infty f^{(n+1)}(\xi)\,\phi_n(x-\xi) \, d\xi, \quad (6.49)$$

since the integrand here is zero for $\xi > x$.

The first $n+1$ terms in (6.48) form a polynomial of degree n, so they are annihilated by the operator R_n. Also since R_n operates on functions in so far as they are functions of x, it only operates on the function ϕ_n in the integral in the form (6.49); this is the reason for expressing the integral in this form, in which the limits are independent of x. Hence

$$R_n f(x) = \frac{1}{n!}\int_a^\infty f^{(n+1)}(\xi)\, R_n \phi_n(x-\xi) \, d\xi.$$

Since a has been chosen to be smaller than the smallest argument x_m occurring in $R_n f$, it follows that the arguments of all the terms in $R_n \phi_n(x-\xi)$ are positive for $\xi < a$; but $\phi_n(z) = z^n$ for positive z, so $R_n \phi_n(x-\xi) = 0$ for $\xi < a$. So the lower limit of the integral can be replaced by $-\infty$, and finally

$$R_n f(x) = \int_{-\infty}^\infty f^{(n+1)}(\xi) G(\xi) \, d\xi, \quad (6.50)$$

where

$$G(\xi) = \frac{1}{n!} R_n \phi_n(x-\xi). \quad (6.51)$$

If $R_n f(x)$ is a function of x, then $G(\xi)$ is a function of x as well as of ξ; if $R_n f(x)$ is not a function of x, as is the case for the operator in (6.46), then $G(\xi)$ is not a function of x.

The function $G(\xi)$ consists of polynomial segments between the values of x_j involved in $R_n f(x)$, and is zero outside the range of these values. It is also independent of the function on which R_n operates, hence

$$|R_n f(x)| \leqslant K \cdot \max |f^{(n+1)}(x)| \text{ in } x_m \leqslant x \leqslant x_M,$$

where

$$K = \int_{-\infty}^{\infty} |G(\xi)| \, d\xi;$$

K is independent of the function f on which R operates.

In many cases $G(\xi)$ is of constant sign over the range where it is not zero, and then a better formula for the error can be obtained. The mean value theorem, applied to (6.50), then gives

$$R_n f(x) = f^{(n+1)}(X) \int_{-\infty}^{\infty} G(\xi) \, d\xi, \tag{6.52}$$

where $x_m \leqslant X \leqslant x_M$; the integrand of (6.50) is zero outside these limits so X must lie in this range. Also for $f(x) = x^{n+1}/(n+1)!$, $f^{(n+1)}(x) = 1$ everywhere, so that in this case (6.52) gives

$$\int_{-\infty}^{\infty} G(\xi) \, d\xi = R_n x^{n+1}/(n+1)!$$

and hence in general

$$R_n f(x) = f^{(n+1)}(X) R_n x^{n+1}/(n+1)!. \tag{6.53}$$

As Milne points out, the evaluation of $R_n x^{n+1}$ on the right-hand side of (6.53) is often much easier than the determination of the polynomial segments of $G(\xi)$ and their integration. In (6.53), $R_n x^{n+1}$ can be replaced by $R_n (x-b)^{n+1}$ for any constant b if this is more convenient for the evaluation of this quantity.

Example: To obtain a formula for the error of trapezium rule integration

$$\int_{x_0}^{x_1} f \, dx = \tfrac{1}{2}(\delta x)[f_0 + f_1].$$

Here

$$Rf(x) = \int_{x_0}^{x_1} f \, dx - \tfrac{1}{2}(\delta x)(f_0 + f_1),$$

which is identically zero for $f(x) = x$, but not for $f(x) = x^2$. Hence R is an R_1, and

$$R_1 \phi_1(x-\xi) = \int_{x_0}^{x_1} \phi_1(x-\xi) \, dx - \tfrac{1}{2}(\delta x)[\phi_1(x_0-\xi) + \phi_1(x_1-\xi)].$$

For $\xi < x_0$, $x-\xi$ is positive over the whole range $x = x_0$ to x_1, so $\phi_1(x-\xi) = x-\xi$ for all relevant ξ, and

$$1! \, G_1(\xi) = R_1 \phi_1(x-\xi) = \tfrac{1}{2}[(x-\xi)^2]_{x=x_0}^{x_1} - \tfrac{1}{2}(\delta x)[x_0 - \xi + x_1 - \xi],$$

which is zero, as it should be. For $x_0 < \xi \leqslant x_1$, $\phi_1(x-\xi) = 0$ for $x < \xi$, so

$$1! \, G_1(\xi) = R_1 \phi_1(x-\xi) = \tfrac{1}{2}[(x-\xi)^2]_{x=\xi}^{x_1} - \tfrac{1}{2}(\delta x)(x_1-\xi) = \tfrac{1}{2}(x_1-\xi)(x_0-\xi).$$

For $\xi > x, \phi_1(x-\xi)$ is zero over the whole range of x; so $G_1(\xi) = 0$. Hence altogether

$$G_1(\xi) = \tfrac{1}{2}(x_1-\xi)(x_0-\xi) \quad \text{for } x_0 \leqslant \xi \leqslant x_1$$
$$= 0 \quad \text{otherwise.}$$

Hence for a general function $f(x)$,

$$R_1 f = \tfrac{1}{2} \int_{x_0}^{x_1} f''(\xi)(x_1-\xi)(x_0-\xi)\, d\xi.$$

In this case $G(\xi)$ is zero or negative, and is of so simple a form that it is easy to evaluate $\int_{-\infty}^{\infty} G(\xi)\, d\xi$ directly. Substitution of $\xi = x_0+(x_1-x_0)\eta$ gives

$$\int_{-\infty}^{\infty} G(\xi)\, d\xi = \tfrac{1}{2} \int_{x_0}^{x_1} (x_1-\xi)(x_0-\xi)\, d\xi = -\tfrac{1}{2}(\delta x)^3 \int_{0}^{1} \eta(1-\eta)\, d\eta = -\tfrac{1}{12}(\delta x)^3.$$

Alternatively, taking $f(x) = (x-x_0)^2/2!$ and using (6.53) we have

$$R_1(x-x_0)^2/2! = \tfrac{1}{2}[\tfrac{1}{3}(x_1-x_0)^2 - \tfrac{1}{2}(\delta x)(x_1^2+x_0^2)]$$
$$= \tfrac{1}{12}(\delta x)[2(x_1^2+x_1 x_0+x_0^2) - 3(x_1^2+x_0^2)]$$
$$= -\tfrac{1}{12}(\delta x)^3,$$

so that $R_1 f = -\tfrac{1}{12} f''(X)(\delta x)^3$, where $x_0 \leqslant X \leqslant x_1$.

6.71. Use of formulae for the error

If a formula for interpolation, integration, etc., is such that the operator R of the previous section is of degree n, the error of the formula involves the $(n+1)$th derivative of the function to which it is applied. But we have seen that for a function specified only by a table of values, the numerical determination of derivatives beyond the first or second is an unreliable process and one to be avoided if possible. Even when the function to which the interpolation or integration formula is to be applied is given by a formula which can be differentiated, the formulae for the higher derivatives may be too complicated to be convenient for numerical evaluation. Thus a formula which depends on the values of derivatives beyond the first or second is of limited practical use.

VII

INTEGRATION OF ORDINARY DIFFERENTIAL EQUATIONS

7.1. Step-by-step methods

ONE class of methods for the numerical integration of ordinary differential equations consists of those in which the solution is evaluated step by step through a series of equal intervals in the independent variable, so that when the solution has been carried to $x = x_j$, the next step consists of evaluating the change in the solution through the interval δx from x_j to x_{j+1}. In such a process we follow out in the course of the numerical work the development of the solution as the independent variable increases. For simple equations this can be made a straightforward and easy process to carry out; it can be provided with adequate current checks to assure the worker that the integration is proceeding correctly, and in the writer's experience it is one of the most satisfying forms of numerical work to carry out.

7.11. One-point and two-point boundary conditions

From the point of view of a step-by-step process, the nature of the boundary and other conditions to be satisfied is more important than the nature of the equation itself; and as regards the boundary conditions what matters is not *what* they are but *where* they are. If all the conditions which the solution must satisfy are boundary conditions given at one point of the range of integration (usually one end of it), the solution can be started from there with all relevant quantities known; and, apart from the possible occurrence of singularities or of instability in the process of integration, evaluation of a solution usually gives no difficulty. Such conditions are known as 'one-point' boundary conditions, and a problem in which the conditions are of this type has been called by Richardson† a 'marching problem' as the solution is obtained by marching step by step from the initial data.

But if some conditions are specified at one point, $x = a$, of the range and others at another, $x = b$ (usually $x = a, b$ will be the ends of the range) or if there is a relation between the behaviour of the solution at the two ends of the range such as a condition that the solution y should be periodic, which for a first-order equation is $y(b) = y(a)$, or some

† L. F. Richardson, *Phil. Trans. Roy. Soc.* **226** (1927), 300.

integral condition on the solution as a whole such as $\int_a^b y^2\,dx = 1$, the evaluation of the solution may not be so straightforward. Conditions which are specified at two points of the range are called 'two-point' boundary conditions; a set of conditions at more than two points is possible but unusual. A problem in which the conditions on the solution are not one-point boundary conditions Richardson has called a 'jury problem'.

If the equation, and the conditions which the solution must satisfy, are linear, it may be possible to evaluate the solution as the sum of a particular integral satisfying the conditions at one point of the range, and a complementary function. But in many cases such a procedure is a formal possibility only and not a useful one for practical numerical work; and if the equation is non-linear it is not available.

A step-by-step solution has to start from some point of the range with definite numerical values of sufficient quantities to define a solution; for an nth-order equation these will usually be y and its first $(n-1)$ derivatives, but they may be the values $y_0, y_1, y_2, ..., y_{n-1}$ at the beginnings of the first n intervals. With one-point boundary conditions this point is naturally taken as the point from which to start the integration. With other conditions it is best to start from the point at which the values of the greatest number of values of y or its derivatives are specified by the given conditions on the solution. The other starting conditions have to be estimated and adjusted, either by trial or by the use of a complementary function when this is practicable, until a solution satisfying the other conditions is obtained.

We will consider first the step-by-step evaluation of a solution from *given* initial conditions, and later return to the consideration of the determination of solutions satisfying other conditions.

7.2. Second-order equation with first derivative absent

The simplest numerical process is that for a second-order equation with the first derivative absent

$$y'' = f(x,y), \tag{7.1}$$

in which $f(x,y)$ need *not* be linear in y. This is integrated by using the formula for twofold integration from y'' to y, without an intermediate calculation of y' (§ 6.44):

$$y_1 - 2y_0 + y_{-1} = \delta^2 y_0 = (\delta x)^2 [y_0'' + \tfrac{1}{12}\delta^2 y_0'' - \tfrac{1}{240}\delta^4 y_0''] + O(\delta x)^8. \tag{7.2}$$

One procedure will be explained first in some detail; there are several variants of it, some of which will be mentioned later. It will be supposed that the term $\frac{1}{240}\delta^4 y_0''$ in (7.2) is negligible, so that the integration formula is being used in the form

$$\delta^2 y_0 = (\delta x)^2[y_0'' + \tfrac{1}{12}\delta^2 y_0''].\tag{7.3}$$

Suppose the integration has reached $x = x_0$, and we are concerned with the integration through the interval δx to $x = x_1$. At this stage we have y_0 and $y_0'' = f(x_0, y_0)$ and the *backward* differences from these. The procedure is then as follows. Estimate $\delta^2 y_0''$, and obtain an approximation to $\delta^2 y_0$ from (7.3). Add this to $\delta y_{-\frac{1}{2}}$ to give an approximation to $\delta y_{\frac{1}{2}}$, and add this to y_0 to give an approximation to y_1. From this calculate y_1'' and hence $\delta^2 y_0'' = y_1'' - 2y_0'' + y_{-1}''$. Let ϵ be the difference between this value of $\delta^2 y_0''$ and that estimated. A change of the estimate of $\delta^2 y_0''$ by ϵ makes a change $\frac{1}{12}(\delta x)^2 \epsilon$ in y_1. If this is less than $\frac{1}{2}$ in the last figure retained in y, the estimate is adequate; if not, the estimate is revised and the calculation of the interval repeated; but the interval length (δx) should be taken so that this is seldom necessary. A convenient arrangement of the work is as follows:

x	y''	$\delta^2 y''$		y	$\delta^2 y$
x_{-2}	$y_{-2}'' = f(x_{-2}, y_{-2})$			y_{-2}	
		$\delta y_{-1\frac{1}{2}}''$		$\delta y_{-1\frac{1}{2}}$	
x_{-1}	$y_{-1}'' = f(x_{-1}, y_{-1})$	$\delta^2 y_{-1}''$	$(y_{-1}'' + \tfrac{1}{12}\delta^2 y_{-1}'')$	y_{-1}	$\delta^2 y_{-1}$
		$\delta y_{-\frac{1}{2}}''$		$\delta y_{-\frac{1}{2}}$	
x_0	$y_0'' = f(x_0, y_0)$	$\boxed{\delta^2 y_0''}$	$(y_0'' + \tfrac{1}{12}\delta^2 y_0'')$	y_0	$\delta^2 y_0$
		$\delta y_{\frac{1}{2}}''$		$\delta y_{\frac{1}{2}}$	
x_1	$y_1'' = f(x_1, y_1)$			y_1	

The quantities above the heavy lines are those which are known when the integration has reached $x = x_0$; the quantity $\delta^2 y_0''$ enclosed in a 'box' is that which is estimated and if necessary adjusted, and the arrows show the sequence in which the various quantities are calculated.

To start the integration, two values of y are required, and it is advisable to have three to provide a check and to give an indication of the values of $\delta^2 y''$. These initial values will often be obtainable from a solution in series without requiring the evaluation of a large number of terms. In some cases it may be necessary to carry out a few steps of an integration at a small interval before starting the main integration.

Example: $y'' = (1 - x^2)y$, $y(0) = 0$, $y'(0) = 1$, $\delta x = 0{\cdot}1$. $y(0{\cdot}1)$ and $y(0{\cdot}2)$ evaluated from the series solution:

$$y = x + \tfrac{1}{6}x^3 - \tfrac{1}{24}x^5 + O(x^7).$$

x	$1-x^2$	y''	$\delta^2 y''$	y	$\delta^2 y$	$\delta^4 y$ (check)
0·0	1·00	0		0	0	
			992	-51	10016_6	
0·1	0·99	·0992	-51	·10016_6	98_8	
			941	-53	10115_4	93_6
0·2	0·96	·1933	-104	·20132_0	192_4	-10_3
			837	-57	10307_8	83_3
0·3	0·91	·2770	-161	·30439_8	275_7	-16_3
			676	-65	10583_5	67_0
0·4	0·84	·3446	-226	·41023_3	342_7	-22_6
			450	-71	10926_2	44_4
0·5	0·75	·3896	-297	·51949_5	387_1	
			153		11313_3	
0·6	0·64	·4049		·63262_8		

Here the numbers above the broken line are obtained from the series solution. In this example, y is an odd function of x, so that we have $\delta^2 y''(0) = 0$, as well as the value $\delta^2 y''(0\cdot1) = -0\cdot0051$. The value $\delta^2 y(0\cdot1) = 0\cdot000988$ is obtained in two ways, namely (a) from the first three values of y'' and the integration formula (7.2), and (b) from the first three values of y. Agreement between these values forms a check on the starting conditions, and also checks that the $\delta^2 y''$ term in the integration formula has been taken with the right sign; this term has the coefficient $+\frac{1}{12}$ here, whereas in the formula for a single integration, the first term in the correction to the trapezoidal formula has the coefficient $-\frac{1}{12}$. This makes it rather easy to make a mistake of sign at this point, and it is as well to have a check that the right sign has been taken.

If the integration has been taken to $x = 0\cdot5$, the numbers above the full line will have been calculated; we will consider the integration through the next step, $x = 0\cdot5$ to $0\cdot6$. From the run of the third differences $\delta^3 y''$, the next value may be expected to be about -76, giving $\delta^2 y''(0\cdot5)$ about -302; a twelfth of this is -25 which gives

$$\delta^2 y(0\cdot5) = (0\cdot01)(0\cdot3896 - 0\cdot0025) = 0\cdot003871.$$

This is entered in the $\delta^2 y$ column and checked by forming the value of $\delta^2 [\delta^2 y(0\cdot4)]$. By operating on both sides of (7.3) with δ^2, we have

$$\delta^2(\delta^2 y)_0 = (\delta x)^2 [\delta^2 y_0'' + \tfrac{1}{12}\delta^4 y_0''], \tag{7.4}$$

and use of this formula provides a good check on the values of $\delta^2 y$; it should be noted that the contribution from $\delta^4 y_0''$ may have to be included in (7.4) although it is negligible in (7.2).

The value of $y(0\cdot6)$ is then built up from the value of $\delta^2 y(0\cdot5)$, and from it the value of $y''(0\cdot6)$ is obtained from the differential equation. This value is

$$y''(0\cdot6) = 0\cdot4049,$$

whence $\delta^2 y''(0\cdot5) = -297$; the estimate was adequate and no recalculation of this interval is necessary. The calculation has reached the stage from which we started, only one interval further on, and a similar calculation for the next interval can now be undertaken.

The differences of the values of y'' form a check against random mistakes in these values, and use of formula (7.4) provides a current check of the values of $\delta^2 y$. The other process which needs checking is the twofold summation of these differences to give the solution y.

There are various ways of carrying out this check. If values of y have been built up by two successive summations, of $\delta^2 y$ to δy and of δy to y, as illustrated in this example, a good check is provided by evaluating the second differences of y by the method of § 4.45, which does not involve the calculation of first differences, and verifying that the values so obtained reproduce the values of $\delta^2 y$. This check can be applied as each value of y is obtained, but is best carried out occasionally, say every ten intervals, in such a way as to verify the values obtained since the previous check.

Another check, which can only be carried out on a series of values of y, is provided by taking a set of alternate values of y and differencing them to second differences, taking the corresponding values of y'' and differencing as far as necessary for use in formula (7.2), and verifying that these values of $\delta^2 y$, and of y'' and its differences, do satisfy formula (7.2) with (δx) equal to twice the integration interval. It will usually be necessary to use higher orders of differences in y'' in this check than in the integration, but central differences of higher order than the second are available at this stage.

Example: To check the solution of $y'' = (1-x^2)y$ obtained above. Copying the values of y'' and y at intervals $\delta x = 0\cdot2$, and differencing them, we have the second to sixth columns in the following table:

x	y''	$\delta^2 y''$	$\delta^4 y''$	y	$\delta^2 y$	$(\delta x)^2(y'' + \frac{1}{12}\delta^2 y'' - \frac{1}{240}\delta^4 y'')$
$0\cdot0$	0	0		0		
$\cdot2$	$\cdot1933$	-420	-70	$\cdot20132_0$	759_3	$4(1933-35_0-0_3) = 759_1$
$\cdot4$	$\cdot3446$	-910		$\cdot41023_3$		
$\cdot6$	$\cdot4049$					

The last column gives the calculation of $\delta^2 y(0\cdot2)$, for $\delta x = 0\cdot2$, from the values of y'' and its differences. Agreement to a unit in the sixth decimal with the value of $\delta^2 y$ is not to be expected; but this figure is only a guarding figure.

The interval δx used, and the number of figures kept in the different parts of the calculation, will depend on the equation, the data occurring in it, and the accuracy required in the results. This example is representative of the accuracy which it is convenient to keep in many calculations concerned with integration of equations occurring in scientific or technical problems. The last figure in y in this example is a guarding figure only, and could well be omitted if the function $f(x, y)$ in the equation involved some experimentally determined function which is not known to better than 1 part in 1000. In working to this accuracy, the first estimate of $\delta^2 y''$ in each interval, its division by 12, the addition of the result to y'', can be done mentally; so can the multiplication by

K

$(\delta x)^2$ when δx is a power of 10, as will often be the case. Then the first number written down is $(y''+\frac{1}{12}\delta^2 y'')$ or $\delta^2 y$, and the value of $\delta^2 y$ is immediately checked by differencing. Such an integration can be carried out quite quickly.

The smaller the interval (δx) taken, the better the estimate of $\delta^2 y''$ can be made, and the smaller the quantity $(\delta x)^2$ by which this is multiplied. But it is not advisable to take very small intervals, first, because the amount of work required to cover a given range of x increases as the length of integration interval used decreases, and, secondly, because effects of rounding errors in the values of $\delta^2 y$ may accumulate rather rapidly in the double summation to give y. If a large number of small intervals are taken, additional guarding figures may have to be taken to ensure that the cumulative effects of rounding errors are negligible to the accuracy required in the final results, and this makes the amount of work involved increase rather more than proportionately to the number of intervals. The interval length (δx) should therefore be taken, roughly speaking, about as large as is compatible with ease in the practical numerical working of the integration. As a rough working rule it should be taken so that for only about one interval in five does the calculation for an interval have to be repeated. If many have to be repeated the interval should be halved.

If $\delta^2 y''$ is not too large, then a good approximation to $\delta^2 y_0$ is $(\delta x)^2 y_0''$, so that to this approximation, for a function satisfying equation (7.1),

$$y_1 = 2y_0 - y_{-1} + (\delta x)^2 f(x_0, y_0).$$

Thus for such a function we always have a good approximation to the function one interval ahead of where we know y''. It is this feature which makes the numerical integration of such an equation such a straightforward process.

The procedure for two simultaneous equations

$$y'' + f(x, y, z) = 0, \qquad z'' + g(x, y, z) = 0$$

or more, with all first derivatives absent, is similar.

7.21. Change of the interval of integration

It will not always be advisable to keep the same interval length throughout an integration. It may happen that the suitable interval length (δx) varies by a factor 10 or even 100 over the range of x to be covered; then the use, over the whole range, of the small interval necessary over part of it might make the calculation so long as to be almost impracticable.

As already emphasized in §6.41, it is advisable at any change of interval length to take an overlap between the integrations carried out with the two different interval lengths. The most usual changes of interval length are by factors 2, $2\frac{1}{2}$, or $\frac{1}{2}$. To increase the interval length by a factor 2, all that is necessary is to take alternate values of y and the corresponding values of y'', for two or three intervals before the point at which the change of interval length is to be made, difference them, and check the formula (7.2) for the function values and differences at this new interval, and continue as if these were intervals of the integration at the new interval. It may be necessary to keep an extra decimal in y'' to get the same accuracy in y.

To decrease the interval length by a factor 2, some interpolation is required, but only of the simplest kind, namely the 'half-way' interpolation considered in §5.21. Suppose that integration has been carried out with intervals $\delta x = h$ up to $x = X$, and it is required to continue with intervals $\delta x = \frac{1}{2}h$. The integration with intervals $\delta x = h$ should be carried for one or two intervals beyond $x = X$, to give the central differences needed in the half-way interpolation. Then $y(X-\frac{1}{2}h)$ and $y''(X-\frac{1}{2}h)$ should be interpolated and $y''(X-\frac{1}{2}h)$ also calculated from the value of $y(X-\frac{1}{2}h)$ and the differential equation, to check. Then

$$\delta^2 y(X-\tfrac{1}{2}h) = y(X-h) - 2y(X-\tfrac{1}{2}h) + y(X)$$

should be calculated and compared with the value obtained from formula (7.2) at the smaller interval. This checks the interpolation of $y(X-\frac{1}{2}h)$; this check is most important since the whole subsequent integration would be vitiated by a mistake in this value. The integration then proceeds, starting from the values of $y(X-\frac{1}{2}h)$ and $y(X)$.

Example: To continue the integration of $y'' = (1-x^2)y$ from $x = 0.5$, using intervals $(\delta x) = 0.05$.

The value of $\delta^4 y(0.5)$ for $(\delta x) = 0.1$ will be about -29_7, so the interpolated value of $y(0.45)$ is

$$y(0.45) = 0.41023_3 + \tfrac{1}{2}(10926_2) - \tfrac{1}{16}(342_7 + 387_1) + \tfrac{3}{256}(-22_6 - 29_7)$$

$$= 0.41023_3 + 5463_1 - 45_{62} - 0_{61} = 0.46440_2.$$

The interpolated value of $y''(0.45)$ is

$$y''(0.45) = 0.3446 + \tfrac{1}{2}(450) - \tfrac{1}{16}(-226 - 297)$$

$$= 0.3446 + 225 + 33 = 0.3704$$

(the fourth-difference contribution is negligible), whereas the value calculated from the differential equation is

$$y''(0.45) = [1 - (0.45)^2](0.46440_2) = 0.37036$$

which, to four decimals, agrees with the interpolated value. Thus, starting from $x = 0.4$, we have the following values

x	y''		$\delta^2 y''$	$y''+\frac{1}{12}\delta^2 y''$	y		$\delta^2 y$
0·4	·3446				·41023$_3$		
		258				5416$_9$	
·45	·3704		−66	·3698$_5$	·46440$_2$		92$_4$
		192				5509$_3$	
·5	·3896				·51949$_5$		

The value of $\delta^2 y(0.45)$ derived from the values of y'' is 92_{46}, the difference between this value and the value 92_4 derived from the values of y is within the tolerance for the effect of the rounding error in the interpolated value. The integration can therefore be continued from these values.

Note: In the integration of this equation to this accuracy, it would not actually be necessary, or advisable, to decrease the interval of integration at this point; this case is only considered here as an example of the procedure.

The treatment of a change of interval length by a factor $2\frac{1}{2}$ is similar. Suppose, for example, the integration has been taken to $x = 0.30$ by intervals of 0.02 and it is desired to change to intervals of 0.05. The values of y and y'' at $x = 0.25$ are obtained by half-way interpolation between the values at $x = 0.24$ and 0.26, $y''(0.25)$ is checked as above, and $y(0.25)$ checked by verifying formula (7.2) at the larger interval.

7.22. Variants of the method

There are several variants of this method, some of which can be combined.

Instead of evaluating y'' for each value of x, forming $(y''+\frac{1}{12}\delta^2 y'')$ and multiplying this by $(\delta x)^2$, we could evaluate $(\delta x)^2 y''$ and form $\delta^2 y$ as

$$\delta^2 y_0 = (\delta x)^2 y_0'' + \frac{1}{12}\delta^2[(\delta x)^2 y''].$$

At a change of interval length, the entries in the column of $(\delta x)^2 y''$ would be different for the two lengths of interval.

Another variant is as follows. If we operate on both sides of formula (7.2) with the repeated central sum operator $\sigma^2 = \delta^{-2}$, it becomes

$$y_0 = (\delta x)^2[\sigma^2 y_0'' + \frac{1}{12}y_0'' - \frac{1}{240}\delta^2 y_0'']. \tag{7.5}$$

If this formula is used, the *aggregate* contributions from the $\frac{1}{12}\delta^2 y_0'' - \frac{1}{240}\delta^4 y_0''$ terms in (7.2) are evaluated separately for each interval, instead of being built up from contributions from successive intervals. This avoids accumulation of rounding and truncation errors in these contributions.

The process of starting the integration is rather more complicated, as initial values for the double sum $\sigma^2 y''$ have to be evaluated. The process does not avoid estimation, since if the integration has been carried to $x = x_0$, then for the end of the step from x_0 to x_1 we have

$$y_1 = (\delta x)^2[\sigma^2 y_1'' + \frac{1}{12}y_1'' - \frac{1}{240}\delta^2 y_1''];$$

neither y_1 nor y_1'' is known at this stage, only the value of $\sigma^2 y_1''$ and the relation $y_1'' = f(x_1, y_1)$ between y_1 and y_1''; so this is an implicit equation for y_1, and unless it happens to be linear the solution of it may well be more trouble than the integration process.

If the equation to be solved is linear, say

$$y'' = f(x)y + g(x) \qquad (7.6)$$

then the solution, to the accuracy given by neglecting the $\delta^4 y''$ term in (7.2), can be obtained without any estimation as follows. In (7.2)

$$\delta^2 y_0'' = y_1'' - 2y_0'' + y_{-1}''$$

and if y'' is given by (7.6) this is

$$\delta^2 y_0'' = (f_1 y_1 - 2f_0 y_0 + f_{-1} y_{-1}) + (g_1 - 2g_0 + g_{-1})$$

so that (7.2) can be written

$$[1 - \tfrac{1}{12}(\delta x)^2 f_1]y_1 - 2[1 - \tfrac{1}{12}(\delta x)^2 f_0]y_0 + [1 - \tfrac{1}{12}(\delta x)^2 f_{-1}]y_{-1}$$
$$= (\delta x)^2 [f_0 y_0 + g_0 + \tfrac{1}{12}\delta^2 g_0],$$

or $\qquad \delta^2[\{1 - \tfrac{1}{12}(\delta x)^2 f\}y]_0 = (\delta x)^2[f_0 y_0 + g_0 + \tfrac{1}{12}\delta^2 g_0]. \qquad (7.7)$

This treatment is usually ascribed to Numerov;[†] it has also been given independently by Manning and Millman[‡] and, as applied to a pair of simultaneous equations, by Wilkes.[§]

Written as a relation between three successive values of y, (7.7) is

$$[1 - \tfrac{1}{12}(\delta x)^2 f_1]y_1 = [2 + \tfrac{5}{6}(\delta x)^2 f_0]y_0 - [1 - \tfrac{1}{12}(\delta x)^2 f_{-1}]y_{-1} + (\delta x)^2[g_0 + \tfrac{1}{12}\delta^2 g_0].$$
$$(7.8)$$

A method, due to Olver, for correcting for the truncation errors in this formula will be considered later (§ 7.52).

Both these variants require special treatment at a point at which the interval length (δx) changes.

7.3. First-order differential equations

For a first-order equation the following method, when applicable, seems the most convenient. It is based on the use of the integration formula

$$y_1 - y_0 = \tfrac{1}{2}(\delta x)[(y_0' + y_1') - \tfrac{1}{6}(\delta x)\{\delta y_{\frac{1}{2}}'' - \tfrac{1}{60}\delta^3 y_{\frac{1}{2}}''\}], \qquad (7.9)$$

expressing an integral in terms of the integrand and the *differences of its derivative* (see § 6.22). It is applicable if the function f in the equation

$$y' = f(x, y)$$

† B. Numerov, *Publ. de l'Observ. astrophysique central de Russie*, **2** (1933), 188.
‡ M. F. Manning and J. Millman, *Phys. Rev.* **53** (1938), 673.
§ M. V. Wilkes, *Proc. Camb. Phil. Soc.* **36** (1940), 204.

is either given by an analytical formula, so that there is no difficulty in evaluating

$$y'' = \frac{\partial f}{\partial x} + \frac{\partial f}{\partial y}\frac{dy}{dx} = \frac{\partial f}{\partial x} + f\frac{\partial f}{\partial y}$$

to any accuracy required, or if $\partial f/\partial x$ and $\partial f/\partial y$ can be determined by numerical differentiation to the accuracy required in using the formulae of the method.

Two advantages of formula (7.9) have already been pointed out in § 6.22, namely, the small coefficient of the $\delta^3 y''$ term in the square bracket, and the fact that if this term (and higher terms) are neglected, so that the formula becomes

$$y_1 - y_0 = \tfrac{1}{2}(\delta x)[(y_0' + y_1') - \tfrac{1}{6}(\delta x)(y_1'' - y_0'')], \tag{7.10}$$

it does not involve the values of any quantities at points outside the interval through which the integration is being taken.

Further, the values of y'' calculated for use in the integration formula can be used to give approximations to the successive values of y by use of the formula

$$\delta^2 y_0 = (\delta x)^2[y_0'' + \tfrac{1}{12}\delta^2 y_0'']$$

with the term in $\delta^2 y_0''$ either omitted or estimated.

If the numbers occurring in the integration are arranged with those referring to the same value of x in a *column*, instead of in a row, the work can be arranged in the following example.

Example:

$$y' = 1 - 2xy; \qquad y = 0 \text{ at } x = 0 \quad (\text{see § 6.43, equation (6.35)}).$$

In this case $y'' = -2xy' - 2y$. It would be possible in this case to use a series to start the integration, but this will not be used, so as to show the procedure when the use of a series is not convenient.

x	0·0	0·1	0·0	0·1	0·2	0·3	0·4
$-2xy$	0	$-\cdot020$	0	$-\cdot0199$	$-\cdot0779$	$-\cdot1696$	$-\cdot2880$
$y' = 1 - 2xy$	1	$\cdot980$	1·0000	0·9801	0·9221	0·8304	0·7120
$-2xy'$	0	$-\cdot196$		$-\cdot1960$	$-\cdot3688$	$-\cdot4982$	$-\cdot5696$
$-2y$	0	$-\cdot200$		$-\cdot1987$	$-\cdot3894$	$-\cdot5652$	$-\cdot7199$
Sum $= y''$	0	$-\cdot396$	0	$-\cdot395$	$-\cdot758$	$-1\cdot063$	$-1\cdot289$
		-396		-395	-363	-305	-226
				32	58	79	

$y_0' + y_1'$		1·980		1·9801	1·9022	1·7525	1·5424
$-\tfrac{1}{6}(\delta x)(y_1'' - y_0'')$		$+\cdot007$		$+\cdot0066$	60	51	38
Sum $= S$		1·987		1·9867	1·9082	1·7576	1·5462
$S\,\delta x = \delta(2y)$		$\cdot1987$		$\cdot19867$	$\cdot19082$	$\cdot17576$	$\cdot15462$
$2y$	0	$\cdot1987$	0	$\cdot19867$	$\cdot38949$	$\cdot56525$	$\cdot71987$

Est. $\Big\{$ $2(\delta x)^2(y'' + \tfrac{1}{12}\delta^2 y'')$				-790	-1506	-2112	
Next $\delta(2y)$				$\cdot19077$	$\cdot17576$	$\cdot15464$	
Next $2y$	0·20			$\cdot38944$	$\cdot56525$	$\cdot71989$	

Since in this equation the values of $2y$ occur in the formula for y' and y'', it is convenient in this case to accumulate values of $2y$ rather than y.

For the first interval the values of y_0, y_0', and y_0'' are available and a first estimate of the value of $2y(0\cdot1)$ is obtained by using these values in the first three terms of a Taylor series; this gives $2y(0\cdot1) = 0\cdot20$. From this, approximate values of $y'(0\cdot1)$ and $y''(0\cdot1)$ are found, and integration carried through the interval $x = 0$ to $0\cdot1$, giving a better value of $2y(0\cdot1)$, namely $0\cdot1987$, from which better values of y' and y'' at the end of the first interval and a better final value of y are obtained. Use of this better value of y does not change the values of y' and y'' to the accuracy to which they are being used in the integration, and the revised integration through the first interval can then be taken as the first step in the main integration.

Suppose now that the integration has reached $x = 0\cdot3$, so that the quantities to the left of the heavy line are known. The run of the second differences of $\delta^2 y''$ suggests that the value at $0\cdot3$ will be about 80, so that

$$\delta^2[2y(0\cdot3)] = (0\cdot01)2[-1\cdot063+0\cdot007] = -0\cdot02112.$$

This is written in on the last line but two, and the approximate value of $2y(0\cdot4) = 0\cdot71989$ is built up from it. The values $y'(0\cdot4)$, $y''(0\cdot4)$ are calculated from this value of $2y$, and then the integration carried out, giving $2y(0\cdot4) = 0\cdot71987$. The difference of this value from the trial value $0\cdot71989$ is not such as to affect y' or y'' to the accuracy to which they are kept. The integration has now been taken to $x = 0\cdot4$, and the sequence of operations can now be repeated for the next interval. *Notes*: (i) Since with the interval taken the values of $\delta y''$ are divided by 60 before being added to those of y', it is adequate to keep y'' to one decimal fewer than y'.

(ii) It would be practicable to keep another decimal in $2y$ without using a smaller interval δx.

7.31. Another method for a first-order equation

If in the equation in the form $y' = f(x, y)$, the function f is not such that y'' can be obtained to an accuracy adequate for use in the method of the preceding section, a formula involving only y' and its differences can be used. The appropriate central-difference formula, with an error term of the same order as that of (7.10), is

$$y_1-y_0 = \tfrac{1}{2}(\delta x)[y_0'+y_1'-\tfrac{1}{12}(\delta^2 y_0'+\delta^2 y_1')]. \tag{7.11}$$

But this is not so convenient, because $\delta^2 y_1'$ involves y_2', which is not known until the *next* interval, from y_1 to y_2, has been completed, and because the error term is larger than that of formula (7.10).

When the integration has reached x_0, only y_0, y_0', and backward differences from y_0 are available. There is an integration formula using backward differences from the beginning of the interval, but it is not satisfactory for practical use since the coefficients of the neglected higher-order differences are so large; that of the fourth difference is $\tfrac{251}{720}$ instead of $\tfrac{11}{720}$ for formula (7.10). Even if the trapezoidal approximation is used, it is necessary to estimate y_1 to give y_1', and to adjust this estimate until it agrees with the result of integration with the corresponding value of y_1'; and without the value of y_0'' it is more difficult to obtain a good approximation for the first estimate. Even when y_1' is known, $\delta^2 y_1'$ also has to be estimated, and this estimate cannot be confirmed until the *next* interval has been completed. An examination of the differences of y' and of y in the worked example of the previous section will show the advantage of having values of y'' available so that the only estimate that has to be made is one of $\delta^2 y''$.

7.32. Second-order equation with the first derivative present

The most convenient practical treatment of a second-order equation with the first derivative present depends on the form of the equation. For a linear equation

$$y'' + f(x)y' + g(x)y = h(x) \tag{7.12}$$

the terms in y' can be eliminated by the use of

$$Y = y \exp\left[\tfrac{1}{2} \int f(x)\, dx\right];$$

this gives

$$Y'' + [g(x) - \tfrac{1}{2}f'(x) - \tfrac{1}{4}\{f(x)\}^2]Y = h(x) \exp\left[\tfrac{1}{2} \int f(x)\, dx\right] \tag{7.13}$$

which reduces the equation to the form treated in § 7.2. This is likely to be a convenient reduction for the homogeneous equation, in which $h(x) = 0$. If $h(x)$ is not zero, the exponential factor may make the right-hand side of (7.13) vary too rapidly to be convenient for numerical work; though since Y has to be divided by a corresponding exponential factor to give the solution y required, it may be possible to drop the less significant digits of Y as the solution proceeds.

If the equation is linear in y', though not in y:

$$y'' + f(x)y' + g(x, y) = 0, \tag{7.14}$$

the term in y' can be eliminated by the same change of variable, though the resulting equation is not so convenient as (7.14). If, however, $g(x, y)$ is periodic in x and a periodic solution of y is required, this reduction of the equation is not very convenient, as the function Y will not in general be periodic. Then it is probably best to use the equation in the form (7.14).

A general method of treating the general second-order equation

$$y'' + f(x, y, y') = 0 \tag{7.15}$$

is to regard it as two simultaneous first-order equations

$$y' = z, \qquad z' + f(x, y, z) = 0,$$

the latter being integrated first in each interval. That is, y'' is first integrated to give y', and then y' is integrated to give y. The value of y at the end of the interval can be estimated by use of

$$\delta^2 y_0 = (\delta x)^2 [y_0'' + \tfrac{1}{12}\delta^2 y_0'']$$

of which only the term $\tfrac{1}{12}\delta^2 y_0''$ has to be estimated, and for the integration of y' to give y, y_1'' is known so that the integration formula (7.8) can be used for this integration. If the function $f(x, y, y')$ in equation (7.15) is such that y''' can be evaluated to adequate accuracy from values of x, y, and y', then the method of § 7.3 can also be used for the integration of y'' to give y'. For example, for the van der Pol equation

$$y'' - (1 - y^2)y' + ky = 0$$

we have $\qquad\qquad y''' - (1 - y^2)y'' + 2y(y')^2 + ky' = 0$

and can use the method of § 7.3 twice in each interval, once to integrate y'' to give y' and then to integrate y' to give y. This reduction of a second-order equation to two first-order equations should *not* generally be used for a second-order equation with the first derivative absent.

7.33. Equations of order higher than the second

If it is required to treat numerically an equation of order higher than the second, it is best to break down the integration through each interval into a sequence of single and twofold integrations. In each interval the highest derivative should be integrated first, and the lower-order derivatives in succession; then, apart perhaps from the integration of the highest-order derivatives, formula (7.9) can be used for any single integration required.

7.4. Taylor series method†

There is another method, which is in principle applicable to equations, of suitable form, of any order. Its limitation is that it is only suitable for equations in which the relation between the derivatives is given by an analytical formula, so that it can be differentiated formally as many times as is required. For example, in the case of the equation

$$y' = x^2 - y^2 \qquad\qquad (7.16)$$

we have in succession

$$y'' = 2(x - yy'), \qquad y''' = 2[1 - \{yy'' + (y')^2\}] \left.\vphantom{\begin{array}{c}a\\b\end{array}}\right\}. \quad (7.17)$$
$$y^{iv} = -2[yy''' + 3y'y''], \quad y^{v} = -2[yy^{iv} + 4y'y''' + 3(y'')^2] \ \ \text{etc.}$$

It would be possible here to substitute for y' from (7.16) in the first of

† See, for example, J. C. P. Miller, *British Association Mathematical Tables*, Part-volume B, *The Airy Integral* (1946), Introduction, § 5.

equations (7.17) before differentiating, but this would lead to more complicated formulae, and it is better to carry out the substitution numerically rather than algebraically.

Consider first a first-order equation such as (7.16), and suppose that the solution has been taken to $x = x_0$, so that y_0 is known. Then y_0'', y_0''', y_0^{iv},... can be calculated in turn from a set of relations such as (7.17), and then y_1 can be calculated from the Taylor series

$$y_1 = y(x_0+\delta x) = y_0+(\delta x)y_0'+\frac{1}{2!}(\delta x)^2y_0''+\frac{1}{3!}(\delta x)^3y_0'''+....$$

It is convenient to arrange the numerical work so that the terms containing odd powers of δx and those containing even powers are added up separately:

$$\left.\begin{aligned} S_{\text{even}} &= y_0+\frac{1}{2!}(\delta x)^2y_0''+\frac{1}{4!}(\delta x)^4y_0^{iv}+\frac{1}{6!}(\delta x)^6y_0^{vi}+... \\ S_{\text{odd}} &= (\delta x)y_0'+\frac{1}{3!}(\delta x)^3y_0'''+\frac{1}{5!}(\delta x)^5y_0^{v}+... \end{aligned}\right\}. \quad (7.18)$$

Then
and
$$\left.\begin{aligned} y_1 &= S_{\text{even}}+S_{\text{odd}} \\ y_{-1} &= S_{\text{even}}-S_{\text{odd}} \end{aligned}\right\} . \quad (7.19)$$

This calculation of y_{-1}, the starting-point for the previous interval, from y and its derivatives at $x = x_0$ is a very good check; y_0 has been calculated from y and its derivatives at x_{-1}, so that almost all the numbers involved in the calculation of y_{-1} from y_0 by (7.19) are different from those involved in the original calculation of y_0 from y_{-1}.

There is no particular reason for working with the derivatives themselves rather than with convenient multiples of them. In this case the convenient multiples are the quantities $Y^{(n)}$ defined by

$$Y^{(n)} = \frac{1}{n!}(\delta x)^n y^{(n)};$$

these are sometimes called 'reduced derivatives'. That is,

$$Y^{(0)} = y, \qquad Y^{(1)} = (\delta x)y', \qquad Y^{(2)} = \tfrac{1}{2}(\delta x)^2 y'', \quad ....$$

Then, for example, (7.16), (7.17) become

$$Y^{(1)} = (\delta x)[x^2-\{Y^{(0)}\}^2],$$
$$Y^{(2)} = (\delta x)[x\,\delta x-Y^{(0)}Y^{(1)}],$$
$$Y^{(3)} = \tfrac{1}{3}(\delta x)[(\delta x)^2-2Y^{(0)}Y^{(2)}-\{Y^{(1)}\}^2],$$
$$Y^{(4)} = -\tfrac{1}{2}(\delta x)[Y^{(0)}Y^{(3)}+Y^{(1)}Y^{(2)}] \quad \text{etc.,}$$

and (7.18) becomes

$$S_{\text{even}} = Y_0^{(0)} + Y_0^{(2)} + Y_0^{(4)} + Y_0^{(6)} + \cdots \\ S_{\text{odd}} = Y_0^{(1)} + Y_0^{(3)} + Y_0^{(5)} + \cdots \Bigg\}. \qquad (7.20)$$

No special procedure is necessary for starting the integration.

For a second-order equation y_1' has to be calculated from a Taylor series as well as y_1. We have

$$y_{\pm 1}' = y_0' \pm (\delta x) y_0'' + \frac{1}{2!} (\delta x)^2 y_0''' \pm \frac{1}{3!} (\delta x)^3 y_0^{iv} + \cdots,$$

and hence

$$Y_{\pm 1}^{(1)} = (\delta x) y_{\pm 1}' = Y_0^{(1)} \pm 2 Y_0^{(2)} + 3 Y_0^{(3)} \pm 4 Y_0^{(4)} + \cdots;$$

so that if we write

$$S_{\text{even}}' = 2 Y_0^{(2)} + 4 Y_0^{(4)} + 6 Y_0^{(6)} + \cdots, \qquad S_{\text{odd}}' = Y_0^{(1)} + 3 Y_0^{(3)} + 5 Y_0^{(5)} + \cdots,$$

the reduced first derivative at $x = x_1$ is

$$Y_0^{(1)} = S_{\text{even}}' + S_{\text{odd}}'$$

and the check on the integration is provided by

$$Y_{-1}^{(1)} = S_{\text{odd}}' - S_{\text{even}}'.$$

By taking the series (7.20) to several terms, it is practicable to make the truncation error of considerably higher order in (δx) than it is in the case of formula (7.9) or (7.11), and so to work with a larger interval δx or alternatively to a greater number of significant figures. Results to a large number of figures will probably not be required except for equations which do satisfy the conditions for this method to be practicable, and in such cases it is a very powerful method.

7.5. Other procedures

A number of other procedures have been proposed for the numerical integration of differential equations. A few will be summarized in the following sections.

7.51. Richardson's 'deferred approach to the limit'

In the procedures so far explained it has been the purpose to make each interval of the integration correct, within the tolerance for rounding error, before going on to the next. This is done by keeping the truncation error in each interval less than the rounding error. An alternative procedure is to carry out a whole integration using a very simple integration formula for which the truncation error is greater than the rounding error, and only correcting for the truncation error after the whole integration is completed. Such a process has been called by L. F. Richardson[†] a 'deferred approach to the limit'; a process of this kind is applicable to quadrature as well as to the numerical integration of differential equations.

If in integrating the first-order equation

$$y' = f(x, y)$$

we use simply the trapezoidal formula

$$\delta y_{\frac{1}{2}} = y_1 - y_0 = \tfrac{1}{2}(\delta x)(f_0 + f_1), \qquad (7.21)$$

the result y at a given value of x will depend on the interval length x used in the integration as well as on x. Let us express this by writing this result as $y(x, \delta x)$; the solution of the differential equation is the limit of this as $\delta x \to 0$, namely $y(x, 0)$.

Now in each interval the error in δy calculated by (7.21) is of order $(\delta x)^3$. The number of intervals required to cover a given range of x is inversely proportional to δx; hence the aggregate truncation error is of order $(\delta x)^2$. Such an error in y results in an error in y' of order $(\delta x)^2$, which makes an additional error of order $(\delta x)^3$ in each δy, which is of the same order as the truncation error in that interval alone. Thus the aggregate error at any given x is of order $(\delta x)^2$.

If now two separate integrations are carried out, using the same integration formula (7.21), with different interval lengths (δx), then the leading term in the aggregate truncation error can be eliminated by extrapolating to $\delta x = 0$, linearly in $(\delta x)^2$, at each value of x. The most convenient way of doing this in practice is by use of one set of intervals $\delta x = h$ and another set $\delta x = 2h$, the process is represented graphically in Fig. 12; a convenient numerical process is represented by the formula

$$y(x, 0) = y(x, h) - \tfrac{1}{3}[y(x, 2h) - y(x, h)]. \qquad (7.22)$$

This process has been called by Richardson 'h^2-extrapolation'. It is important to ensure that cumulative rounding errors do not vitiate this extrapolation to $\delta x = 0$.

It is in principle possible to carry out this process of extrapolation to $\delta x = 0$ from results calculated for more than two different interval lengths, but this is not a satisfactory procedure in many cases.

† L. F. Richardson, *Phil. Trans. Roy. Soc.* **226** (1927), 300.

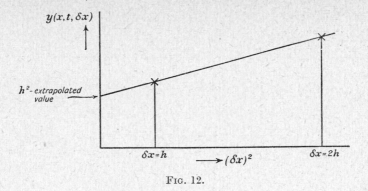

FIG. 12.

7.52. Iterative processes

The solution of the equation

$$y' = f(x, y), \qquad y(x_0) = y_0$$

can formally be obtained by constructing a sequence of function $y_{(n)}(x)$ by

$$y_{(n+1)}(x) = y_0 + \int_{x_0} f\{x, y_{(n)}(x)\}\, dx. \qquad (7.23)$$

If the integral is evaluated by quadrature, this process of iterative quadrature is the numerical equivalent of Picard's process in the formal analytical theory of differential equations. It is sometimes useful for starting an integration, but unless a good approximation is available to use as a first approximation $y_0(x)$ in the right-hand side of (7.23), it is seldom useful for carrying the integration of an equation with one-point boundary conditions over a range of x, because the convergence of the successive functions $y_{(n)}$ to the solution of the equation is too slow. A form of iterative quadrature may, however, be useful in dealing with problems with two-point boundary conditions (see § 7.6).

As an example of another, more practical, kind of iterative process, consider the equation

$$y'' = f(x, y). \qquad (7.24)$$

A sequence of functions $y_{(n)}$ can be formed by

$$\delta^2 y_{(n)} = (\delta x)^2 [f\{x, y_{(n)}(x)\} + \tfrac{1}{12}\delta^2 y''_{(n-1)} - \tfrac{1}{240}\delta^4 y''_{(n-1)}]. \qquad (7.25)$$

Here only the leading term on the right-hand side depends on the function $y_{(n)}$ currently being evaluated; the 'correcting' terms, involving $\delta^2 y''$, $\delta^4 y''$ are derived from the previously calculated function $y_{(n-1)}$. This avoids any estimation of $\delta^2 y''$, and enables $\delta^4 y''$ and $\delta^6 y''$, and higher differences, to be included.

A different iterative process is obtained if y'' on the left-hand side of (7.24) is expressed in terms of y and its differences.

From formula (4.43) we have

$$(\delta x)^2 y_0'' = \delta^2 y_0 - \tfrac{1}{12}\delta^4 y_0 + \tfrac{1}{90}\delta^6 y_0 - \tfrac{1}{560}\delta^8 y_0 + O(\delta x)^{10},$$

so that if y satisfies equation (7.24),

$$\delta^2 y = (\delta x)^2 f(x,y) + \tfrac{1}{12}\delta^4 y - \tfrac{1}{90}\delta^6 y + \tfrac{1}{560}\delta^8 y + O(\delta x)^{10}. \tag{7.26}$$

Then a sequence of functions $y_{(n)}$ can be formed by means of the iterative formula

$$y_{(n+1)} = (\delta x)^2 [\sigma^2 f\{x, y_{(n+1)}\} + \tfrac{1}{12}\delta^2 y_{(n)} - \tfrac{1}{90}\delta^4 y_{(n)} + O(\delta x)^6], \tag{7.27}$$

where σ^2 is the twofold sum operator as in §7.22. Here the 'correcting' terms in the evaluation of $y_{(n+1)}$ are expressed in terms of the differences of the previous function $y_{(n)}$ itself, instead of in terms of the differences of its second derivative. A similar treatment can be applied to first-order equations, and various examples of its application have been given by Fox and Goodwin.†

For a linear (but not necessarily homogeneous) equation this process can be shortened as follows.‡ Let the equation be

$$y'' = f(x)y + g(x). \tag{7.28}$$

Substitution of $[f(x)y + g(x)]$ for the general function $f(x,y)$ in (7.26) gives

$$\delta^2 y = (\delta x)^2 [f(x)y + g(x)] + \tfrac{1}{12}\delta^4 y - \tfrac{1}{90}\delta^6 y + \tfrac{1}{560}\delta^8 y + O(\delta x)^{10},$$

and operation on both sides with $(1 + \tfrac{1}{12}\delta^2)$ gives

$$\delta^2 [\{1 - \tfrac{1}{12}(\delta x)^2 f\} y] = (\delta x)^2 f(x)y + (g + \tfrac{1}{12}\delta^2 g) - \tfrac{1}{240}\delta^6 y + \tfrac{13}{15120}\delta^8 y + O(\delta x)^{10}. \tag{7.29}$$

If the terms of sixth and higher orders in (δx) are neglected, this is equation (7.7). Let z be the solution of this approximate equation, with the same initial conditions as those specified for y; that is,

$$\delta^2 [\{1 - \tfrac{1}{12}(\delta x)^2 f\} z] = (\delta x)^2 f(x)z + (g + \tfrac{1}{12}\delta^2 g), \tag{7.30}$$

and let

$$y = z + \eta.$$

Then, on subtracting (7.30) from (7.29), it follows that η satisfies

$$\delta^2 [\{1 - \tfrac{1}{12}(\delta x)^2 f\} \eta] = (\delta x)^2 f(x)\eta - \tfrac{1}{240}\delta^6 y + \tfrac{13}{15120}\delta^8 y + O(\delta x)^{10}. \tag{7.31}$$

From equation (7.31) it follows that η is of order $(\delta x)^4$, hence $\delta^6 y$ differs from $\delta^6 z$ by terms of order $(\delta x)^{10}$. Hence (7.31) can be replaced, with an error of order $(\delta x)^{10}$, by

$$\delta^2 [\{1 - \tfrac{1}{12}(\delta x)^2 f\} \eta] = (\delta x)^2 f(x)\eta - \tfrac{1}{240}\delta^6 z + \tfrac{13}{15120}\delta^8 z. \tag{7.32}$$

---

† L. Fox and E. T. Goodwin, *Proc. Camb. Phil. Soc.* **45** (1949), 373.
‡ This treatment is due to F. W. J. Olver. For a similar treatment of a non-linear equation see Olver, ibid. **46** (1950), 570, § 4.

Then if z is calculated from formula (7.30) and η from formula (7.32), neither of which involve any estimation, the aggregate truncation error in $y = z + \eta$ is of order $(\delta x)^8$.

7.6. Two-point boundary conditions

As an example of the treatment of two-point boundary conditions, consider the solution of
$$y'' = f(x, y)$$
subject to the conditions
$$y = y_0 \text{ at } x = 0, \qquad y = y_a \text{ at } x = a.$$
A step-by-step integration, starting from $x = 0$, has to start from definite numerical values of y at the beginning and end of the first interval, and the result at any later value of x is determined by these two values of y. The former is given to be y_0, but the latter, $y(\delta x)$, is not specified. If the variation of the solution $y(a)$ at $x = a$ with the value of $y(\delta x)$ is not too rapid, the following process can be used to find the solution satisfying the condition at $x = a$. A set of integrations is carried out for a set of trial values of $y(\delta x)$, and the value of $y(a)$ obtained as a function of $y(\delta x)$. Interpolation (graphical or numerical) can then be used to obtain a close approximation, say y_1, to the value of $y(\delta x)$ which gives a solution for which $y(a)$ has the required value y_a. A further one or two integrations with values of $y(\delta x)$ in the immediate neighbourhood of y_1 then enables the solution satisfying the given condition at $y = a$ to be obtained by linear interpolation.

If the value of $y(a)$ is very sensitive to the value of $y(\delta x)$, such a process is not practicable in this simple form. Consider the variation of y at a fixed x with the trial value of $y(\delta x)$; this is $\partial y(x)/\partial y(\delta x)$. This is a function of x, and, for a non-linear differential equation, corresponds to a 'complementary function' of a linear differential equation. It might behave approximately as e^{x^2}, in which case it would increase by a factor of about 10^{10} over a range of x from 0 to 5. This would mean that unless the choice of $y(\delta x)$ were correct to $0 \cdot 00001$, all trial solutions would have values of $|y(a)|$ of the order of 10^5 or larger. If the condition at $x = a$ were $y(a) = 1$, interpolation between two trial solutions with values of $y(\delta x)$ differing by $0 \cdot 00001$ would determine $y(\delta x)$ closely but would not determine the solution at all well except near $x = 0$. Further, the effects of rounding errors in the early intervals of the integration build up in much the same way as the function $\partial y(x)/\partial y(\delta x)$, so that it would be necessary to keep a large number of figures, and probably to work to fifteen or twenty decimals.

Such a situation is not rare; in the writer's experience it is more likely than not to occur in equations with two-point boundary conditions which arise in real problems (as distinct from those which are made up to serve as text-book examples). In such a situation, however, a procedure of the same kind can be used, proceeding by stages in the x direction. Two solutions with different values of $y(\delta x)$ are carried to such a value of x, say x_{ii}, that their behaviour indicates clearly enough whether the required solution lies between them or not; if not, other solutions are evaluated until a pair is found between which the required solution does lie. Let these be y_I and y_{II}, with values $y_1(\delta x)$ and $y_{II}(\delta x)$ at the end of the first interval.

From the behaviour of the solutions y_I and y_{II} at $x = x_{ii}$, and the expected behaviour of the solution required, an estimate is made of the fraction θ of the difference between the functions y_I and y_{II} such that

$$y_I + \theta(y_{II} - y_I)$$

is a fair approximation to the required solution. Linear interpolation will probably not be valid at $x = x_{ii}$, but should be good enough to give one decimal in θ, which is all that is wanted. Another solution, y_{III}, is then started, not from $x = 0$ but from some value of x_i at which linear interpolation between the solution y_I and y_{II} is valid to the accuracy to which the calculation is carried. Whether linear interpolation is valid can usually be tested by comparing (a) the value of $y''(x_i)$ interpolated linearly between the values for solutions y_I and y_{II}, that is,

$$y_I''(x_i) + \theta[y_{II}''(x_i) - y_I''(x_i)],$$

and (b) the value of $y''(x_i)$ calculated from the interpolated value of $y(x_i)$. If the difference between these two values of $y''(x_i)$ is not enough to affect the last digit of $y(x_i + \delta x)$, then, in the usual contexts in which this procedure is required, the linear interpolation is adequate.

According to the behaviour of y_{III}, either another solution is started from x_i, or a solution is started by linear interpolation between y_{III} and y_{II} or y_I at a point x_{iii} further out, by a repetition of the process for selecting and starting the evaluation of the solution y_{III}. This process may have to be repeated several times before the value $x = a$ is reached.

7.61. Iterative quadrature

In the process considered in the previous section the solution satisfying the two-point boundary conditions is reached by evaluating a sequence of functions each of which *does* satisfy the differential equation but *does not* satisfy *all* the boundary conditions. An alternative procedure in some cases is to approach the solution required through a sequence of functions each of which satisfies *all* the boundary conditions, but does *not* satisfy the equation.

Consider, for example, the equation

$$y''' = -(1+y^2)y'' \qquad (7.33)$$

with boundary conditions

$$y = 0, \qquad y' = 0 \quad \text{at } x = 0, \qquad y' \to 1 \quad \text{as } x \to \infty. \qquad (7.34)$$

Let $y_{(n)}(x)$ be a sequence of functions defined by

$$y'''_{(n+1)} = -(1+y^2_{(n)})y''_{(n+1)}. \qquad (7.35)$$

If at any stage of the work $y_{(n)}$ is a known function of x, this is an equation for the next function of the sequence, namely $y_{(n+1)}$; it is linear and homogeneous in this unknown function and there is no difficulty in obtaining a solution of (7.35) satisfying *all three* of the boundary conditions (7.34). One integration gives

$$y''_{(n+1)} = A \exp\left[-\int_0^x (1+y^2_{(n)})\, dx\right],$$

where A is, so far, an undetermined integration constant. Another integration gives

$$y'_{(n+1)} = A \int_0^x \exp\left\{-\int_0^x (1+y^2_{(n)})\, dx\right\} dx\,;$$

the condition $y'(0) = 0$ has been satisfied by choosing the lower limit of the integral; the condition $y'(\infty) = 1$ can now be satisfied by choice of A, and gives

$$y'_{(n+1)} = \frac{\int_0^x \exp\left\{-\int_0^x (1+y^2_{(n)})\, dx\right\} dx}{\int_0^\infty \exp\left\{-\int_0^x (1+y^2_{(n)})\, dx\right\} dx},$$

and another integration from lower limit $x = 0$ satisfies the condition on $y(0)$, giving

$$y_{(n+1)} = \frac{\int_0^x\int_0^x \exp\left\{-\int_0^x (1+y^2_{(n)})\, dx\right\} dx\,dx}{\int_0^\infty \exp\left\{-\int_0^x (1+y^2_{(n)})\, dx\right\} dx}. \qquad (7.36)$$

This may appear a rather elaborate form of equation (7.35), but it contains the boundary conditions (7.34) in addition, and is in fact quite convenient for numerical work.

5353 L

Unless $y_{(n+1)} = y_{(n)}$ to the accuracy of the numerical work, $y_{(n+1)}$ is not a solution of equation (7.33), so that the separate members of the sequence $y_{(n)}(x)$ are not solutions of the equation though they do satisfy *all* the boundary conditions. But if the process converges, in a numerical sense that after a finite number of repetitions of the iterative process $y_{(n+1)}$ becomes equal to $y_{(n)}$ to the accuracy to which the numerical work is taken, then to this accuracy such a function $y_{(n+1)}$ is a solution of the equation (7.33).

A process of this kind, when available, is particularly useful in cases in which, using a step-by-step integration, $y(a)$ is very sensitive to $y(\delta x)$. This sensitiveness is an indication of a kind of instability in the step-by-step process; but this instability does not correspond to any instability in the physical system to which the equation refers, just because in the physical system the behaviour of the system is fixed at both ends of the range. It does not appear either in a treatment such as that of the present section, which approaches the physical situation more closely in that it insists at each stage that the approximate solution is tied at both ends, however it behaves intermediately.

Another method, which also works through a sequence of approximate solutions satisfying the boundary conditions at both ends of the range, is an application of the 'relaxation method' of Southwell (see § 8.5 and end of § 8.53).

7.62. Characteristic value problems

In the equations considered in §§ 7.6 and 7.61, the parameter which was adjustable to fit the two-point boundary conditions was $y(\delta x)$; variations of this are equivalent to variations in y_0', since for a second-order equation $y(\delta x)$ is determined in terms of y_0 and y_0' (compare § 7.4). So that in effect the adjustable parameter is one of the initial conditions.

In another important class of problems the adjustable parameter is a constant in the equation itself, for example the constant λ in the equation

$$y'' + [\lambda + f(x)]y = 0 \qquad (7.37)$$

with boundary conditions

$$y(a) = y(b) = 0 \qquad (7.38)$$

and the further condition that the solution is not identically zero. The values of λ for which the equation (7.37) has such solutions are called the 'characteristic values' of λ. Depending on the form of $f(x)$ and the values of a and b, there may be one or more discrete values of λ and perhaps a continuous range. For example, for the equation

$$y'' + \left(\frac{2}{x} + \lambda\right)y = 0$$

with the condition that y should be 0 at $x = 0$ and finite at $x = \infty$, there is an infinite set of discrete characteristic values $\lambda = -1/n^2$ (n integral) and a continuous set $\lambda > 0$.

The determination of characteristic values and corresponding solutions can be carried out by evaluating trial solutions with trial values of λ, using a process very similar to that of § 7.6.[†]

For many forms of the function $f(x)$ for which solutions of (7.37) are wanted in practice, there is a finite least value of λ; this can often be determined approximately by using Rayleigh's principle.[‡] This states that if z is an approximation to the solution of (7.37) for the lowest value of λ, then

$$\int_a^b z\{z'' + f(x)z\}\, dx \Big/ \int_a^b z^2\, dx \qquad (7.39)$$

differs from λ by a quantity of order $\int_a^b (y-z)^2\, dx$, so that a rough estimate of z substituted in (7.39) gives a fair value of λ. This may often give a good first trial value to use in the numerical integration of equation (7.37).

7.7. Further notes on numerical integration of ordinary differential equations

With a first-order linear equation, $y' + f(x)y = g(x)$, there is a strong temptation to follow the standard text-book method and reduce the solution of the equation to a quadrature by use of an integrating factor. There are occasions for which this is useful (see § 7.61 for example). But the writer's experience has been that in the great majority of cases arising for solution in practice, this is a temptation to be resisted, and that it is considerably easier to evaluate the solution by numerical integration of the equation as it stands than to evaluate the integrals in the solution in quadrature. An example has been given in § 1.1.

On the other hand, in a second-order equation linear in the first derivative, it may be worth while making a change of variable to remove the term involving the first derivative, especially if the equation is linear and homogeneous. This has been considered in § 7.32.

---

† For another procedure, see § 8.7. See also W. E. Milne, *Journ. of Research of Nat. Bur. of Standards*, **45** (1950), 245.

‡ See G. Temple and W. G. Bickley, *Rayleigh's Principle* (Oxford, 1933).

7.71. The Madelung transformation

For evaluating oscillatory solutions of a second-order homogeneous linear equation with the first derivative absent:

$$y''+f(x)y = 0, \tag{7.40}$$

a transformation due to Madelung[†] is sometimes useful.

Let us write
$$y = F(x)\exp\left[i \int g(x)\,dx\right], \tag{7.41}$$

where F and g are to be real; this is equivalent to describing the oscillating function y at each point in terms of a local amplitude $F(x)$ and local phase $\phi(x) = \int g(x)\,dx$. The real and imaginary parts of (7.41) clearly give two linearly independent solutions of (7.40). Substitution of (7.41) into (7.40) and separation of real and imaginary parts gives

$$F''-Fg^2+fF = 0, \tag{7.42}$$

$$2F'g+Fg' = 0. \tag{7.43}$$

The second of these two equations is integrable and gives

$$F^2g = \text{const.} = A \quad \text{(say)}, \tag{7.44}$$

and substitution in (7.42) then gives

$$F''-A^2/F^3+fF = 0. \tag{7.45}$$

Thus the evaluation of the two functions F and g can be separated, equation (7.45) being first solved for F, and g then determined.

Equation (7.45) is not linear, but it may be easier to integrate than the original equation (7.40), since the rapidly oscillating part of y has been taken out by the factor $\exp\left[i \int g(x)\,dx\right]$, and the function F describing the local amplitude of this oscillation will often vary relatively slowly.[‡]

7.72. The Riccati transformation

For equation (7.40) with $f(x)$ negative, the Riccati transformation

$$\eta = y'/y = d(\log y)/dx, \qquad \eta'+\eta^2+f(x) = 0 \tag{7.46}$$

is sometimes useful, especially if $f(x)$ is negative over a considerable range of x. If $f(x)$ is negative and slowly varying, and $|f(x)|$ is large, a solution of equation (7.46) can sometimes be obtained by writing it in the form

$$\eta = \pm[-f(x)-\eta']^{\frac{1}{2}} \tag{7.47}$$

[†] E. Madelung, *Zeit. für Phys.* **67** (1931), 516.
[‡] For an example of the use of this transformation, see D. R. Hartree, R. L. Kronig, and H. Pedersen, *Physica*, **1** (1934), 895.

and solving this by iteration. The first approximation is

$$\eta = [-f(x)]^{\frac{1}{2}};$$

numerical differentiation then gives an approximation to η' in (7.47) and hence a better value of η. This is one of the few situations in which numerical differentiation may be useful as a tool in a practical numerical process.

VIII

SIMULTANEOUS LINEAR ALGEBRAIC EQUATIONS AND MATRICES

8.1. Direct and indirect methods for simultaneous linear equations

THE necessary and sufficient condition that a system of linear simultaneous equations should have a solution, and that the solution should be unique, is that the determinant of the coefficients should be non-zero. In this chapter, except in § 8.6, it will be assumed that this condition is satisfied, so that we shall only be concerned with the determination of a solution when a unique solution exists.

Any text-book of algebra shows that the solution of such a set of equations can be expressed in terms of ratios of determinants, and one way of evaluating the solution of the equations would be to evaluate these determinants numerically. But though there may be no one best way of evaluating the solution, it can be said with some certainty that the direct evaluation of the determinants and of the expression for the solution in terms of them is *never* the best way, though of course the evaluation of a solution by any other method must come in the end to the same thing as the evaluation of the solution in terms of determinants.

The general form of a set of such equations will be written

$$\left.\begin{aligned} a_{11}x_1 + a_{12}x_2 + a_{13}x_3 + \ldots &= b_1 \\ a_{21}x_1 + a_{22}x_2 + a_{23}x_3 + \ldots &= b_2, \quad \text{etc.} \end{aligned}\right\} \tag{8.1}$$

or shortly
$$\sum_j a_{ij}x_j = b_i \quad (i = 1, 2, \ldots, n),$$

or in matrix form
$$\mathbf{Ax} = \mathbf{b}.$$

The equation $\sum a_{ij}x_j = b_i$ with any particular value of i will be called the 'ith equation' and n will be used throughout for the number of equations and of unknowns. $\mathbf{I}$ will be written for the unit matrix, that is the matrix of which all the diagonal elements are 1 and all the non-diagonal elements 0.

There is probably no one way for evaluating the solution of such a set of equations which can be said to be the best in all circumstances. The most effective practical method to use depends on various characteristics of the equations and of the solutions required and on the experience of the individual who has the task of carrying out the numerical work.

The character of the equations is concerned with such matters as whether the coefficients are all small integers or not, whether many are zero, and whether those which are non-zero are arranged in some systematic way, whether they are all exactly known or are subject to uncertainty as a consequence of being either experimental measures or results of other calculations subject to rounding errors, and whether the diagonal coefficients are large compared with the non-diagonal coefficients or not.

Relevant characteristics of the solutions required are whether a solution is wanted for one set of values of the b_j's only or for many such sets, and whether the characteristic values of the matrix $\mathbf{A}$ are required as well as the solution of the equation.

There are two main kinds of method, sometimes called 'direct' and 'indirect'.

'Direct' methods are those in which one application of the computing procedure leads to the solution, to an accuracy depending on the nominal accuracy of the calculations. The evaluation of the expression for the solution in terms of determinants, and the method of elimination, are examples.

'Indirect' methods are those in which the solution is approached by successive approximation, by a number of repetitions of the same computing procedure. For hand calculations an advantage, when such a method is applicable, is that in the early stages only a limited number of figures need be kept, and the accuracy increased as the solution is approached.

If an approximation $x_1 = \xi_1, x_2 = \xi_2,...$, in general $x_i = \xi_i$, to the solution of the equations has been obtained, the quantities

$$R_i = \sum_j a_{ij}\xi_j - b_i \qquad (8.2)$$

are called the 'residuals' of the various equations; they measure the extent to which the approximate solution $x_i = \xi_i$ fails to satisfy the equations. The corrections $\Delta\xi_j = (x_j - \xi_j)$ to the approximate solution satisfy the equations

$$\sum_j a_{ij}\Delta\xi_j = c_i = -R_i \qquad (8.3)$$

with the same coefficients as the original equations. In various methods of evaluating a solution it is possible to proceed by a process of approximation, obtaining first an approximate solution, calculating the residuals for this approximate solution, then solving (8.3) for corrections to the approximate solution, and perhaps repeating this process.

8.11. Matrices

If, as assumed, the determinant of the coefficients is non-zero then the matrix $\mathbf{A}$ of the coefficients has an inverse $\mathbf{A}^{-1}$, and the solution is formally

$$\mathbf{x} = \mathbf{A}^{-1}\mathbf{b}. \tag{8.4}$$

If many solutions for different sets of values b_i are wanted, then it may be worth while to evaluate $\mathbf{A}^{-1}$ first and then to evaluate solutions from (8.4); one process for the inversion of a matrix is considered in §8.3 and another in §8.41. In general the calculation of $\mathbf{A}^{-1}$ will be affected by rounding errors, so the matrix used as $\mathbf{A}^{-1}$ in evaluating a solution from (8.4) will not be exactly the inverse of the matrix $\mathbf{A}$ of the coefficients of the original equations. The results of evaluating (8.4) with this approximate $\mathbf{A}^{-1}$ may therefore have to be treated as an approximation $\boldsymbol{\xi}$ to the solution and improved as explained at the end of the previous section.

A matrix in which all elements below the diagonal are zero is called an 'upper triangular' matrix and one in which all the elements above the diagonal are zero is called 'lower triangular'. The determinant of a triangular matrix is the product of its diagonal elements.

8.12. Ill-conditioned equations

If the determinant D of the coefficients is expanded in terms of the elements of any one row or column, for example

$$D = \sum_k A_{jk} a_{jk} \tag{8.5}$$

(the sum being over k only, j being fixed), it may happen that D is small compared with some of the individual terms in this sum. Then the value of D, and so the solution of the equations, is very sensitive to small changes in the values of the coefficients, and an approximate solution obtained by a numerical method which is subject to rounding errors is likely to be very sensitive to these errors. If, for example, D is of the order of unity but some of the individual terms in (8.5) are of the order of 2000, then a change of 0·1 per cent. in the coefficient a_{jk} in one of these large terms may change the value of D from $+1$ to -1, and the solutions in the two cases, and for intermediate values of this coefficient a_{jk}, may be entirely different.

A very elementary example is provided by the equations

$$x+2y = 4, \qquad 1000x+2001y = 4003$$

for which $D = 2001-2000 = 1$, and the solution is

$$x = -2, \qquad y = 3.$$

If the coefficient of y in the second of these equations is changed by $-0\cdot1$ per cent. to 1999, the solution becomes

$$x = 10, \qquad y = -3$$

and if it is changed by $+0\cdot1$ per cent. to 2003, the solution becomes

$$x = 2, \qquad y = 1.$$

If the coefficients in these equations are known *exactly*, then the solution can be determined to any accuracy required. But if the coefficients are subject to some uncertainty, either through being derived from observations which can only be made to a finite degree of accuracy, or through being themselves results of other calculations which may be affected by rounding errors, then clearly not even the sign and first significant figure of the solution can be determined unless the uncertainties in the coefficients are less than $0\cdot1$ per cent. A set of equations for which D is small compared with some of the individual terms in the sum (8.5) is called 'ill-conditioned'.

It is sometimes said that a set of equations is ill-conditioned if the determinant D of the coefficients is small; but this is an inadequate statement because the relevant standard of smallness is unspecified. Consider a set of thirty equations for which $D = 1$. The relations between the variables expressed by the equations are not altered if each equation is multiplied by 1000; but D then becomes 10^{90} which is not 'small' in any ordinary use of the word.

'Ill-conditioned', applied to a set of equations, is sometimes used merely as a qualitative term of abuse; but it is capable of being given a quantitative significance. Let $\lambda^{(1)}, \lambda^{(2)},..., \lambda^{(n)}$ be the characteristic values of the matrix of the coefficients a_{jk}, and let $|\lambda^{(m)}|, |\lambda^{(M)}|$ be the greatest and least of the quantities $|\lambda^{(j)}|$; then $|\lambda^{(M)}/\lambda^{(m)}|$ is a quantitative measure of ill-conditionedness; when this ratio is nearly unity the equations are well-conditioned, when it is large compared with 1 they are ill-conditioned; when $\lambda^{(m)}$ is zero the determinant D of the coefficients is zero and either the equations have no solution or the solution is not unique.

Unfortunately the numerical determination of this measure of ill-conditionedness is as long a process as the evaluation of the solution of the equations, and the same applies to some other measures of condition which have been suggested by Turing.† So it is not very useful in practice

† A. M. Turing, *Quart. J. Mech. and Applied Math.* **1** (1948), **287**.

for giving advance warning that the equations concerned are ill-conditioned. In many cases the intermediate results obtained in the course of the numerical process of solving the equations exhibit characteristic symptoms when the equations are ill-conditioned. These symptoms depend on the particular process and will be mentioned in the course of consideration of the individual processes.

Sometimes inspection of a set of equations will suggest that they are ill-conditioned. Expressed geometrically, any one of the equations is the equation of a hyper-plane in n-dimensional space, and the coefficients in the equation are the components of a vector normal to this hyper-plane. If these normals are all in much the same direction then the hyper-planes are nearly parallel so that their intersections are at very acute angles, and the common point of them all, which represents the solution of the equations, is not well determined. For example, it is clear on inspection that for the equations (constructed by T. S. Wilson and quoted by J. Morris)†

$$\left.\begin{array}{c} 5x_1+7x_2+6x_3+5x_4 = 23 \\ 7x_1+10x_2+8x_3+7x_4 = 32 \\ 6x_1+8x_2+10x_3+9x_4 = 33 \\ 5x_1+7x_2+9x_3+10x_4 = 31 \end{array}\right\} \qquad (8.6)$$

the normals to the hyper-planes make only small angles with each other, so that this set of equations is ill-conditioned. But it is only occasionally that an ill-conditioned set of equations can be recognized as such by inspection.

A characteristic feature of ill-conditioned equations is that a set of values for the unknowns which differs considerably from the solution of the equations may, nevertheless, give small residuals for all the equations. For example, for the equations (8.6) the residuals for certain sets of values of x_1, x_2, x_3, x_4 are as follows:

x_1	x_2	x_3	x_4	
$+14\cdot6$	$-7\cdot2$	$-2\cdot5$	$+3\cdot1$	$R_1 = -R_2 = -R_3 = R_4 = 0\cdot1$
$+\ 2\cdot36$	$+0\cdot18$	$+0\cdot65$	$+1\cdot21$	$R_1 = -R_2 = -R_3 = R_4 = 0\cdot01$

whereas the exact solution is $x_1 = x_2 = x_3 = x_4 = 1$. Thus in this case values of the residuals which are less than 1/2000 of the values of the b's in the equations still do not guarantee the accuracy even of the first figure in the x's. This is an extreme case, but it illustrates the need for caution in taking the smallness of residuals as a guide to the accuracy of the solution when the equations are ill-conditioned.

† J. Morris, *Phil. Mag.* (7) **37** (1946), 106.

8.13. Normal equations

For a set of values of $(x_1, x_2,..., x_n)$, *not* necessarily a solution of the equations, let $2S$ be written for the sum of the squares of the residuals (8.2), that is,

$$S = \tfrac{1}{2} \sum_i R_i^2.$$

Then S is a quadratic function of $(x_1, x_2,..., x_n)$ which is zero for those values of $(x_1, x_2,..., x_n)$ which form the solution of the equations, and is positive for all other sets of values. Hence the determination of the solution of these equations is equivalent to finding the set of values of $(x_1, x_2,..., x_n)$ which make S a minimum. This set is given by

$$\frac{\partial S}{\partial x_j} = 0 \quad \text{(all } j\text{)}$$

or

$$\sum_i R_i \frac{\partial R_i}{\partial x_j} = 0. \tag{8.7}$$

Now

$$\partial R_i / \partial x_j = a_{ij} = (\tilde{a})_{ji},$$

where $\tilde{\mathbf{A}}$ is the transpose of the matrix $\mathbf{A}$. Hence the set of equations (8.7) is

$$\sum_i \tilde{a}_{ji} R_i = 0$$

or

$$\sum_{ik} [(\tilde{a}_{ji} a_{ik}) x_k - \tilde{a}_{ji} b_i] = 0 \tag{8.8}$$

or in matrix form

$$(\tilde{\mathbf{A}}\mathbf{A})\mathbf{x} - \tilde{\mathbf{A}}\mathbf{b} = 0.$$

The set of equations (8.8) is sometimes called the set of 'normal equations' corresponding to the original equations (8.1). They are derived from the positive definite quadratic form S, and the matrix $(\tilde{\mathbf{A}}\mathbf{A})$ is necessarily symmetrical; these features are advantageous in some methods of carrying out the solution numerically.

On the other hand, the ratio $|\lambda^{(M)}/\lambda^{(m)}|$ for the normal equations is greater than that for the original equations,† so that the normal equations are less well-conditioned than the original equations, and when the original equations are at all severely ill-conditioned, the normal equations are very much worse. Hence, methods which do not depend on the matrix of the coefficients being symmetrical, or on the equations being derived from a positive definite quadratic form, are often preferable.

8.2 Elimination

A straightforward direct method is one based on successive elimination of the variables. This is a development of the process of elementary algebra with attention given to three points, namely systematic

† See Olga Taussky, *M.T.A.C.* **4** (1950), 111.

arrangement of the work, provision of a current check, and control of rounding errors. The points are all important and become more important the greater the number of equations and unknowns.

In elementary algebra emphasis is properly given to the importance of verifying that an alleged solution does actually satisfy the equations. This final check should always be carried out. But in the evaluation of the solution of a set of more than three equations it is hardly sufficient since if it fails it gives no indication of the location of the mistake, and the whole work has to be repeated with an appreciable probability of repeating the same mistake. A *current* check is required, both to help in locating a mistake and to prevent much further work being based on erroneous intermediate results.

To eliminate x_k between the ith and jth equations, in which the coefficients of x_k are a_{ik} and a_{jk} respectively, we have to multiply the equations by α_j and α_i respectively, and add, choosing α_j so that

$$\alpha_j a_{ik} + \alpha_i a_{jk} = 0.$$

Formally, there is an infinite number of ways of choosing the multipliers α_i and α_j; but in practice there are only two ways which are generally useful. One is to take one of the multipliers as unity, that is to say to take

$$\left. \begin{array}{ll} \alpha_i = 1, & \alpha_j = -a_{jk}/a_{ik} \\ \alpha_j = 1, & \alpha_i = -a_{ik}/a_{jk} \end{array} \right\}, \tag{8.9}$$

or

the other is to take

$$\alpha_j = \pm a_{jk}, \qquad \alpha_i = \mp a_{ik}. \tag{8.10}$$

The division involved in the choice represented by (8.9) will usually involve rounding errors in each elimination. Since the results of eliminating one variable are used later in the elimination of other variables, it is important to keep these rounding errors under control, and this is best done as follows. One of the multipliers is taken as unity; we choose that one of the alternatives (8.9) which makes the modulus of the other multiplier less than unity. Then at each stage of the elimination the rounding errors from previous stages are always multiplied by numbers of modulus less than unity.

This is a general method. If, however, the coefficients are all fairly small integers, it is possible to carry out the elimination without introducing any rounding errors, by using the choice (8.10) of the multipliers, which avoids any division. If this can be done without the coefficients becoming inconveniently large it is probably the preferable choice. It may be possible to keep the coefficients from becoming large by making suitable linear combinations of the equations, with integral coefficients, in the course of the elimination process; since no rounding off is involved there is no loss of numerical accuracy in such a procedure. As a simple example, with the equations

$$(1)\ 23x+31y = b_1, \qquad (2)\ 44x+65y = b_2$$

one should *not* try to eliminate x by multiplying the first equation by 44 and the second by -23 and adding; the first step should be to form the linear combination $2\times(1)-(2)$:

$$(3) = 2\times(1)-(2), \qquad 2x-3y = 2b_1-b_2,$$

before continuing the elimination.

8.21. General elimination process

To eliminate the variable x_k from a set of equations, specified by different values of i, we may take one equation, say the jth, and for each value of i form

$$(i\text{th equation})+(\alpha_i)\times(j\text{th equation}), \tag{8.11}$$

where α_i is given by the second of formulae (8.9). If the numerical work is suitably arranged, it is not necessary to write out the equations in full at each stage. It is enough to write down, for each equation, the coefficients and the constant term in appropriate columns. A current check can be provided by keeping a record, with each equation, of the sum of the coefficients and the constant term, and forming the linear combination expressed by (8.11) not only for the coefficients but also for this check sum. The value of this check sum for the ith equation will be written s_i; that is

$$s_i = b_i + \sum_l a_{il}.$$

Thus for using the jth equation to eliminate x_k from the ith equation, we have the following scheme:

	Coefficients of		Constant	Check
	x_k	x_l	term	sum
ith equation	a_{ik}	a_{il}	b_i	s_i
jth equation	a_{jk}	a_{jl}	b_j	s_j
$[\alpha_i = -a_{ik}/a_{jk}]$	$a_{ik}+\alpha_i a_{jk}$	$a_{il}+\alpha_i a_{jl}$	$b_i+\alpha_i b_j$	$s_i+\alpha_i s_j$
Result	$=0$	$=a_{il}'$	$=b_i'$	$=s_i'$

$$\left.\right\} \tag{8.12}$$

The check consists in verifying that s_i' calculated as $s_i+\alpha_i s_j$ is in agreement (within the tolerance for rounding errors) with the sum of the other entries in the corresponding line, namely $b_i'+\sum_l a_{il}'$. The jth equation here is sometimes called the 'pivotal equation', and the coefficient a_{jk}, which is the divisor in the evaluation of the coefficient $\alpha_i = -a_{ik}/a_{jk}$, is called the 'pivotal coefficient' or 'pivot' for this elimination; it is the coefficient, in the pivotal equation, of the variable to be eliminated.

Example: To use the first of the three equations:

$$31{\cdot}74x_1 + 43{\cdot}61x_2 - 16{\cdot}94x_3 + 16{\cdot}94x_4 = 41{\cdot}37,$$
$$6{\cdot}86x_1 + 9{\cdot}81x_2 + 7{\cdot}68x_3 + 3{\cdot}96x_4 = 16{\cdot}81,$$
$$35{\cdot}85x_1 - 32{\cdot}92x_2 + 13{\cdot}81x_3 + 5{\cdot}94x_4 = 21{\cdot}84,$$

to eliminate x_2 from the second and third.

The pivotal coefficient is the coefficient 43·61 in the first equation, and the multipliers are

$$\alpha_2 = -9{\cdot}81/43{\cdot}61 = -0{\cdot}22495, \qquad \alpha_3 = +32{\cdot}92/43{\cdot}61 = 0{\cdot}75487$$

Line no. and operation	Coefficient of				Constant term	Check sum	Notes
	x_1	x_2	x_3	x_4			
(1)	31·74	43·61	−16·94	16·94	41·37	116·72	
(2)	6·86	9·81	7·68	3·96	16·81	45·12	
(3)	35·85	−32·92	13·81	5·94	21·84	44·52	
(4) = $\alpha_2 \times$ (1)	−7·140	−9·810	3·811	−3·811	−9·306	−26·256	$\alpha_2 = -0{\cdot}22495$
(5) = (2)+(4)	−0·280	0	11·491	0·149	7·504	18·864	cross sum = 18·864
(6) = $\alpha_3 \times$ (1)	23·960	32·920	12·877	−12·877	31·229	88·108	$\alpha_3 = 0{\cdot}75487$
(7) = (3)+(6)	59·810	0	26·687	−6·937	53·069	132·628	cross sum = 132·629

Notes: (i) It is convenient to keep a note, on the left-hand side, of the operations carried out to obtain the successive lines of the calculation. This simplifies the location and correction of mistakes should any be made, and is also useful if the calculation has to be repeated with other values of the constant terms b_i.

(ii) In working, it is best to set each α_i on the setting levers or keyboard of a machine, then first multiply by the coefficient a_{jk} of the variable which it is required to eliminate, to check that α_i has been set correctly, then multiply by the other coefficients a_{jl} in the pivotal equation. These products can be written down, as in the above example in lines (4) and (6), or the entries in lines (5) and (7) can be formed and written down directly.

(iii) The results of elimination of x_2 from the third equation in the above example illustrate a kind of mistake which is not detected by the check explained above. The check is satisfied but two entries in line (7) are wrong; in line (6) the coefficients of x_3 and x_4 should read $-12{\cdot}787$ and $+12{\cdot}787$ respectively, and the corresponding entries in line (7) need correcting accordingly. The failure of the check to indicate the presence of the mistakes arises from the fact that the coefficient of x_4 in line (6) is just copied from that of x_3 with a change of sign, and if the latter coefficient is wrong, then so is the former and the effects of the two mistakes cancel in the check. This shows that special care is necessary when two coefficients in the pivotal equation are equal and opposite in sign. It also emphasizes that in the solution of a system of equations the current check on the eliminations alone is not sufficient; this current check should *always* be supplemented by a verification that an alleged solution does satisfy the original equations.

8.22. Evaluation of a solution by elimination

One way of arranging the solution of a system of equations by the elimination process is as follows. Use one equation as pivotal equation to eliminate one variable from all the equations. It is convenient to consider the variables and equations renumbered (if necessary) so that the variable eliminated is x_1, and the equation used as pivotal equation at this stage is the first. The result will be a single equation containing x_1:

$$a_{11}x_1 + a_{12}x_2 + a_{13}x_3 + \ldots + a_{1n}x_n = b_1 \qquad (8.13)$$

and a system of $(n-1)$ equations not involving x_1, of which a typical one is

$$a'_{i2}x_2 + a'_{i3}x_3 + \ldots + a'_{in}x_n = b'_i, \qquad (8.14)$$

where a'_{il} and b'_i are given by (8.12) with $j = 1$. Then another variable, which can similarly be taken as x_2, is eliminated from equations (8.14), and so on.

If the equation used as the pivotal equation to eliminate x_1 is chosen so that $|a_{11}| \geqslant |a_{i1}|\ (i > 1)$, then none of the multipliers $\alpha_i = -(a_{i1}/a_{11})$ in this elimination is greater than 1 in magnitude, a condition which we have already seen to be desirable to keep control of rounding errors. Similarly, the equation used as the pivotal equation to eliminate x_2 should be chosen so that $|a'_{22}| \geqslant |a'_{i2}|\ (i > 2)$, and so on.

Once an equation has been used as a pivotal equation in the elimination of one variable in this process, it is left unaltered in the further stages of the elimination process. Then this process leads finally to a system of equations of which the first is (8.13), the second is that member (say with $j = 2$) of the set (8.14) which is used as the pivotal equation for the elimination of x_2 from this set of equations, and so on. This system is

$$\left.\begin{array}{c} a_{11}x_1 + a_{12}x_2 + a_{13}x_3 + a_{14}x_4 + \ldots = b_1 \\ a'_{22}x_2 + a'_{23}x_3 + a'_{24}x_4 + \ldots = b'_2 \\ a''_{33}x_3 + a''_{34}x_4 + \ldots = b''_3, \quad \text{etc.} \end{array}\right\}, \qquad (8.15)$$

of which the mth equation contains $n-m+1$ of the variables, and the coefficients form an upper triangular matrix.

The last of this set of equations involves x_n only, the last but one involves x_n and x_{n-1} only, the last but two involves x_n, x_{n-1} and x_{n-2} only, and so on. This whole system of equations can therefore be solved by starting from the *last* and working backwards so as to determine the values of $x_n, x_{n-1}, x_{n-2}, \ldots$ in this order, using at each stage the values of the x_k's previously obtained. This process is known as 'back substitution'. In it, the value of each unknown is determined from that equation which was used as pivotal equation to eliminate it in the elimination process.

In the calculation the usual symptom of an ill-conditioned set of equations is that the coefficient of x_n in the last equation of the set (8.15) is small compared with the values of the coefficients in the equation used for the elimination of x_{n-1}; this is illustrated in the following example. Another symptom (of which this is a particular case) which may appear is that the elimination of one of the unknowns between two equations, say equations (A) and (B), by forming the linear combination $(A)+\alpha(B)$ (with $|\alpha| \leqslant 1$), results in an equation in which *all* the coefficients have values which are small compared with their values in equation (A).

Example:

To solve the equations

$$-23x_1+11x_2+x_3 = 0, \qquad 11x_1-3x_2-2x_3 = 3, \qquad x_1-2x_2+x_3 = -2.$$

Line no. and operation	Coefficients of x₁	x₂	x₃	b	Check sum	Notes
(1)	−23	11	1	0	−11	
(2)	11	−3	−2	3	9	
(3)	1	−2	1	−2	−2	
(4) $= \alpha_2 \times (1)$	−11	5·261	0·478	0	−5·261	$\alpha_2 = 11/23 = 0.47826$
(5) $= (2)+(4)$		**2·261**	−1·522	3	3·739	
					3·739	cross sum
(6) $= \alpha_3 \times (1)$	−1	0·478	0·043	0	−0·478	$\alpha_3 = 1/23 = 0.04348$
(7) $= (3)+(6)$		−1·522	1·043	−2	−2·478	
					−2·479	cross sum
(8) $= \alpha_3 \times (5)$		1·522	−1·025	2·020	2·517	$\alpha_3 = \dfrac{1·522}{2·261} = 0.6732$
(9) $= (7)+(8)$			**0·018**	0·020	0·038	
					0·038	cross sum
(10) $= x_3$			1	1·111	2·111	
(11) $= 1·522x_3$			1·522	1·691	3·213	
(12) $= (5)+(11)$		2·261		4·691	6·952	
(13) $= x_2$		1		2·075	3·075	cross sum checks
(14) $= -11 \times (13)$		−11		−22·825	−33·825	
(15) $= (1)+(14)$ −(10)	−23			−23·936	−46·936	
(16) $= x_1$	1			1·041	2·041	

Final check		Residuals
$x_1 = 1·041$	$-23x_1+11x_2+x_3 = -0·007$	$-0·007$
$x_2 = 2·075$	$11x_1-3x_2-2x_3 = 3·004$	$+0·004$
$x_3 = 1·111$	$x_1-2x_2+x_3 = -1·998$	$+0·002$

Notes: (i) The 'pivots' are distinguished in this example by being printed in heavy type (in manuscript an underline or 'box' could be used), the coefficient of the last remaining variable being counted as a 'pivot' for this purpose. The largest coefficient is chosen as the first pivot, and the result of eliminating x_1 is given by lines (5) and (7). In these equations the coefficient of x_2 in line (5) is the greatest, and this is taken as the next pivot.

(ii) In line (7) there is a difference of a unit in the last figure between the number derived from the other relevant entries in the same *column* and that derived from the cross sum along the *row*. This is an effect of rounding errors, and occasional small discrepancies in the check, such as this, must be expected. In the further calculation, the value derived from the cross sum should be used in such cases.

(iii) If the coefficients are known to have exact integral values, then it is significant to keep any number of figures in the calculation. In this example three decimals have been kept. Any required accuracy could be attained by keeping enough figures, though before the solution is carried out it may be difficult to judge how many are needed to give a specified accuracy in the solution. In the present case it might be expected that the three decimals kept should be enough to give the solution to 1 per cent., allowing for rounding errors; but as will be seen (under (iv) below), the 'solution' in this case is not even accurate to two figures.

If the coefficients were only known to two decimals there would be no significance in keeping more than three. If, for example, the coefficient a_{22} were only known to lie in the range -3.00 ± 0.01, then the entry 2.261 in line (5) might stand for any number in the range 2.251 to 2.271, and the only purpose of keeping even the third decimal is to avoid rounding errors accumulating in the second decimal.

(iv) By taking another decimal in x_1 only ($x_1 = 1.0407$) these residuals can be reduced to -0.001, $+0.001$, $+0.002$ to three decimals, so that at first sight it would appear that this solution is correct to at least two decimals. It is not, however: the correct solution is $x_1 = 1$, $x_2 = 2$, $x_3 = 1$, and the solution is not even correct to one decimal. This is a consequence of the ill-conditioned character of the equations. There is a warning of this character of the equations at line (9) of the working, at which the coefficient of x_3 is very small compared with that in equation (7).

(v) If the coefficients are known to have exact integral values, the value of the last pivotal coefficient can sometimes be improved as follows. The product of the pivots is the determinant of the coefficients of the original equations,† and this must be an integer if the coefficients are integers. In this example the product of the pivots as evaluated is

$$-23 \times 2.261 \times 0.018 = -0.94.$$

The second factor is certainly not in error by more than 1 in 1000, and the extreme possibilities of rounding errors cannot affect the third by more than 10 per cent.; so the value of this product lies between -0.84 and -1.04. But it must be integral, and must therefore be -1; hence the value of the last pivot is

$$-1/(-23 \times 2.261) = 0.0192,$$

the fourth decimal being certainly correct.

This argument must *not* be used unless the coefficients are *known* to be integral; otherwise it might give a false idea of the accuracy of the solution.

† A factor (-1) may be introduced if the order of the variables or of the equations is changed in the elimination process.

(vi) If ξ_1, ξ_2, ξ_3 is an approximate solution, and R_1, R_2, R_3 the residuals obtained by putting $x_j = \xi_j$, then the corrections $(x_j - \xi_j)$ to the approximate solution can be obtained by solving the equations (8.3) in a similar manner.

8.23. Alternative arrangement of the elimination process

In the above arrangement of the elimination process, each pivotal equation is left unchanged in later stages of the process. An alternative procedure is to use each pivotal equation to eliminate an unknown from the pivotal equations previously used, as well as from later equations.

In the above example, for instance, the pivotal equation (5) can be used to eliminate x_2 from equation (1) as well as from equation (3).

This procedure avoids the process of back-substitution, but the elimination process is longer, and the total amount of work involved is about the same.

8.3. Inverse of a matrix by elimination

One way of inverting a matrix $\mathbf{A}$ is to obtain a set of solutions of the equations

$$\sum_j a_{ij} x_j = b_i \tag{8.16}$$

for different sets of values of the b's, namely the sets

$$b_1 = 1, \qquad b_2 = 0, \qquad b_3 = 0, \quad \ldots;$$
$$b_1 = 0, \qquad b_2 = 1, \qquad b_3 = 0, \quad \ldots;$$

and in general for the sets

$$b_k = 1, \qquad b_l = 0 \quad (l \neq k). \tag{8.17}$$

The solution x_j of the equations (8.16) will depend on the value of k in (8.17). For any particular value of k, let us write the solution

$$x_j = c_{jk}.$$

Then for any set of values of the b's in (8.16)

$$x_j = \sum_k c_{jk} b_k;$$

that is, the c_{jk}'s are the elements of the matrix which is the inverse of $\mathbf{A}$.

The solution of the equations for the different sets of values (8.17) of the b's can be carried out simultaneously by a slight extension of the process of § 8.22, using a separate column for the coefficients of each value of b_k in the original equations.

Example: To solve the equations

$$-23x_1 + 11x_2 + x_3 = b_1,$$
$$11x_1 - 3x_2 - 2x_3 = b_2,$$
$$x_1 - 2x_2 + x_3 = b_3$$

for general values of b_1, b_2, and b_3. The left-hand sides of these equations are the same as in the previous example; the right-hand sides have general values. In this example the elimination will be carried out by the special process mentioned in §8.21 as avoiding divisions, and the rounding errors associated with them, in the elimination process.

Equation no. and operation	Coefficients of			Coefficients of			Check sum	Notes
	x_1	x_2	x_3	b_1	b_2	b_3		
(1)	-23	11	1	1	0	0	-10	
(2)	11	-3	-2	0	1	0	7	
(3)	1	-2	1	0	0	1	1	
(4) = (1)−(3)	-24	13	0	1	0	-1	-11	cross sum checks
(5) = (2)+2×(3)	13	-7	0	0	1	2	9	cross sum checks
(6) = (4)+2×(5)	2	-1	0	1	2	3	7	cross sum checks
(7) = (4)+12×(6) = x_2	0	1	0	13	24	35	73	cross sum checks
(8) = (6)+(7)	2	0	0	14	26	38	80	
(9) = ½(8) = x_1	1	0	0	7	13	19	40	cross sum checks
(10) = 2×(7)+(3)	1	0	1	26	48	71	147	
(11) = (10)−(9) = x_3	0	0	1	19	35	52	107	cross sum checks

Hence

$$x_1 = 7b_1 + 13b_2 + 19b_3,$$
$$x_2 = 13b_1 + 24b_2 + 35b_3,$$
$$x_3 = 19b_1 + 35b_2 + 52b_3,$$

and

$$\begin{pmatrix} -23 & 11 & 1 \\ 11 & -3 & -2 \\ 1 & -2 & 1 \end{pmatrix}^{-1} = \begin{pmatrix} 7 & 13 & 19 \\ 13 & 24 & 35 \\ 19 & 35 & 52 \end{pmatrix}.$$

Notes: (i) In this example advantage has been taken of the simple numerical values of the coefficients to lighten the numerical work of the elimination process. The particularly simple values of the coefficients of x_3 suggest that this is the unknown to eliminate first.

(ii) In line (6) no elimination is carried out, but a linear combination of the equations is made so as to keep down the magnitudes of the numbers occurring in the calculation.

(iii) By avoiding division and so keeping the work free from rounding errors, the exact solution is obtained without any attention having to be given to the number of figures kept at the various stages of the work. Further, the ill-conditioned nature of the equations (see note (iv) below) gives no difficulty in obtaining a solution. Also the numbers occurring are simple enough in this case for the whole calculation to be done without the aid of a desk machine.

(iv) The large values of the elements of the inverse matrix show why such a poor approximation to the solution, as represented by the 'solution' obtained in §8.22, gives such small residuals.

If (ξ_1, ξ_2, ξ_3) is an approximation to the solution, and R_1, R_2, R_3 are the residuals obtained on substituting $x_1 = \xi_1$, $x_2 = \xi_2$, $x_3 = \xi_3$ into the equations, then the corrections to the approximate solution are

$$(x_1 - \xi_1) = 7R_1 + 13R_2 + 19R_3,$$
$$(x_2 - \xi_2) = 13R_1 + 24R_2 + 35R_3,$$
$$(x_3 - \xi_3) = 19R_1 + 35R_2 + 52R_3,$$

so that if $R_1 = R_2 = R_3 = 0.01$, then $x_3 - \xi_3 = 1.06$; that is, the error in an approximate value of x_3 may be over 100 times the residuals in the equations, although in the equations this unknown only occurs with coefficients 1 and 2.

8.4. Choleski's method†

In the elimination method explained above the number of quantities written down in the process of solution of a system of n equations is of order n^3. When n is more than about 6 or 8, there may be advantages in arranging the work so that the number of intermediate quantities recorded is considerably smaller, of order n^2 rather than of order n^3.

The method usually ascribed to Choleski, of which there are several variants, is one in which the amount of recording of intermediate results is reduced in this way. It depends on the resolution of the matrix $\mathbf{A}$ of the coefficients into the product $\mathbf{LU}$ of two matrices, of which $\mathbf{L}$ is lower triangular with the diagonal elements unity, and $\mathbf{U}$ is upper triangular. Then the system of equations

$$\mathbf{Ax} = \mathbf{LUx} = \mathbf{b}$$

can be written

$$\mathbf{Ly} = \mathbf{b}, \tag{8.18}$$

$$\mathbf{Ux} = \mathbf{y}. \tag{8.19}$$

Written out, equations (8.18) are

$$\left. \begin{array}{r} y_1 = b_1 \\ l_{21}y_1 + y_2 = b_2 \\ l_{31}y_1 + l_{32}y_2 + y_3 = b_3 \\ \cdot \quad \cdot \quad \cdot \quad \cdot \quad \cdot \quad \cdot \end{array} \right\}, \tag{8.20}$$

since all the diagonal elements of $\mathbf{L}$ are unity; from these equations $y_1, y_2, y_3, \ldots$ can be obtained in succession. And equations (8.19) written out, are

$$\left. \begin{array}{r} u_{11}x_1 + u_{12}x_2 + u_{13}x_3 + \ldots + u_{1n}x_n = y_1 \\ u_{22}x_2 + u_{23}x_3 + \ldots + u_{2n}x_n = y_2 \\ \cdot \quad \cdot \quad \cdot \quad \cdot \quad \cdot \quad \cdot \quad \cdot \quad \cdot \quad \cdot \quad \cdot \\ u_{n-1,n-1}x_{n-1} + u_{n-1,n}x_n = y_{n-1} \\ u_{nn}x_n = y_n \end{array} \right\} \tag{8.21}$$

and, once the values of the y_j's have been found from (8.20), those of the x_k's can be found in succession from equations (8.21), starting with the *last* and working backwards.

To resolve the matrix $\mathbf{A}$ into the product $\mathbf{LU}$ the *rows* of $\mathbf{A}$ are taken

---

† See, for example, L. Fox, H. D. Huskey, and J. H. Wilkinson, *Quart. J. Mech. and Applied Math.* **1** (1948), 149; A. M. Turing, ibid. 287. For another method of a similar type see P. D. Crout, *Trans. Amer. Inst. Elect. Eng.* **60** (1941), 1235.

in order, the elements of **L** being derived from elements of **A** *below* the diagonal, and those of **U** from those of **A** *on and above* the diagonal. Let

$$\begin{pmatrix} a_{11} & a_{12} & a_{13} & a_{14} & \cdot & \cdot \\ a_{21} & a_{22} & a_{23} & a_{24} & \cdot & \cdot \\ a_{31} & a_{32} & a_{33} & a_{34} & \cdot & \cdot \\ \cdot & \cdot & \cdot & \cdot & \cdot & \cdot \end{pmatrix}$$

$$= \begin{pmatrix} 1 & 0 & 0 & 0 & \cdot & \cdot \\ l_{21} & 1 & 0 & 0 & \cdot & \cdot \\ l_{31} & l_{32} & 1 & 0 & \cdot & \cdot \\ \cdot & \cdot & \cdot & \cdot & \cdot & \cdot \end{pmatrix} \begin{pmatrix} u_{11} & u_{12} & u_{13} & u_{14} & \cdot & \cdot \\ 0 & u_{22} & u_{23} & u_{24} & \cdot & \cdot \\ 0 & 0 & u_{33} & u_{34} & \cdot & \cdot \\ \cdot & \cdot & \cdot & \cdot & \cdot & \cdot \end{pmatrix}.$$

Then for the first row of Λ we have

$$u_{1r} = a_{1r}. \tag{8.22}$$

For the second row of **A**

$$\left. \begin{aligned} a_{21} &= l_{21} u_{11}, & l_{21} &= a_{21}/u_{11} \\ a_{2r} &= l_{21} u_{1r} + u_{2r}, & u_{2r} &= a_{2r} - l_{21} u_{1r} \quad (r \geqslant 2) \end{aligned} \right\}. \tag{8.23}$$

For the third row of **A**

$$\left. \begin{aligned} a_{31} &= l_{31} u_{11}, & l_{31} &= a_{31}/u_{11} \\ a_{32} &= l_{31} u_{12} + l_{32} u_{22}, & l_{32} &= (a_{32} - l_{31} u_{12})/u_{22} \\ a_{3r} &= l_{31} u_{1r} + l_{32} u_{2r} + u_{3r}, & u_{3r} &= a_{3r} - l_{31} u_{1r} - l_{32} u_{2r} \quad (r \geqslant 3) \end{aligned} \right\}. \tag{8.24}$$

and in general, for the pth row of **A**

$$\left. \begin{aligned} l_{pr} &= \left(a_{pr} - \sum_{s<r} l_{ps} u_{st} \right) \Big/ u_{rr} \quad (r < p) \\ u_{pr} &= a_{pr} - \sum_{s<p} l_{ps} u_{st} \qquad\qquad (r \geqslant p) \end{aligned} \right\}. \tag{8.25}$$

If the elements of **L** and **U** are calculated in the order indicated by the sequence of these formulae, then the evaluation of each involves just one unknown, one element of **A** which has not been used before, and quantities already calculated. The accumulation of the products in these formulae, and the divisions by u_{rr} in the calculation of the elements of **L**, can all be done without writing down any intermediate results; the quantities which have to be written down in the course of this resolution of **A** into factors are the n^2 components of **L** and **U**.

The work can be checked by the use of column and row sums. Fox† recommends the following arrangement of the work

							Row sum
A	a_{11}	a_{12}	a_{13}	a_{14}	.	.	Σ_1
	a_{21}	a_{22}	a_{23}	a_{24}	.	.	Σ_2
	a_{31}	a_{32}	a_{33}	a_{34}	.	.	Σ_3
	.	.	.	.	.	.	.
L	1	0	0	0	.	.	
	l_{21}	1	0	0	.	.	
	l_{31}	l_{32}	1	0	.	.	
	.	.	.	.	.	.	
$\tilde{U} =$	u_{11}	0	0	0	.	.	
transpose	u_{12}	u_{22}	0	0	.	.	
of U	u_{13}	u_{23}	u_{33}	0	.	.	
	.	.	.	.	.	.	
s = column sum of $\tilde{U}$	s_1	s_2	s_3	.	.	.	

Check: Sum $[(r\text{th row of } \mathbf{L}) \times \text{row } s] = \text{row sum } \Sigma_r.$

In this arrangement, in which the matrix $\mathbf{U}$ is written out in the form of its transpose, the factors which have to be multiplied in forming the sums in formulae (8.25) occur in the same column, and correct selection of them is easier than it would be if one set of factors were in a row and the other set in a column.

The advantage of this method is that the number of quantities which has to be written down is only of order n^2. On the other hand, too little is written down to indicate how the numbers which are written down were obtained, and this makes diagnosis of mistakes difficult; the use of row and column sums gives a good indication of freedom from mistakes when none have been made, but the checks are too few to be of much help in identifying or locating a mistake if one is indicated.

The absence of intermediate results to make it clear how each number in the course of the calculation is obtained means that the computor must depend on his memory for the required sequence of operations. This sequence is slightly different for every one of the elements of $\mathbf{L}$ and of $\mathbf{U}$, and though it might become familiar enough to anyone who had much work of this kind to do, the writer's experience is that it is too complicated to be satisfactory for occasional use. The method seems to be one for the professional expert and the specialist rather than for the occasional user; but it is so strongly recommended by those who have had enough practice to become completely familiar with the sequence of operations required that it has been included here.

† L. Fox, *Journ. Roy. Stat. Soc.*, Ser. B, **12** (1950), 120.

8.41. Inverse of a matrix by Choleski's method

The inverse of a lower triangular matrix L can be found by taking the identity $L L^{-1} = I$, or in expanded form, with C for L^{-1}

$$\begin{pmatrix} 1 & 0 & 0 & 0 & . & . & . \\ l_{21} & 1 & 0 & 0 & . & . & . \\ l_{31} & l_{32} & 1 & 0 & . & . & . \\ & & & . & . & & \end{pmatrix} \begin{pmatrix} c_{11} & c_{12} & c_{13} & . & . & . \\ c_{21} & c_{22} & c_{23} & . & . & . \\ c_{31} & c_{32} & c_{33} & . & . & . \\ & & . & . & . & . \end{pmatrix}$$

$$= \begin{pmatrix} 1 & 0 & 0 & 0 & . & . & . \\ 0 & 1 & 0 & 0 & . & . & . \\ 0 & 0 & 1 & 0 & . & . & . \\ & & . & . & . & . & . \end{pmatrix},$$

and working through line by line of the unit matrix. The first line gives

$$c_{11} = 1, \qquad c_{1j} = 0 \quad (j > 1).$$

The second line gives

$$l_{21} c_{11} + c_{21} = 0, \quad \text{whence } c_{21} = -l_{21},$$
$$l_{21} c_{12} + c_{22} = 1, \quad \text{whence } c_{22} = 1, .$$
$$l_{21} c_{1j} + c_{2j} = 0, \quad \text{whence } c_{2j} = 0 \quad (j > 2),$$

and so on. The numerical calculation can be arranged in the same way as for the factorization of A into a product LU. The inverse of an upper triangular matrix can be treated in the same way, starting with the *last* row of the unit matrix.

If $$A = LU,$$

then $$A^{-1} = U^{-1} L^{-1},$$

so that a matrix can be inverted by factorizing it as a product LU, inverting U and L separately, and finally multiplying them to form A^{-1}. Like the Choleski method for the solution of a single set of equations, however, it is a method which is more suitable for the specialist who has a lot of work of this particular kind to do than for the occasional user.

8.5. Relaxation method

An indirect method which is very powerful in some cases is one called the 'relaxation' method. It was originally developed by Southwell† for application in problems of structural engineering, and some of the terminology of the method is derived from this particular application. But its range of application is much wider.

† R. V. Southwell, *Proc. Roy. Soc.* A, **151** (1935), 56; see also ibid. **184** (1945), 253; *Relaxation Methods in Engineering Science* (Oxford, 1940).

For any approximation $x_j = \xi_j$ to the solution of equations (8.1), the 'residuals' of the equations are defined by (8.2). For the solution of the equations, all the residuals are 0. In the relaxation method attention is concentrated on the residuals, and the method consists in making changes in the x's in a systematic manner so as to reduce the magnitudes of the residuals to negligible amounts.

The first process is to draw up an 'operations table' giving the change of each residual for a unit change of each single x_j. Then a set of initial values of x_j is taken and the residuals calculated, and changes of the x_j's then made in such a way as to decrease the residuals; the steps of this part of the work are recorded in a 'relaxation table' in which the *changes* of the x's and the resulting *total* residuals are recorded.

Example: To find, correct to two decimal places, the solution of the equations

$$\left. \begin{array}{l} 9x_1 - 2x_2 + x_3 = 50 \\ x_1 + 5x_2 - 3x_3 = 18 \\ -2x_1 + 2x_2 + 7x_3 = 19 \end{array} \right\}. \qquad (8.26)$$

For the first equation the residual R_1, for any trial values of x_1, x_2, x_3 is

$$R_1 = 9x_1 - 2x_2 + x_3 - 50.$$

Hence for a change $\Delta x_1 = 1$ of x_1 alone, the change of R_1 is $\Delta R_1 = 9$; similarly for a change $\Delta x_2 = 1$ of x_2 alone, the change of R_1 is $\Delta R_1 = -2$, and for a change $\Delta x_3 = 1$ of x_3 alone, the change of R_1 is $\Delta R_1 = +1$. These values of ΔR_1 are entered in the *first column* of the operations table.

Similarly, the residual for the second equation is

$$R_2 = x_1 + 5x_2 - 3x_3 - 18,$$

and for the same changes Δx_1, Δx_2, Δx_3, the changes in R_2 are $\Delta R_2 = +1$, $+5$, and -3 respectively, and so on. Thus in this arrangement of the work, the matrix of these entries in the operations table is the transpose of the matrix of the coefficients in the equation. The working is shown on the opposite page.

Notes: (i) In this example, a change Δx_1 of x_1 affects R_1 mainly, and R_2, R_3 to a smaller extent, and similarly for changes Δx_2 and Δx_3. A change Δx_1, made in such a way as to reduce $|R_1|$ considerably, is called a 'relaxation' of x_1, and the relaxation process consists of making a sequence of such relaxations. There is clearly no point in choosing Δx_1 so as to make R_1 exactly zero, since R_1 will be affected by subsequent relaxations Δx_2 and Δx_3. It will usually be adequate to take single-digit numbers for the relaxations; this greatly lightens the numerical work, and makes it possible to carry out the greater part of it mentally and speedily.

(ii) The relaxation table begins with any trial set of values of x_1, x_2, x_3 and the corresponding residuals. The simplest first trial set is $x_1 = x_2 = x_3 = 0$, and the residuals are then just the negatives of the constant terms in the equations.

In this case the residual R_1 is the greatest, and a large part of this can be removed, with smaller changes in the other residuals, by a relaxation $\Delta x_1 = 5$. The resulting changes in all the residuals are given by multiplying line (1) of the operations table by 5. In the example on p. 169, these changes are shown in brackets; they would not be written down in actual working; each would be evaluated mentally and

	Δx_1	Δx_2	Δx_3	ΔR_1	ΔR_2	ΔR_3	Notes
Operations	1	0	0	9	1	−2	Line (i)
table	0	1	0	−2	5	2	Line (ii)
	0	0	1	1	−3	7	Line (iii)

	Δx_1	Δx_2	Δx_3	R_1	R_2	R_3	Notes
	$x_1 = 0$	$x_2 = 0$	$x_3 = 0$	−50	−18	−19	
Relaxation	5	(0)	(0)	(45)	(5)	(−10)	Line (i)
table				−5	−13	−29	×5
	(0)	(0)	4	−1	−25	−1	
	(0)	5	(0)	−11	0	9	
	1	(0)	(0)	−2	1	7	
	(0)	(0)	−1	−3	4	0	
	(0)	−1	(0)	−1	−1	−2	
	$x_1 = 6$	$x_2 = 4$	$x_3 = 3$	−1	−1	−2	Check
			×10				
	$10x_1 = 60$	$10x_2 = 40$	$10x_3 = 30$	−10	−10	−20	
			3	−7	−19	1	
		4		−15	1	9	
	2			3	3	5	
			−1	2	6	−2	
		−1		4	1	−4	
	−1			−5	0	−2	
	$10x_1 = 61$	$10x_2 = 43$	$10x_3 = 32$	−5	0	−2	Check
			×10				
	610	430	320	−50	0	−20	
	5			−5	5	−30	
			4	−1	−7	−2	
		1		−3	−2	0	
	$100x_1 = 615$	$100x_2 = 431$	$100x_3 = 324$	−3	−2	0	Check
			×10				
	6150	4310	3240	−30	−20	0	
		4		−38	0	8	
	4			−2	4	0	
	6154	4314	3240	−2	4	0	Check

added to the previous value of the corresponding residual, and only the new residual would be written down. For example, the value $\Delta R_1 = 9$ in the operations table, multiplied by $\Delta x_1 = 5$, gives 45, which added to the old R_1 ($= -50$) gives the new R_1 ($= -5$) and only this is written down. In subsequent lines in the relaxation table the only entries in the R_j columns are those which would be written down in actual working. Similarly, the bracketed zeros in the Δx_j columns might be omitted, as they have been later in the relaxation table.

After the first relaxation $\Delta x_1 = 5$ the largest residual is $R_3 = -29$ and most of this is removed by a further relaxation $\Delta x_3 = 4$; then R_2 is greatest and can be reduced to zero by $\Delta x_2 = 5$. The contributions to R_1 from these relaxations Δx_3

and Δx_2 have been such that $|R_1|$ can be reduced substantially by a further relaxation $\Delta x_1 = 1$, and the procedure continues until the residuals are so small that they cannot be improved without making relaxations of magnitude smaller than unity.

At this stage it is convenient to avoid decimal points by multiplying the entries in the relaxation table by 10. But before doing this it is advisable to check that the calculation has been carried out correctly so far. This is done by adding up the changes Δx_1 and adding the result to the initial value taken (here zero), and similarly for x_2, x_3. The resulting values of x_1, x_2, x_3 are then substituted in the equations and the residuals calculated; they should agree with the last line so far obtained in the operations table. If they do not, there is no need to go back and look for the mistake; these values of x_1, x_2, x_3 form as good a set of trial values as the set $(0, 0, 0)$ actually used—indeed they are probably much better—and can be used as the starting values of a further calculation.

(iii) When a set of small residuals has been obtained *and checked*, the values of x and the residuals can be multiplied by 10 and the process continued, and this operation can be repeated as often as required. In this example it is repeated until it gives the result

$$1000(x_1, x_2, x_3) = (6154, 4314, 3240)$$

or, to two decimals, $(x_1, x_2, x_3) = (6{\cdot}15, 4{\cdot}31, 3{\cdot}24).$

It will be seen that although the number of operations may be large, each is very simple and, except for the checking operations, each involves only numbers of two digits, and often only of one digit.

8.51. Group relaxations

There is no need to restrict oneself to relaxations of the variables singly. In this example a relaxation Δx_2 makes appreciable contributions to R_1 and R_3, and the process of reducing the residuals would clearly be quicker and easier if we could make correlated changes in the variables in such a way as to affect only one residual considerably. It is often possible by trial to find linear combinations of the variables with this property. In this example we have:

	Δx_1	Δx_2	Δx_3	ΔR_1	ΔR_2	ΔR_3
X_3	0	1	2	0	-1	16
	0	4	-1	-9	23	1
X_2	1	4	-1	0	24	-1

A multiple of X_3 can clearly be used to reduce R_3 without affecting R_1 and with only quite a small effect on R_2, and similarly a multiple of X_2 can be used to reduce R_2. Relaxations which are multiples of X_2 or X_3 are called 'group relaxations' by Southwell. Use of them corresponds to making a linear transformation of the variables so that in the transformed variables the non-diagonal coefficients in the equations are small compared with the diagonal coefficients. But we do not have to carry out the transformation formally by introducing the new variables and expressing the equations in terms of them. The process of carrying out the numerical work makes this transformation for us.

Use of these group relaxations does not, of course, preclude us from using relaxations of a single variable if the values of the residuals indicate that such a procedure would be appropriate.

Example

		Δx_1	Δx_2	Δx_3	ΔR_1	ΔR_2	ΔR_3	
Operations		1	0	0	9	1	-2	
table		0	1	0	-2	5	2	
		0	0	1	1	-3	7	
	X_2	1	4	-1	0	24	-1	
	X_3	0	1	2	0	-1	16	
Relaxation		x_1	x_2	x_3	R_1	R_2	R_3	
table		0	0	0	-50	-18	-19	
		5			-5	-13	-29	
	$2X_3$		2	4	-5	-15	3	
	X_2	1	4	-1	-5	9	2	
		6	6	3	-5	9	2	Check
				$\times 10$				
		60	60	30	-50	90	20	
	$-4X_2$	-4	-16	4	-50	-6	24	
		5			-5	-1	14	
	$-X_3$		-1	-2	-5	0	-2	
		61	43	32	-5	0	-2	Check
				$\times 10$				
		610	430	320	-50	0	-20	
		6			4	6	-32	
	$2X_3$		2	4	4	4	0	
		616	432	324	4	4	0	Check
				$\times 10$				
		6160	4320	3240	40	40	0	
	$-2X_2$	-2	-8	2	40	-8	2	
		-4			4	-12	10	
				-2	2	-6	-4	
			1		0	-1	-2	
		6154	4313	3240	0	-1	-2	Check
		6·154	4·313	3·240		Solution		

8.52. Use and limitations of the relaxation method

Temple† has shown that if the simultaneous equations are derived from a positive definite quadratic form, then the relaxation process formally converges. However, this is neither a necessary nor a sufficient condition for it to be a practicable process in actual numerical work; it

† G. Temple, *Proc. Roy. Soc.* A, **169** (1938), 476.

is quite impracticable for the ill-conditioned equations (8.6) which can be derived from a positive definite quadratic form, whereas it is quite practicable for equations (8.26) which are not so derivable. What matters much more is that it should be easy to find a set of relaxations, either of individual variables or group relaxations, each of which has a considerably greater effect on one of the residuals than on any other.

Although the relaxation method is one of successive approximation, there is no limit in principle to the accuracy to which the solution can be taken. In the structural engineering context for which the method was originally devised by Southwell† there is no significance in carrying the solution beyond a certain limited degree of accuracy, and its first presentation in this context appears to have given the impression that it is fundamentally approximate in character; but it is no more so than any other numerical process which is subject to rounding errors. When it is used in contexts in which no approximation is involved in the equations to which it is applied, it may be possible, and significant, to carry the calculation through to a relatively high accuracy; and because of the simplicity of the process this may be the easiest way of deriving results to such accuracy.

For example, the recurrence relation for the Bessel functions

$$J_{n+1}(x) - (2n/x)\, J_n(x) + J_{n-1}(x) = 0$$

provides a set of simultaneous linear equations for $J_n(x)$ as a function of n for given x; and given, say, $J_n(x)$ for $n = N \geqslant x$ and the condition $J_n(x) \to 0$ as $n \to \infty$, it is possible to solve these equations to any accuracy required by an application of the relaxation process. The process is a simple and quick one, and Fox‡ has recorded that starting only from $J_{10}(10)$, he has obtained eighteen-decimal values of $J_n(10)$, for values of n from 11 to the value $(n = 37)$ at which $J_n(10) < 10^{-18}$, without difficulty. This process is most effective for calculating $J_n(x)$ for $n > x$, which is just the range over which the use of the recurrence relation to evaluate $J_{n+1}(x)$ from $J_n(x)$ and $J_{n-1}(x)$ becomes unsatisfactory (see § 11.3).

In one particular application, namely to the solution of ordinary differential equations with two-point boundary conditions (see § 8.53) or of partial differential equations of elliptic type (§ 10.2), the relaxation process is combined with the use of finite-difference approximations to derivatives, and this is perhaps part of the reason why the relaxation process has come to be regarded as essentially approximate. But this

---

† R. V. Southwell, *Proc. Roy. Soc.* A, **151** (1935), 56.
‡ L. Fox, *Proc. Camb. Phil. Soc.* **45** (1949), 50.

is a mistaken idea; the approximation is in the reduction of the differential equation to a set of simultaneous algebraic equations by use of finite differences. This approximation is involved whatever numerical process is used for the evaluation of a solution of these simultaneous equations, and the relaxation process, if used, is quite distinct from this approximation.

If a number of sets of equations with the same set of coefficients but with different values of $(b_1, ..., b_n)$ have to be solved, no advantage can be taken of this in the relaxation process, and for this reason this process is not well adapted to the inversion of a matrix.

The main difficulty likely to arise in using the process is slow convergence, and this will be most likely to occur when many of the coefficients in the equations are of the same order of magnitude, so that a relaxation of one of the unknowns makes changes of similar magnitude in a number of residuals. This situation is likely to occur when the equations are ill-conditioned, but is not necessarily a symptom of this condition.

8.53. Linear differential equations and linear simultaneous equations

Consider the linear differential equation

$$y'' = f(x)y + g(x) \tag{8.27}$$

with two-point boundary conditions, $y = y_0$ at $x = x_0$, $y = y_n$ at $x = x_n = x_0 + n(\delta x)$. To the approximation in which $(\delta x)^2 y''$ can be replaced by $\delta^2 y$, this differential equation is equivalent to the set of algebraic equations

$$\delta^2 y_j = (\delta x)^2 [f_j y_j + g_j],$$

or

$$y_{j+1} - [2 + (\delta x)^2 f_j] y_j + y_{j-1} = (\delta x)^2 g_j, \tag{8.28}$$

for $1 \leqslant j \leqslant n-1$, with y_0 and y_n given. This is a set of linear algebraic equations for $(n-1)$ unknowns, and could be solved numerically by any of the methods for the solution of such equations.

A convenient process in many cases is one that has been suggested and developed by Thomas and by Fox. It is a version of the Choleski method (§ 8.4), which in this case is very simple because of the specially simple forms of the matrices concerned.

Equations (8.28), arranged with the known quantities on the right-hand side, are

$$\left. \begin{array}{l} -[2 + (\delta x)^2 f_1] y_1 + y_2 = -y_0 + (\delta x)^2 g_1 \\ y_{j-1} - [2 + (\delta x)^2 f_j] y_j + y_{j+1} = (\delta x)^2 g_j \quad (2 \leqslant j \leqslant n-2) \\ y_{n-2} - [2 + (\delta x)^2 f_{n-1}] y_{n-1} = -y_n + (\delta x)^2 g_{n-1} \end{array} \right\}. \tag{8.28 a}$$

For short, let $\phi_j = (\delta x)^2 f_j$, and

$$c_1 = -y_0 + (\delta x)^2 g_1, \; c_j = (\delta x)^2 g_j \; (2 \leqslant j \leqslant n-2), \; c_{n-1} = -y_n + (\delta x)^2 g_{n-1};$$

also let $\mathbf{y} = (y_1, y_2, ..., y_n)$, $\mathbf{c} = (c_1, c_2, ..., c_n)$. Then equations (8.28 a), in matrix form, are

$$\mathbf{A}\mathbf{y} = \mathbf{c}, \tag{8.28 b}$$

where $\mathbf{A}$ is the matrix

$$\mathbf{A} = \begin{pmatrix} -(2+\phi_1) & 1 & 0 & 0 & . & . & 0 & 0 & 0 \\ 1 & -(2+\phi_2) & 1 & 0 & . & . & 0 & 0 & 0 \\ 0 & 1 & -(2+\phi_3) & 1 & . & . & 0 & 0 & 0 \\ . & . & . & . & . & . & . & . & . \\ 0 & 0 & 0 & 0 & . & . & 1 & -(2+\phi_{n-2}) & 1 \\ 0 & 0 & 0 & 0 & . & . & 0 & 1 & -(2+\phi_{n-1}) \end{pmatrix}$$

It can easily be verified that for this matrix $\mathbf{A}$ the lower and upper triangular matrices of § 8.4 are

$$\mathbf{L} = \begin{pmatrix} 1 & 0 & 0 & . & . & 0 & 0 & 0 \\ -l_1 & 1 & 0 & . & . & 0 & 0 & 0 \\ 0 & -l_2 & 1 & . & . & 0 & 0 & 0 \\ . & . & . & . & . & . & . & . \\ 0 & 0 & 0 & . & . & -l_{n-3} & 1 & 0 \\ 0 & 0 & 0 & . & . & 0 & -l_{n-2} & 1 \end{pmatrix}, \tag{8.28 c}$$

$$\mathbf{U} = \begin{pmatrix} -1/l_1 & 1 & 0 & . & . & 0 & 0 \\ 0 & -1/l_2 & 1 & . & . & 0 & 0 \\ 0 & 0 & -1/l_3 & . & . & 0 & 0 \\ . & . & . & . & . & . & . \\ 0 & 0 & 0 & . & . & -1/l_{n-2} & 1 \\ 0 & 0 & 0 & . & . & 0 & -1/l_{n-1} \end{pmatrix},$$

where $\quad 1/l_1 = (2+\phi_1), \; l_{j-1} + (1/l_j) = (2+\phi_j) \quad (2 \leqslant j \leqslant n-1)$

so that $l_1 = 1/(2+\phi_1), \quad l_j = 1/(2+\phi_j - l_{j-1}) \quad (2 \leqslant j \leqslant n-1)$. (8.28 d)

From these relations the l_j's can be evaluated in succession, in order of increasing j.

Also equation (8.28 b) becomes $\mathbf{LU}\mathbf{y} = \mathbf{c}$, so that if $\mathbf{z} = -\mathbf{U}\mathbf{y}$, then $\mathbf{L}\mathbf{z} = -\mathbf{c}$, and for the matrix $\mathbf{L}$ given by (8.28 c) it follows that

$$z_1 = -c_1, \quad z_j = -c_j + l_{j-1} z_{j-1} \quad (2 \leqslant j \leqslant n-1), \tag{8.28 e}$$

from which the z_j's can be evaluated in succession, in the order of j increasing; then from the equation $\mathbf{z} = -\mathbf{U}\mathbf{y}$ it follows that

$$y_{n-1} = l_{n-1} z_{n-1}, \quad y_j = l_j(y_{j+1} + z_j) \quad (1 \leqslant j \leqslant n-2) \tag{8.28 f}$$

from which the y_j's can be evaluated in succession, in the order of j decreasing.

The process is a direct one, and, if solutions of (8.28 b) are required for the same function $f(x)$ and several different vectors $\mathbf{c}$, the matrix $\mathbf{A}$, and so the values of the l_j's, are the same for all vectors $\mathbf{c}$, so the evaluation of the l_j's only has to be done once. This may be necessary if it is required to improve the approximation to the solution of the differential equation (8.27) by including higher orders of differences in the replacement of derivatives by differences. The process is easily adaptable to second-order linear differential equations containing a first-derivative term, and was indeed formulated by Thomas and by Fox for this more general case, but is particularly simple for equations like (8.27) for which the first derivative is absent. It can also be adapted to deal with other forms of two-point boundary conditions. Also higher-order differences can be included in the replacement of y'' by finite differences, as follows.

The set of equations (8.28) has been obtained by replacing the derivative in (8.27) by the simplest finite-difference approximation to it. In the solution of the equations in the approximate form (8.28), y'' is never evaluated; so in taking higher orders of differences into account, it is more convenient to use those of y than those of y''. The next approximation to y''_j is given by

$$(\delta x)^2 y''_j = \delta^2 y_j - \tfrac{1}{12}\delta^4 y_j;$$

use of this approximation in (8.27) gives

$$y_{j+1} - [2 + (\delta x)^2 f_j]y_j + y_{j-1} = (\delta x)^2 g_j + \tfrac{1}{12}\delta^4 y_j. \tag{8.29}$$

This set of equations should be solved by an iterative process, the values of $\delta^4 y$ on the right-hand side in one iteration being obtained from the results of the previous iteration; higher orders of differences of y can be included on the right-hand side of (8.29) if appreciable. One should *not* try to solve it by expressing $\delta^4 y_j$ in terms of function values and treating (8.29) as a recurrence relation between five successive values of y; this would be equivalent to replacing equation (8.27) by a fourth-order equation and would probably introduce spurious 'solutions'.

The terms $\tfrac{1}{12}\delta^4 y_j$ (and higher difference terms if appreciable) can be incorporated in the c_j's.

Example: To find an approximation to the solution of the equation

$$y'' = x^2 y - 1 \tag{8.30}$$

with $y = 0$ at $x = \pm 4$.

From the symmetry of the equation and the boundary conditions, it follows that y is an even function of x. Hence we need only consider the range $x = 0$ to 4, and impose a condition of symmetry about $x = 0$.

Let us take $\delta x = \tfrac{1}{2}$ and reckon j from $j = 0$ at $x = 0$. Then equation (8.28) becomes

$$y_{j+1} - (2 + \tfrac{1}{16}j^2)y_j + y_{j-1} = -\tfrac{1}{4} + \tfrac{1}{12}\delta^4 y_j \quad \text{for} \quad 1 \leqslant j \leqslant 7, \tag{8.31}$$

and the condition of symmetry, $y_{-1} = y_1$, gives for $j = 0$ the equation

$$-y_0 + y_1 = -\tfrac{1}{8} + \tfrac{1}{24}\delta^4 y; \qquad (8.32)$$

so that

$$\phi_j = \tfrac{1}{16}j^2, \, l_0 = 1; \; c_0 = -\tfrac{1}{8} + \tfrac{1}{24}\delta^4 y_0, \, c_j = -\tfrac{1}{4} + \tfrac{1}{12}\delta^4 y_j \quad (1 \leqslant j \leqslant 7); \quad (8.32\,\text{a})$$

and equations (8.28 d), (8.28 e) apply for $1 \leqslant j \leqslant 7$.

The working can be arranged as shown on p. 177; some intermediate results, which it would not be necessary to write down if working with a desk machine, are included to show the sequence of operations.

In this working, the calculation is split into three sections by heavy lines. The first section, to the left of the first heavy line, is concerned with the calculation of the l_j's. The values of $(2 + \phi_j)$ are filled in first from the formula for ϕ_j, then the l_j's calculated in succession from formulae (8.28 d). The second section is concerned with a first approximation to y_j, neglecting the fourth-difference terms in (8.31), (8.32). The z_j's are calculated first, by working downwards through the columns to the left of the thin line; each value of z_j is multiplied by the value of l_j in the *same* line, and the product is written in the *next lower* line in the column headed $l_{j-1}z_{j-1}$, and added to the $(-c_j)$ in that line to give the next z_j.

The next three columns are concerned with the evaluation of y_j starting from $y_8 = 0$ and working *upwards*; as each y_j is calculated it is entered in the *next higher* line in the column headed y_{j+1} and added to the z_j in that line; the sum is then multiplied by l_j in that line.

The next three columns are concerned with the evaluation of the $\delta^4 y$ terms in formula (8.32 a). The third section of the calculation is a repetition of the procedure of the second section with the $\delta^4 y_j$ contributions to the c_j's included.

Notes: (i) The symmetry of the solution about $y = 0$ has been used in evaluation $\delta^2 y_0$ and $\delta^4 y_0$.

(ii) Since y is required to be zero at $x = 4$ $(j = 8)$, $y''(4) = -1$, so

$$\delta^2 y_8 = (\delta x)^2 y''(4) + O(\delta x)^4 = -0.250 \text{ approximately.}$$

This value (enclosed in brackets) has been used to give a value of $\delta^4 y_7$.

(iii) The calculation could be repeated with values of $\delta^4 y$ derived from the second iteration.

(iv) Smaller intervals (δx) should be used if greater accuracy in the results were required.

(v) This process may not be satisfactory when the function f in equation (8.27) is negative over a considerable range of x.

An alternative procedure is to use a relaxation process.† It is best to start such a process with quite a coarse subdivision of the range over which the solution is wanted (such as $\delta x = 1$ in the above example) and to divide it further as the approximation improves. Beyond a certain stage of the subdivision, depending on the behaviour of y as a function of x and the accuracy required in the solution, it is often better, as suggested by Fox,† to keep some higher differences in the replacement of y'' by finite differences.

† L. Fox, *Proc. Camb. Phil. Soc.* **45** (1949), 50.

j	$2+\phi_j$	$-l_{j+1}$	$1/l_j$	l_j	$-c_0$	$+l_{j-1}z_{j-1}$	z_j	y_{j+1}	z_j+y_{j+1}	y_j	$\delta^2 y_j$	$\delta^4 y_j$	$\tfrac{1}{12}\delta^4 y_j$
0				1	$+0\cdot125$		$0\cdot125$	$1\cdot209$	$1\cdot334$	$1\cdot334$	-250	152	$+6$
1	$2\cdot0625$	-1	$=1\cdot0625$	$0\cdot9412$	$0\cdot25$	$+0\cdot125$	$=0\cdot375$	$0\cdot910$	$1\cdot285$	$1\cdot209$	-174	75	$+6$
2	$2\cdot25$	$-0\cdot9412$	$=1\cdot3088$	$0\cdot7641$	$0\cdot25$	$+0\cdot353$	$=0\cdot603$	$0\cdot588$	$1\cdot191$	$0\cdot910$	-23	-47	-4
3	$2\cdot5625$	$-0\cdot7641$	$=1\cdot7984$	$0\cdot5560$	$0\cdot25$	$+0\cdot461$	$=0\cdot711$	$0\cdot347$	$1\cdot058$	$0\cdot588$	$+81$	-89	-7
4	$3\cdot00$	$-0\cdot5560$	$=2\cdot4440$	$0\cdot4092$	$0\cdot25$	$+0\cdot395$	$=0\cdot645$	$0\cdot202$	$0\cdot847$	$0\cdot347$	$+96$	-44	-4
5	$3\cdot5625$	$-0\cdot4092$	$=3\cdot1533$	$0\cdot3171$	$0\cdot25$	$+0\cdot264$	$=0\cdot514$	$0\cdot124$	$0\cdot638$	$0\cdot202$	67	-10	-1
6	$4\cdot25$	$-0\cdot3171$	$=3\cdot9329$	$0\cdot2543$	$0\cdot25$	$+0\cdot163$	$=0\cdot413$	$0\cdot074$	$0\cdot487$	$0\cdot124$	28	-13	-1
7	$5\cdot0625$	$-0\cdot2543$	$=4\cdot8082$	$0\cdot2080$	$0\cdot25$	$+0\cdot105$	$=0\cdot355$	0	$0\cdot353$	$0\cdot074$	-24	-174	-15
8										0	(-250)		

j	l_j	$-c_0$	$+l_{j-1}z_{j-1}$	z_j	y_{j+1}	z_j+y_{j+1}	y_j	$\delta^2 y_j$	$\delta^4 y_j$
0	1	$0\cdot119$		$0\cdot119$	$1\cdot194$	$1\cdot313$	$1\cdot313$	-238	158
1	$0\cdot9412$	$0\cdot244$	$+0\cdot119$	$=0\cdot363$	$0\cdot906$	$1\cdot269$	$1\cdot194$	-169	62
2	$0\cdot7641$	$0\cdot254$	$+0\cdot342$	$=0\cdot586$	$0\cdot590$	$1\cdot186$	$0\cdot906$	-28	-28
3	$0\cdot5560$	$0\cdot257$	$+0\cdot455$	$=0\cdot712$	$0\cdot349$	$1\cdot061$	$0\cdot590$	$+75$	-82
4	$0\cdot4092$	$0\cdot254$	$+0\cdot396$	$=0\cdot650$	$0\cdot204$	$0\cdot854$	$0\cdot349$	96	-51
5	$0\cdot3171$	$0\cdot251$	$+0\cdot266$	$=0\cdot517$	$0\cdot125$	$0\cdot642$	$0\cdot204$	66	-5
6	$0\cdot2543$	$0\cdot251$	$+0\cdot164$	$=0\cdot415$	$0\cdot077$	$0\cdot492$	$0\cdot125$	31	-15
7	$0\cdot2080$	$0\cdot265$	$+0\cdot105$	$=0\cdot370$	0	$0\cdot370$	$0\cdot077$	-29	-171
8							0	(-250)	

Entries in columns headed y_j calculated from formulae (8.28 f).

8.6. Characteristic values and vectors of a matrix

The 'characteristic values' (also called 'latent roots') λ of a matrix are those numbers for which the system of equations

$$\mathbf{A}\mathbf{x} = \lambda \mathbf{x} \qquad (8.33)$$

has a solution other than $\mathbf{x} \equiv 0$, and the solution $\mathbf{x}$ in such a case is called a 'characteristic vector' (or 'latent vector') of the matrix or a 'characteristic solution' of the equations.

Written out, the system of equations (8.33) is

$$\left.\begin{array}{l} (a_{11}-\lambda)x_1+a_{12}x_2+a_{13}x_3+... = 0 \\ a_{21}x_1+(a_{22}-\lambda)x_2+a_{23}x_3+... = 0 \\ a_{31}x_1+a_{32}x_2+(a_{33}-\lambda)x_3+... = 0 \\ \cdot \quad \cdot \quad \cdot \quad \cdot \quad \cdot \quad \cdot \quad \cdot \quad \cdot \quad \cdot \quad \cdot \quad \cdot \end{array}\right\}, \qquad (8.34)$$

and the condition that this set of equations should have a non-trivial solution is that the determinant of its coefficients should be zero. An algebraic equation of the nth degree in λ can be obtained by multiplying out the determinant, though for $n > 2$ it is seldom that this provides the easiest or quickest way of evaluating characteristic values numerically. But this formal equation gives three results which are useful in the numerical work. The equation is

$$(-1)^n[\lambda^n-\Big(\sum_j a_{jj}\Big)\lambda^{n-1}+...]+D = 0, \qquad (8.35)$$

where D is the determinant of the matrix. Hence
  (i) the equation for λ has n roots (multiple roots, if any, being counted according to their multiplicity);
 (ii) the sum of the roots is the sum of the diagonal elements of the matrix;
(iii) the product of the roots is the determinant of the matrix.
The characteristic values λ, arranged in order of decreasing $|\lambda|$, will be written $\lambda^{(1)}, \lambda^{(2)}, \lambda^{(3)},...$, and the solution x_j for $\lambda = \lambda^{(p)}$ will be written $x_j^{(p)}$.

Since equations (8.34) are homogeneous, each solution $\mathbf{x}^{(p)}$ is undetermined to the extent of an arbitrary multiplying factor. In the formal treatment of these equations it is convenient to regard this multiplying constant as chosen so that $\sum_j (x_j^{(p)})^2 = 1$; such a solution is called 'normalized'. But for numerical work it is usually more convenient to take it so that the greatest in magnitude of the x_j's is unity.

A commonly occurring type of matrix is a symmetrical matrix, and symmetrical matrices have several properties which are useful in numerical calculations. The characteristic values λ are all real, and the characteristic vectors for different values of λ are orthogonal, that is to say, if $\lambda^{(p)} \neq \lambda^{(q)}$, then

$$\sum_j x_j^{(p)} x_j^{(q)} = 0; \tag{8.36}$$

and if any value of λ is an m-fold root of the equation (8.35), then m mutually orthogonal solutions x_j can be found for this value of λ. Hence it is no restriction to take all the characteristic vectors as mutually orthogonal, and it will be assumed that they are so taken.

Further, the behaviour of the quantity

$$\Lambda = \left(\sum_{jk} x_j a_{jk} x_k \right) \bigg/ \left(\sum_j x_j^2 \right) \tag{8.37}$$

as a function of the vector $\mathbf{x}$ has a property which makes it useful in the approximate calculation of characteristic values. In matrix notation it can be written

$$\Lambda = (\mathbf{xAx})/(\mathbf{xIx}), \tag{8.38}$$

where $\mathbf{I}$ is the unit matrix.

Consider first the result of evaluating Λ for one of the characteristic vectors of the matrix, say for $\mathbf{x} = \mathbf{x}^{(p)}$. From the definition of a characteristic vector, it follows that $\mathbf{Ax}^{(p)} = \lambda^{(p)} \mathbf{x}^{(p)}$, and hence that the value of Λ obtained is just $\Lambda = \lambda^{(p)}$, the corresponding characteristic value. Now consider the value of Λ evaluated for a vector $\mathbf{x}$ differing slightly from $\mathbf{x}^{(p)}$, say for $\mathbf{x} = \mathbf{x}^{(p)} + \boldsymbol{\xi}$. From (8.38), its difference from the value $\lambda^{(p)}$ is given by

$$(\Lambda - \lambda^{(p)})(\mathbf{xIx}) = \mathbf{x}(\mathbf{A} - \lambda^{(p)}\mathbf{I})\mathbf{x}. \tag{8.39}$$

Since $\mathbf{x}^{(p)}$ is a characteristic vector with characteristic value $\lambda^{(p)}$ it follows that $(\mathbf{A} - \lambda^{(p)}\mathbf{I})\mathbf{x}^{(p)} = 0$, and hence

$$(\mathbf{A} - \lambda^{(p)}\mathbf{I})\mathbf{x} = (\mathbf{A} - \lambda^{(p)}\mathbf{I})\boldsymbol{\xi}. \tag{8.40}$$

Since $\mathbf{A}$ is symmetrical, so is $\mathbf{A} - \lambda^{(p)}\mathbf{I}$; hence from (8.39) and (8.40)

$$(\Lambda - \lambda^{(p)})(\mathbf{xIx}) = \mathbf{x}(\mathbf{A} - \lambda^{(p)}\mathbf{I})\boldsymbol{\xi}$$

$$= \boldsymbol{\xi}(\mathbf{A} - \lambda^{(p)}\mathbf{I})\mathbf{x} \quad \text{(since } \mathbf{A} - \lambda^{(p)}\mathbf{I} \text{ is symmetrical)}$$

$$= \boldsymbol{\xi}(\mathbf{A} - \lambda^{(p)}\mathbf{I})\boldsymbol{\xi} \quad \text{(by a second use of (8.40))}.$$

Hence Λ differs from $\lambda^{(p)}$ by a quantity which is second-order in $\boldsymbol{\xi}$; in other words, the quantity Λ defined by (8.37) is stationary for small variations of the vector $\mathbf{x}$ from a characteristic vector.

Hence from a fair approximation to a characteristic vector a relatively good approximation to a characteristic value can be obtained by evaluating formula (8.37), and from a good approximation to a characteristic vector a much better approximation to a characteristic value can be obtained. In application to the equations of vibrating systems of several degrees of freedom, characteristic values represent squares of frequencies of normal modes of vibration; an account of the use of formula (8.37) to determine characteristic values in this context, and developments of it, is given in *Rayleigh's Principle*, by Temple and Bickley.†

It is sometimes convenient to express a symmetrical matrix in terms of its characteristic vectors and characteristic values. Let $\mathbf{xx}$ stand for the matrix whose (j,k)th element is $x_j x_k$. Then if the characteristic vectors $\mathbf{x}^{(p)}$ are normalized, the required expression is

$$\mathbf{A} = \sum_p \lambda^{(p)} \mathbf{x}^{(p)} \mathbf{x}^{(p)};$$

if, as is often more convenient for numerical work, they are not normalized, we have

$$\mathbf{A} = \sum_p \left[\lambda^{(p)} \mathbf{x}^{(p)} \mathbf{x}^{(p)} \Big/ \sum_j (x_j^{(p)})^2 \right]. \tag{8.41}$$

The characteristic vectors of the inverse $\mathbf{A}^{-1}$ of a symmetrical matrix $\mathbf{A}$ are the same as those of $\mathbf{A}$ itself, and the characteristic values of $\mathbf{A}^{-1}$ are the reciprocals of the corresponding characteristic values of $\mathbf{A}$, so that

$$\mathbf{A}^{-1} = \sum_p \left[(1/\lambda^{(p)}) \mathbf{x}^{(p)} \mathbf{x}^{(p)} \Big/ \sum_j (x_j^{(p)})^2 \right]. \tag{8.42}$$

Formally, this provides one method of inverting a matrix. But it may be more convenient in numerical work to invert the matrix by some other process, and then use (8.42) to determine the *small* characteristic values of $\mathbf{A}$ and their characteristic vectors.

8.61. Iterative method for evaluation of characteristic values and characteristic vectors of a symmetrical matrix

The characteristic value $\lambda^{(1)}$ of greatest magnitude can be found as follows. Take an arbitrary vector $\mathbf{x}_{(0)}$, with components $x_{(0)j}$, of which the greatest in magnitude is unity. Form $\mathbf{A}\mathbf{x}_{(0)}$ and express it as a multiple $\lambda_{(1)}$ of a vector $\mathbf{x}_{(1)}$ whose component of greatest value is unity. Then repeat the process with $\mathbf{x}_{(1)}$ in place of $\mathbf{x}_{(0)}$ to give a vector $\mathbf{x}_{(2)}$ and so on. That is, form a sequence of numbers $\lambda_{(m)}$ and of vectors $\mathbf{x}_{(m)}$ so that

$$\mathbf{A}\mathbf{x}_{(m-1)} = \lambda_{(m)} \mathbf{x}_{(m)},$$

where each $\lambda_{(m)}$ is chosen so that the component of $\mathbf{x}_{(m)}$ of greatest magnitude is unity. Then, unless the vector $\mathbf{x}_{(0)}$ happens to have been taken orthogonal to the characteristic vector $\mathbf{x}^{(1)}$ of the matrix,

$$\lambda_{(m)} \to \lambda^{(1)} \quad \text{and} \quad \mathbf{x}_{(m)} \to \mathbf{x}^{(1)} \quad \text{as } m \to \infty.$$

The process thus far is also applicable to non-symmetrical matrices.

The rate at which successive values of $\lambda_{(m)}$ ultimately tend to their

† G. Temple and W. G. Bickley, *Rayleigh's Principle* (Oxford, 1933).

limit depends on $|\lambda^{(1)}/\lambda^{(2)}|$, and is greater the greater the value of this ratio. If after the first few repetitions of the process of calculating $\lambda_{(m)}\mathbf{x}_{(m)} = \mathbf{A}\mathbf{x}_{(m-1)}$, the successive values of $\lambda_{(m)}$ seem to be tending to a limit only slowly, the reason may be that $|\lambda^{(1)}/\lambda^{(2)}|-1$ is small. But it may be that $\mathbf{x}_{(0)}$ happens to have been taken nearly orthogonal to $\mathbf{x}^{(1)}$, and in case it has been so taken, it is as well to start the calculation again with another vector $\mathbf{x}_{(0)}$ roughly orthogonal to the one previously used.

Example: To find $\mathbf{x}^{(1)}, \lambda^{(1)}$ for the symmetrical matrix

$$\mathbf{A} = \begin{pmatrix} -23 & 11 & 1 \\ 11 & -3 & -2 \\ 1 & -2 & 1 \end{pmatrix}.$$

(This is the matrix of the coefficients of the equations considered in the examples of §§ 8.21 and 8.22.)

Starting with $\mathbf{x}_{(0)} = (1,0,0)$ we have

$\mathbf{x}_{(0)} = (1,0,0),$ $\mathbf{A}\mathbf{x}_{(0)} = (-23, 11, 1)$
$$= -23(1, -0{\cdot}48, -0{\cdot}04),$$

$\mathbf{x}_{(1)} = (1, -0{\cdot}48, -0{\cdot}04),$ $\mathbf{A}\mathbf{x}_{(1)} = (-28{\cdot}32, 12{\cdot}52, 1{\cdot}92)$
$$= -28{\cdot}32(1, -0{\cdot}442, -0{\cdot}068),$$

$\mathbf{x}_{(2)} = (1, -0{\cdot}442, -0{\cdot}068),$ $\mathbf{A}\mathbf{x}_{(2)} = (-27{\cdot}93, 12{\cdot}462, 1{\cdot}814)$
$$= -27{\cdot}93(1, -0{\cdot}4461, -0{\cdot}0649),$$

$\mathbf{x}_{(3)} = (1, -0{\cdot}4461, -0{\cdot}0649),$ $\mathbf{A}\mathbf{x}_{(3)} = (-27{\cdot}971, 12{\cdot}468, 1{\cdot}827)$
$$= -27{\cdot}971(1, -0{\cdot}4458, -0{\cdot}0653),$$

$\mathbf{x}_{(4)} = (1, -0{\cdot}4458, -0{\cdot}0653),$ $\mathbf{A}\mathbf{x}_{(4)} = (-27{\cdot}9691, 12{\cdot}4680, 1{\cdot}8263)$
$$= -27{\cdot}9691(1, -0{\cdot}44579, -0{\cdot}06530).$$

Hence, to three decimals in $\lambda^{(1)}$ and five in $\mathbf{x}^{(1)}$

$$\lambda^{(1)} = -27{\cdot}969, \qquad \mathbf{x}^{(1)} = (1, -0{\cdot}44579, -0{\cdot}06530). \qquad (8{\cdot}43)$$

Note: The number of figures in $\lambda_{(m)}$ and $\mathbf{x}_{(m)}$ can be kept small in the early stages and increased as the approximation to $\lambda^{(1)}$, $\mathbf{x}^{(1)}$ improves with repetition of the iterative process.

If the matrix is symmetrical, then having found $\lambda^{(1)}$, $\mathbf{x}^{(1)}$ we can evaluate the matrix $\mathbf{x}^{(1)}\mathbf{x}^{(1)}$ and subtract its contribution from $\mathbf{A}$ (see formula (8.41)), so forming the matrix

$$\mathbf{A} - \lambda^{(1)}\mathbf{x}^{(1)}\mathbf{x}^{(1)}\Big/\sum_j (x_j^{(1)})^2 = \mathbf{A}^{(1)}, \quad \text{say}. \qquad (8.44)$$

For this matrix the characteristic value of greatest magnitude is $\lambda^{(2)}$, and this, and the corresponding vector $\mathbf{x}^{(2)}$, can be found similarly, and the process repeated.

This procedure, however, suffers from progressive loss of significant figures as the successive contributions $\lambda^{(p)}\mathbf{x}^{(p)}\mathbf{x}^{(p)}\Big/\sum_j (x_j^{(p)})^2$ are subtracted off; it also requires that each $\lambda^{(p)}$, $\mathbf{x}^{(p)}$ should be determined accurately before calculation of the next is undertaken. A method free from these defects is given in § 8.63.

8.62. An alternative process

An alternative process, after determining $\lambda^{(1)}$ and $\mathbf{x}^{(1)}$, is as follows. Instead of eliminating $\mathbf{x}^{(1)}$ by evaluating $\lambda^{(1)}\mathbf{x}^{(1)}\mathbf{x}^{(1)}\Big/\sum_j (x_j^{(1)})^2$ and forming the matrix $\mathbf{A}^{(1)}$ (see (8.44)), the procedure used for determining $\lambda^{(1)}$ and $\mathbf{x}^{(1)}$ is repeated, with the modification that $\mathbf{x}_{(0)}$ and each $\mathbf{x}_{(m)}$ is constrained to be orthogonal to $\mathbf{x}^{(1)}$ before being multiplied by $\mathbf{A}$. That is, we form a sequence of numbers $\lambda_{(m)}$ and vectors $\mathbf{x}_{(m)}$ by the relation

$$\lambda_{(m)}\,\mathbf{x}_{(m)} = \mathbf{A}\mathbf{x}_{(m-1)} - \mu_{(m)}\,\mathbf{x}^{(1)},$$

$\mu_{(m)}$ being a number determined by the condition that $\mathbf{x}_{(m)}$ should be orthogonal to $\mathbf{x}^{(1)}$; $\lambda_{(m)}$, as before, is determined so that the component of $\mathbf{x}_{(m)}$ of greatest magnitude is unity.

If the work could be done exactly without rounding errors, then there would be no need to introduce the multipliers $\mu_{(m)}$; if $\mathbf{x}_{(0)}$ were taken *exactly* orthogonal to $\mathbf{x}^{(1)}$, then each vector $\mathbf{A}\mathbf{x}_{(m)}$ would be orthogonal to $\mathbf{x}^{(1)}$. The rounded values of $\mathbf{A}\mathbf{x}_{(m-1)}$ will, however, contain a small multiple of $\mathbf{x}^{(1)}$, and if this is not removed, it will give rise to an error which increases with further repetition of the iterative process, so that ultimately $\mathbf{x}_{(m)}$ would tend to $\mathbf{x}^{(1)}$ and not to $\mathbf{x}^{(2)}$.

When $\mathbf{x}^{(1)}$ and $\mathbf{x}^{(2)}$ have been determined, the successive approximations to $\mathbf{x}^{(3)}$ are similarly constrained to be orthogonal both to $\mathbf{x}^{(1)}$ and to $\mathbf{x}^{(2)}$, and so on.

This process has the advantage that there is no loss of significant figures as the work proceeds. On the other hand, since it makes use of the orthogonal property of the characteristic vectors, this property cannot be used as a check, whereas it forms a valuable check when the characteristic vectors are determined independently of one another. Also it is necessary to determine each characteristic vector accurately before starting to calculate the next.

8.63. Richardson's purification process for characteristic vectors

In determining a characteristic vector $\mathbf{x}^{(q)}$ and corresponding characteristic value $\lambda^{(q)}$ by a method of successive approximation, it is an advantage to start with a trial approximation which is nearly orthogonal to any characteristic vectors about which something may be known from earlier stages of the calculation. One method of doing this has been outlined in § 8.62. Another process has been suggested by L. F. Richardson,† and has two advantages; first, it does not require accurate determination of other characteristic vectors, even those for which $|\lambda^{(p)}|$ is greater than $|\lambda^{(q)}|$ for the characteristic vector sought, and, secondly it enables the characteristic vectors to be calculated independently of one another so that the orthogonal property is available as a check.

Any vector $\mathbf{x}$ (of n components) can be expressed as a linear combination of the characteristic vectors $\mathbf{x}^{(p)}$ of $\mathbf{A}$:

$$\mathbf{x} = b_1 \mathbf{x}^{(1)} + b_2 \mathbf{x}^{(2)} + \dots + b_n \mathbf{x}^{(n)} = \sum_p b_p \mathbf{x}^{(p)}. \tag{8.45}$$

Multiplication by $(\mathbf{A} - l\mathbf{I})$ gives

$$(\mathbf{A} - l\mathbf{I})\mathbf{x} = \sum_p (\lambda^{(p)} - l) b_p \mathbf{x}^{(p)}. \tag{8.46}$$

If one of the characteristic values, say $\lambda^{(r)}$, were known exactly, and l were taken to be $\lambda^{(r)}$, the coefficient of the corresponding term in (8.46) would be zero; that is to say, $(\mathbf{A} - \lambda^{(r)}\mathbf{I})\mathbf{x}$ is orthogonal to $\mathbf{x}^{(r)}$. Similarly $(\mathbf{A} - \lambda^{(r)}\mathbf{I})(\mathbf{A} - \lambda^{(s)}\mathbf{I})\mathbf{x}$ is orthogonal to $\mathbf{x}^{(r)}$ and to $\mathbf{x}^{(s)}$, and so on.

Even if $\lambda^{(r)}$ is not known exactly, the coefficient of $\mathbf{x}^{(r)}$ in (8.46) will be relatively small provided that the value of l taken, say $l^{(r)}$, is such that $|\lambda^{(r)} - l^{(r)}|$ is substantially smaller than most of the other quantities $|\lambda^{(p)} - l^{(r)}|$ for $p \neq r$. Further, by repeating the multiplication by $(\mathbf{A} - l\mathbf{I})$ we have $(\mathbf{A} - l\mathbf{I})^m \mathbf{x} = \sum_p (\lambda^{(p)} - l)^m b_p \mathbf{x}^{(p)},$

so that starting from any arbitrary vector $\mathbf{x}$, the vectors $\mathbf{x}, (\mathbf{A} - l^{(r)}\mathbf{I})\mathbf{x}$, $(\mathbf{A} - l^{(r)}\mathbf{I})^2 \mathbf{x}, \dots$ are more and more nearly orthogonal to $\mathbf{x}^{(r)}$. Similarly if $l^{(r)}, l^{(s)}$ are approximations to $\lambda^{(r)}, \lambda^{(s)}$, and any vector $\mathbf{x}$ is multiplied by $(\mathbf{A} - l^{(r)}\mathbf{I})(\mathbf{A} - l^{(s)}\mathbf{I})$, the result will be a vector nearly orthogonal to $\mathbf{x}^{(r)}$ and to $\mathbf{x}^{(s)}$, and so on.

If $\mathbf{x}^{(q)}$ is a characteristic vector to be determined, an arbitrary vector $\mathbf{x}$ can be described as a mixture of the required vector $\mathbf{x}^{(q)}$ with 'impurities' in the form of multiples of the $\mathbf{x}^{(p)}$'s $(p \neq q)$ in amounts represented by the coefficients b_p in (8.45). The effect of multiplying by $(\mathbf{A} - l^{(r)}\mathbf{I})$ or by $(\mathbf{A} - l^{(r)}\mathbf{I})^m$ can be described as 'purification' of the mixture by removal of most of the $\mathbf{x}^{(r)}$ component from it, and similarly for the effect of multiplication by $(\mathbf{A} - l^{(s)}\mathbf{I})^m$; this suggested the term 'purification process' used by Richardson.

In order that such a purification process should be effective, the values used for quantities like $l^{(r)}, l^{(s)}$ need only be approximations to characteristic values. This has two advantages in practical numerical

† *Phil. Trans. Roy. Soc.* **242** (1950), 439.

work. First, for symmetrical matrices good approximations to characteristic values can be obtained, by use of formula (8.37), from approximations to characteristic vectors which are only moderate; hence if only one characteristic vector is required, it is not necessary to determine the others to any great accuracy. And, secondly, it is possible to use simple rounded values for the l's if this would simplify the numerical work.

Example: To determine $\mathbf{x}^{(2)}$, $\mathbf{x}^{(3)}$ for the matrix

$$\mathbf{A} = \begin{pmatrix} -23 & 11 & 1 \\ 11 & -3 & -2 \\ 1 & -2 & 1 \end{pmatrix}$$

without accurate determination of $\mathbf{x}^{(1)}$.

Suppose that in the example of § 8.61 the successive approximation for $\mathbf{x}^{(1)}$, $\lambda^{(1)}$ has only been taken as far as the second stage, with $\mathbf{x}_{(1)} = (1, -0.48, -0.04)$, and it is desired to find the other characteristic vectors and values. The best available approximation to $\lambda^{(1)}$ at this stage is given by evaluating formula (8.37) for this vector $\mathbf{x}_{(1)}$, and is -28.00. This, however, is so close to the actual value of $\lambda^{(1)}$ for this matrix that use of it would not illustrate how effective the purification process can be although $l^{(1)}$ is only a rough approximation to $\lambda^{(1)}$. So in working the example here, the value $l^{(1)} = -27$ will be taken. Then

$$\mathbf{A} - l^{(1)}\mathbf{I} = \mathbf{A} + 27\mathbf{I} = \begin{pmatrix} 4 & 11 & 1 \\ 11 & 24 & -2 \\ 1 & -2 & 28 \end{pmatrix}.$$

This suggests $\mathbf{x} = (0, 1, 1)$ as a trial vector. For this vector $\mathbf{x}$,

$$(\mathbf{A} + 27\mathbf{I})\mathbf{x} = (12, 22, 26),$$

for which the approximation $24(\frac{1}{2}, 1, 1)$ is adequate at this stage. Hence we start the approximation for the second characteristic vector with $\mathbf{x}_{(0)} = \frac{1}{2}(1, 2, 2)$. This gives

$$\mathbf{A}\mathbf{x}_{(0)} = \frac{1}{2}(1, 1, -1).$$

This differs considerably from $\mathbf{x}_{(0)}$, so that although this $\mathbf{x}_{(0)}$ is approximately orthogonal to $\mathbf{x}^{(1)}$, it is far from $\mathbf{x}^{(2)}$ (we shall see later that it is much more nearly in the direction of $\mathbf{x}^{(3)}$). It is also some way from being orthogonal to the best approximation available to $\mathbf{x}^{(1)}$, namely $(1, -0.48, -0.04)$, so that rather than using $(1, 1, -1)$ as the next trial vector $\mathbf{x}_{(1)}$, we repeat the purification process, which gives

$$(\mathbf{A} + 27\mathbf{I})(1, 1, -1) = (14, 37, -29) = 37(0.38, 1, -0.78)$$

and take $\mathbf{x}_{(1)} = (0.38, 1, -0.78)$ as the next trial vector. This gives

$$\mathbf{A}\mathbf{x}_{(1)} = (1.48, 2.74, -2.40) = 2.74(0.54, 1, -0.88) \tag{8.47}$$

and

$$(\mathbf{x}_{(1)}\mathbf{A}\mathbf{x}_{(1)})/(\mathbf{x}_{(1)}\mathbf{I}\mathbf{x}_{(1)}) = 2.95. \tag{8.48}$$

The further procedure depends on the results required. We will first consider the improvement of the approximation to $\mathbf{x}^{(2)}$, and then the determination of $\mathbf{x}^{(3)}$ without more information about $\mathbf{x}^{(2)}$ than is expressed by (8.47) and (8.48).

(*a*) *Improvement of the approximation to* $\mathbf{x}^{(2)}$. We now have the approximations $\lambda^{(1)} = -28.0$, $\lambda^{(2)} = +2.95$, and the general result that the sum of the characteristic values is the sum of the diagonal elements of the matrix, in this case -25. Hence we can conclude that $\lambda^{(3)}$ is roughly 0.05, so that $l^{(3)} = 0$ is a good approximation to $\lambda^{(3)}$, and multiplication by A itself will be effective in removing from a trial vector $\mathbf{x}$ any 'impurities' in the form of multiples of $\mathbf{x}^{(3)}$. Hence starting from $(0.54, 1, -0.88)$ given by (8.47) as the best approximation yet available to $\mathbf{x}^{(2)}$, we multiply by $(A+27I)$ to remove multiples of $\mathbf{x}^{(1)}$ and by A to remove multiples of $\mathbf{x}^{(3)}$ and to examine the successive approximations of $A\mathbf{x}$ to $\lambda^{(2)}\mathbf{x}$.

Since $l^{(3)} = 0$ appears likely to be a better approximation to $\lambda^{(3)}$ than $l^{(1)} = 27$ is to $\lambda^{(1)}$, it will be best to carry out two or three multiplications by $(A+27I)$ for each multiplication by A; and since the vector $(0.54, 1, -0.88)$ is already the result of a multiplication by A, and so contains only a small admixture of $\mathbf{x}^{(3)}$, let us start by some multiplications by $(A+27I)$:

$$(A+27I)(0.54, 1, -0.88) = (12.28, 31.70, -26.10)$$
$$= 31.70(0.387, 1, -0.823),$$
$$(A+27I)(0.39, 1, -0.82) = 29.93(0.392, 1, -0.821),$$
$$(A+27I)(0.392, 1, -0.821) = 29.954(0.3922, 1, -0.8211).$$

This has produced a vector nearly free from $\mathbf{x}^{(1)}$ but possibly still containing traces of $\mathbf{x}^{(3)}$. To remove these we multiply by A:

$$A(0.3922, 1, -0.8211) = 2.9564(0.3918, 1, -0.8216).$$

The results of further multiplication by A alone diverge. This can be seen as follows. Let $\mathbf{x}$ be an approximation to $\mathbf{x}^{(2)}$:

$$\mathbf{x} = \mathbf{x}^{(2)} + b_1 \mathbf{x}^{(1)} + b_3 \mathbf{x}^{(3)},$$

where b_1 and b_3 are small compared with 1. Then

$$A\mathbf{x} = \lambda^{(2)}[\mathbf{x}^{(2)} + (\lambda^{(1)}/\lambda^{(2)})b_1 \mathbf{x}^{(1)} + (\lambda^{(3)}/\lambda^{(2)})b_3 \mathbf{x}^{(3)}].$$

Now $|\lambda^{(1)}/\lambda^{(2)}|$ is greater than 1, and in this example it is about 10, so that any 'impurity' in $\mathbf{x}$ in the form of a multiple of $\mathbf{x}^{(1)}$ is more prominent in $A\mathbf{x}$ than in $\mathbf{x}$. This building up of $\mathbf{x}^{(1)}$ can be avoided by further multiplications by $(A - l^{(1)}I)$:

$$(A+27I)(0.3918, 1, -0.8216) = 29.953(0.39215, 1, -0.82172),$$
$$(A+27I)(0.39215, 1, -0.82172) = 29.9571(0.39212, 1, -0.82171).$$

This vector $\mathbf{x} = (0.39212, 1, -0.82171)$ gives

$$A\mathbf{x} = 2.9567(0.39217, 1, -0.82171),$$
$$(\mathbf{x}A\mathbf{x})/(\mathbf{x}I\mathbf{x}) = 2.9568.$$

So that to four decimals in $\lambda^{(2)}$ and a possible error of one or two in the fifth decimal in $\mathbf{x}^{(2)}$

$$\lambda^{(2)} = 2.9568, \qquad \mathbf{x}^{(2)} = (0.39212, 1, -0.82171). \tag{8.49}$$

Notes: (i) The convergence would be much quicker if the value $l^{(1)} = -28$ instead of -27 were taken, but this working illustrates that the purification process is effective even if $l^{(1)}$ is only a rough approximation to $\lambda^{(1)}$.

(ii) With a matrix whose elements are integral, as in this example, the numerical work is simplified if the l's are taken to have integral values; in this example all elements of A and of $(A - l^{(1)}I)$ are numbers of two digits only, which makes the multiplications very quick.

(b) *Determination of* $\mathbf{x}^{(3)}, \lambda^{(3)}$. The most striking illustration of the power of the method is provided by the determination of $\mathbf{x}^{(3)}$, the characteristic vector for the *smallest* value of $|\lambda|$, without requiring that $\mathbf{x}_{(1)}$ or $\mathbf{x}_{(2)}$ should be determined more accurately than they are at the stage of the calculation reached at formulae (8.47) and (8.48); comparison of formula (8.47) with the result (8.49) shows that the approximation to $\mathbf{x}^{(2)}$ at that stage is decidedly rough.

We have used $l^{(1)} = -27$ as an approximation to $\lambda^{(1)}$, and can now adopt $l^{(2)} = +3$ as an approximation to $\lambda^{(2)}$; so repeated multiplication of an arbitrary vector $\mathbf{x}$ by $(\mathbf{A}+27\mathbf{I})(\mathbf{A}-3\mathbf{I})$ will produce a sequence of vectors whose directions will converge to that of $\mathbf{x}^{(3)}$. Now

$$(\mathbf{A}+27\mathbf{I})(\mathbf{A}-3\mathbf{I}) = \begin{pmatrix} 4 & 11 & 1 \\ 11 & 24 & -2 \\ 1 & -2 & 28 \end{pmatrix}\begin{pmatrix} -26 & 11 & 1 \\ 11 & -6 & -2 \\ 1 & -2 & -2 \end{pmatrix}$$

$$= -\begin{pmatrix} -18 & 24 & 20 \\ 24 & 19 & 33 \\ 20 & 33 & 51 \end{pmatrix} = \mathbf{B} \quad \text{(say)},$$

and we have seen that $\mathbf{x} = \tfrac{1}{2}(1, 2, 2)$ is nearly orthogonal to $\mathbf{x}^{(1)}$ and differs considerably from $\mathbf{x}^{(2)}$, so let us take it as a first approximation to $\mathbf{x}^{(3)}$. Then successive multiplications by $\mathbf{B}$ give:

$$\mathbf{B}(\tfrac{1}{2}, 1, 1) = -(35, 64, 94) = -94(0 \cdot 37, 0 \cdot 68, 1),$$
$$\mathbf{B}(0 \cdot 37, 0 \cdot 68, 1) = -(29 \cdot 66, 54 \cdot 80, 80 \cdot 84)$$
$$= -80 \cdot 84(0 \cdot 367, 0 \cdot 678, 1),$$
$$\mathbf{B}(0 \cdot 367, 0 \cdot 668, 1) = -80 \cdot 711(0 \cdot 3675, 0 \cdot 6776, 1),$$
$$\mathbf{B}(0 \cdot 3675, 0 \cdot 6776, 1) = -80 \cdot 7108(0 \cdot 36733, 0 \cdot 67766, 1),$$
$$\mathbf{B}(0 \cdot 36733, 0 \cdot 67766, 1) = -80 \cdot 7094(0 \cdot 36739, 0 \cdot 67763, 1),$$
$$\mathbf{B}(0 \cdot 36739, 0 \cdot 67763, 1) = -80 \cdot 7096(0 \cdot 36737, 0 \cdot 67764, 1),$$
$$\mathbf{B}(0 \cdot 36737, 0 \cdot 67764, 1) = -80 \cdot 7095(0 \cdot 36738, 0 \cdot 67764, 1).$$

This process could be continued indefinitely, to give as many decimals in $\mathbf{x}^{(3)}$ as might be required. With a possible error of 1 in the fifth decimal

$$\mathbf{x}^{(3)} = (0 \cdot 36738, 0 \cdot 67764, 1)$$

and with this value of $\mathbf{x}^{(3)}$

$$(\mathbf{x}^{(3)}\mathbf{A}\mathbf{x}^{(3)})/(\mathbf{x}^{(3)}\mathbf{I}\mathbf{x}^{(3)}) = 0 \cdot 01209_3,$$

which is therefore an approximation to $\lambda^{(3)}$.

The collected results for this matrix $\mathbf{A}$ are

$$\left. \begin{aligned} \lambda^{(1)} &= -27 \cdot 969, & \mathbf{x}^{(1)} &= (1, -0 \cdot 44579, -0 \cdot 06530) \\ \lambda^{(2)} &= 2 \cdot 9568, & \mathbf{x}^{(2)} &= (0 \cdot 39212, 1, -0 \cdot 82171) \\ \lambda^{(3)} &= 0 \cdot 012093, & \mathbf{x}^{(3)} &= (0 \cdot 36738, 0 \cdot 67764, 1) \end{aligned} \right\} \qquad (8.50)$$

$\lambda^{(1)}$, $\mathbf{x}^{(1)}$ being given by (8.43) and $\lambda^{(2)}$, $\mathbf{x}^{(2)}$ by (8.49). The best check on these results is provided by verifying that the relations between characteristic vectors and between characteristic values are satisfied.

Since the characteristic vectors have been determined independently of one another, they can be checked by verifying that the orthogonality relations are satisfied. The results (8.50) give

$$\sum_j x_j^{(1)} x_j^{(2)} = -0 \cdot 00001, \qquad \sum_j x_j^{(2)} x_j^{(3)} = -0 \cdot 00001,$$

$$\sum_j x_j^{(3)} x_j^{(1)} = -0 \cdot 00000_5,$$

which differ from zero by amounts within the tolerance for rounding errors.

The sum of the characteristic values should be equal to the sum of the diagonal elements, which is -25 in this case, and this relation is satisfied exactly to three decimals. And since the elements of the matrix are integral, their determinant is integral, the product of the characteristic values should be integral. For the results (8.50), $\lambda^{(1)}\lambda^{(2)}\lambda^{(3)} = -1 \cdot 00007$, which differs from -1 by an amount within the tolerance for rounding errors.

A further check is provided by building up the matrix A from its characteristic vectors and characteristic values according to formula (8.41); this, however, does not give a good check on $\mathbf{x}^{(3)}$, since its contribution is multiplied by the small factor $\lambda^{(3)}$.

Notes: (i) The ratio $|\lambda^{(1)}/\lambda^{(3)}|$ of the greatest and least in magnitude of the characteristic values is about 2300, and the large size of this quantity is an indication of the degree to which the equations $A\mathbf{x} = \mathbf{b}$, with this matrix A, are ill-conditioned. This character of A has not, however, introduced any difficulty in finding the characteristic values in this case.

(ii) If the characteristic values and vectors are found in succession, the last (in this case the third) can be found as follows.

From an arbitrary vector $\mathbf{x}$, a vector $\mathbf{X}$, orthogonal to $\mathbf{x}^{(1)}$ and $\mathbf{x}^{(2)}$ is formed by taking

$$\mathbf{X} = (\mathbf{x} - \mu_1 \mathbf{x}^{(1)} - \mu_2 \mathbf{x}^{(2)}) \tag{8.51}$$

and determining μ_1, μ_2 appropriately. Since $\mathbf{x}^{(2)}$ is orthogonal to $\mathbf{x}^{(1)}$ it follows that the required values of μ_1, μ_2 are

$$\left. \begin{aligned} \mu_1 &= \left(\sum_j x_j^{(1)} x_j \right) \Big/ \sum_j (x_j^{(1)})^2 \\ \mu_2 &= \left(\sum_j x_j^{(2)} x_j \right) \Big/ \sum_j (x_j^{(2)})^2 \end{aligned} \right\}. \tag{8.52}$$

$\mathbf{X}$ should then be multiplied by such a factor that its greatest component is 1, and the process repeated, as a check and to remove effects of rounding errors as far as possible.

If the elements of A are integral, the following alternative process can sometimes be used to determine $\lambda^{(3)}$. As soon as $\lambda^{(1)}$ and $\lambda^{(2)}$ are found to the accuracy

$$\lambda^{(1)} = -27 \cdot 969 \pm 0 \cdot 001, \qquad \lambda^{(2)} = 2 \cdot 957 \pm 0 \cdot 001,$$

it follows, from the relation

$$\lambda^{(1)} + \lambda^{(2)} + \lambda^{(3)} = \text{sum of diagonal elements} = -25,$$

that $\lambda^{(3)}$ lies in the range $\lambda^{(3)} = 0 \cdot 012 \pm 0 \cdot 002$

and hence $\lambda^{(1)}\lambda^{(2)}\lambda^{(3)} = -0 \cdot 99 \pm 0 \cdot 17.$

But since the elements of A are integral, this product must be integral, so must be -1. Hence $\lambda^{(3)} = -1/\lambda^{(1)}\lambda^{(2)} = +0 \cdot 01209.$

(iii) The purification process can be used to hasten the convergence of the approximation to $\lambda^{(1)}, \mathbf{x}^{(1)}$. From the result (8.47) it follows that multiplication by $(A - 3I)$ will be effective in removing multiples of $\mathbf{x}^{(2)}$ from a trial approximation to $\mathbf{x}^{(1)}$. Hence after the second step in the example as worked in § 8.61 we could proceed as follows:

$$(A - 3I)(1, -0 \cdot 442, -0 \cdot 068) = -30 \cdot 930(1, -0 \cdot 44578, -0 \cdot 06531),$$
$$A(1, -0 \cdot 44578, -0 \cdot 06531) = -27 \cdot 9689(1, -0 \cdot 44578, -0 \cdot 06531),$$

reaching the result in two fewer steps than in § 8.61.

This example illustrates some possibilities of Richardson's purification procedure; for developments of the idea, and other examples, reference should be made to Richardson's paper.

8.7. Relaxation process for characteristic vectors

Another method of determining characteristic vectors is a form of relaxation process.

If l is any given number and we try to find by a relaxation process a solution of the equations

$$\left.\begin{array}{l}(a_{11}-l)x_1+a_{12}x_2+a_{13}x_3+\ldots=0 \\ a_{21}x_1+(a_{22}-l)x_2+a_{23}x_3+\ldots=0 \quad \text{etc.}\end{array}\right\} \qquad (8.53)$$

in which not all the x_j's are zero, then unless l is a characteristic value, it will not be possible to reduce all residuals to zero. But if the x_j's are components of a characteristic vector, corresponding to a characteristic value λ, then

$$(a_{11}-l)x_1+a_{12}x_2+a_{13}x_3+\ldots=(\lambda-l)x_1,$$
$$a_{21}x_1+(a_{22}-l)x_2+a_{23}x_3+\ldots=(\lambda-l)x_2,$$
$$\cdot \quad \cdot \quad \cdot \quad \cdot \quad \cdot \quad \cdot \quad \cdot \quad \cdot \quad \cdot \quad \cdot$$

so that the ratio $[(\text{residual of the }j\text{th equation})/x_j]$ will be the same for all values of j.

If therefore we fix one of the x_j's at a non-zero value, and in the relaxation process aim not at reducing all the residuals to zero but at making the residual of each jth equation proportional to x_j, then a change of l, forming an improvement in the approximation to λ, will have the effect of reducing all the residuals simultaneously.

If an approximate characteristic vector $\mathbf{x}$ can be estimated on inspection of the equation, then an approximation Λ to the corresponding characteristic value is given by formula (8.37), and this can be taken as the best available value, at this stage of the calculation, to l.

Example: Consider again the matrix used in the examples in the previous sections, namely

$$\mathbf{A} = \begin{pmatrix} -23 & 11 & 1 \\ 11 & -3 & -2 \\ 1 & -2 & 1 \end{pmatrix}.$$

Inspection suggests that $\mathbf{x} = (2, -1, 0)$ is an approximation to a characteristic vector. For this $\mathbf{x}$, the vector $\mathbf{Ax}$ is

$$\mathbf{Ax} = (-57, 25, 2)$$

and

$$\sum_{jk} x_j A_{jk} x_k \bigg/ \sum_j (x_j)^2 = -139/5 = -27{\cdot}8.$$

With $l = -27{\cdot}8$ the matrix of the coefficients of equations (8.53) is

$$\mathbf{A} - l\mathbf{I} = \begin{pmatrix} 4{\cdot}8 & 11 & 1 \\ 11 & 24{\cdot}8 & -2 \\ 1 & -2 & 28{\cdot}8 \end{pmatrix}$$

and the beginning of the relaxation process, keeping x_1 fixed, is as follows:

	x_1	x_2	x_3	R_1	R_2	R_3	
Operations	0	1	0	11	24·8	−2	
table	0	0	1	1	−2	28·8	

	x_1	x_2	x_3	R_1	R_2	R_3	
Relaxation	2	−1	0	−1·4	−2·8	4·0	
table			−0·14	−1·54	−2·52	−0·032	
		0·1		−0·44	−0·04	−0·232	
			0·01	−0·43	−0·06	0·056	
		0·01		−0·32	0·188	0·036	
	2	−0·89	−0·13	−0·32	0·188	0·036	Checked

Although the residuals are not very closely proportional to the values of the x_j's, they are now of such signs and magnitudes that a change of l which would reduce R_1 to zero would also decrease $|R_2|$ and $|R_3|$ considerably.

When a stage such as this has been reached, it is best to calculate a new approximation to λ; in this case, with

$$\mathbf{x} = (2, -0\cdot89, -0\cdot13),$$

$$\mathbf{Ax} = (-55\cdot92, 24\cdot93, 3\cdot65),$$

$$\sum_{jk} (x_j A_{jk} x_k)\Big/\sum_j (x_j)^2 = 134\cdot50/4\cdot8090 = -27\cdot968$$

and with this value of l, the residuals, to three decimals, are

$$0\cdot016, \quad 0\cdot039, \quad 0\cdot014;$$

as expected, these values are substantially smaller than those at the end of the relaxation table above. A further relaxation can then be carried out starting from these values.

A similar process can be carried out for the other characteristic vectors in order of decreasing $|\lambda|$. For these, however, it is necessary either to eliminate each one from the matrix as it is calculated, as in § 8.61, or to ensure that each as it is calculated is made orthogonal to all those already determined, as in § 8.62.

Characteristic values of linear ordinary differential equations with two-point boundary conditions can be obtained by a combination of this technique with the replacement of derivatives by finite differences as in § 8.53.†

† See L. Fox, *Proc. Camb. Phil. Soc.* **45** (1948), 50, § 8.

IX

NON-LINEAR ALGEBRAIC EQUATIONS

9.1. Solution of algebraic equations

By an 'algebraic' equation is meant, in this chapter, an equation $f(x) = 0$ not involving derivatives or integrals of $f(x)$, and of which a solution is a number, as distinct from a *differential* equation of which a solution is a *function* of the continuous variable x. It does not imply that the function $f(x)$ whose zeros are to be found is an algebraic function. For example the equations

$$x^3 + 5x^2 - 3x - 2 = 0$$

and

$$e^x \sin x = 1$$

are both 'algebraic' in this sense.

$f(x)$ being a given function of x, the problem of finding the roots of $f(x) = 0$ is often best dealt with in two steps, the first concerned with locating the roots roughly, to two or three significant figures, and the second with improving these rough values.

The solution of an algebraic equation can be regarded as a process of inverse interpolation, for if $f(x)$ is tabulated as a function of x, then the determination of the value of x for which $f(x)$ has any given value, of which zero is a special case, is just the situation with which inverse interpolation is concerned. Once a solution has been located approximately, tabulation of the function in the neighbourhood of that solution, followed by a process of inverse interpolation, is one way of determining it more exactly. Another method is to use an iterative process; this is considered in § 9.3.

9.2. Graphical methods

Use of graphs is often a valuable method of locating approximately the roots of an equation $f(x) = 0$. Either the function $f(x)$ itself may be graphed and its intersections with the x-axis determined, or the equation may be written in the form $f_1(x) = f_2(x)$, and its roots determined by the intersection of the graphs of $y = f_1(x)$ and $y = f_2(x)$; it may be possible to avoid some calculation by this process. In some cases graphs using some argument other than x, such as $\log x$ or $1/x$, may be useful. The best procedure will depend on the form of the function $f(x)$, and it is difficult to lay down any general rules.

The following examples give suggestions for handling some kinds of equations:

(i) Equations of the form $f(x) \equiv x^n + ax + b = 0$. Use graphs of $y = x^n$ and $y = -(ax+b)$.

(ii) Equations of the form

$$f(x) \equiv x^n + a_1 x^{n-1} + a_2 x^{n-2} + \ldots + a_{n-1} x + a_n = 0.$$

Evaluate $f(x)$ directly (see § 3.2) or by building up from its differences (see § 4.42) for, say, $x = -5(0 \cdot 2) + 5$; for $|x| > 4$, say, take $y = 1/x$ and evaluate

$$F(y) = a_n y^n + a_{n-1} y^{n-1} + \ldots + a_1 y + a_0.$$

Use graphs of $f(x)$ against x and $F(y)$ against y.

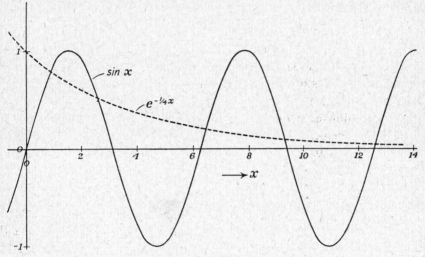

FIG. 13.

(iii) $e^{\frac{1}{4}x} \sin x = 1$. Write this as $\sin x = e^{-\frac{1}{4}x}$, and determine the intersections of $y = e^{-\frac{1}{4}x}$ with $y = \sin x$ (see Fig. 13). This avoids calculation of the products $e^{\frac{1}{4}x} \sin x$.

9.3. Iterative processes

By an iterative process is meant one in which the equation $f(x) = 0$ is expressed in the form

$$x = F(x),$$

and we try to find a solution by constructing a sequence $\{x_n\}$ by the relation

$$x_{n+1} = F(x_n). \tag{9.1}$$

If, to the degree of numerical accuracy to which the work is carried out, $x_{n+1} = x_n$, then this value of x_{n+1} is a solution of the equation to that degree of accuracy.

Let $x = X$ be the solution of the equation, and let

$$x_n = X + \xi_n \tag{9.2}$$

so that ξ_n is the error in x_n, regarded as a solution of the equation. An important feature of an iterative method is the way in which this error varies with the number n of repetitions of the iterative process. This can be examined by expanding the right-hand side of (9.1) in a Taylor series. Then, since $x = X$ satisfies $x = F(x)$, it follows that

$$\xi_{n+1} = a_1\xi_n + a_2\xi_n^2 + a_3\xi_n^3 + ..., \tag{9.3}$$

where $a_k = F^{(k)}(X)/k!$.

If $a_1 \neq 0$, then the errors ξ_n of results of successive repetitions of the iterative process are ultimately related by

$$\xi_{n+1} = a_1\xi_n, \qquad \xi_{n+m} = a_1^m\xi_n;$$

in order that the process should converge, $|a_1| = |F'(X)|$ must be less than 1, and the magnitude of the error then decreases exponentially with n increasing. This means that the number of additional correct significant figures obtained from each repetition of such a process (or, more often, the number of repetitions required to obtain each new correct significant figure) is the same, however many figures have been obtained. Such a process is called 'first-order'.

But if $a_1 = 0$, $a_2 \neq 0$ in (9.2), then the successive errors ξ_n are ultimately related by

$$\xi_{n+1} = a_2\xi_n^2, \quad \text{or} \quad a_2\xi_{n+m} = (a_2\xi_n)^{2^m},$$

where $a_2 = \frac{1}{2}F''(X)$. The number of correct significant figures is approximately doubled for each repetition of the iterative process, so that the better the approximation of x_n to X, the easier it is to improve it further. Such a process is called 'second-order', and once a fair approximation to $x = X$ has been attained, a second-order process is very greatly to be preferred to a first-order one; but it must be started from an approximation good enough to ensure that $|a_2\xi_0| < 1$. It will be shown in § 9.32 that from any first-order process it is possible to derive a second-order process.

If $a_1 = 0$, $a_2 = 0$, $a_3 \neq 0$ in (9.2), then the successive errors ξ_n are ultimately related by

$$\xi_{n+1} = a_3\xi_n^3, \quad \text{or} \quad a_3^{\frac{1}{2}}\xi_{n+m} = (a_3^{\frac{1}{2}}\xi_n)^{3^m};$$

such a process is called 'third-order'. The formula for a third-order process is usually more complicated than that for a second-order process for the same equation, and the convergence of a second-order process is already so fast once a good approximation has been obtained that the advantage of still quicker convergence obtainable from a third-order process may be more than offset by the more complicated formulae which have to be evaluated for each repetition of the iterative process, and third-order processes are not much used in practice. Second-order processes, however, are widely used.

9.31. Examples of iterative processes

(a) *Newton's process for a square root*

An important example of a second-order process is one for a square root, usually known as 'Newton's process'. If b is the number whose square root is required, this process consists of forming the sequence $\{x_n\}$ defined by
$$x_{n+1} = \tfrac{1}{2}[x_n + (b/x_n)].$$
For this process, $X = b^{\frac{1}{2}}$, and $F(x) = \tfrac{1}{2}[x + (b/x)]$, so that
$$F'(x) = \tfrac{1}{2}(1 - b/x^2), \qquad F'(X) = 0,$$
$$F''(x) = b/x^3, \qquad\qquad F''(X) = 1/X,$$
so that $a_1 = 0$, $a_2 \neq 0$ in (9.3), and the process is second order.

As an example of the application of this process, consider the evaluation of $\sqrt{12}$, starting from $x_0 = 2$.

$$x_0 = 2, \quad\; x_1 = \tfrac{1}{2}(2 + \tfrac{12}{2}) = 4,$$
$$x_1 = 4, \quad\; x_2 = \tfrac{1}{2}(4 + \tfrac{12}{4}) = \tfrac{7}{2} = 3\cdot5,$$
$$x_2 = \tfrac{7}{2}, \quad\; x_3 = \tfrac{1}{2}(\tfrac{7}{2} + \tfrac{24}{7}) = \tfrac{97}{28} = 3\cdot4643,$$
$$x_3 = 3\cdot4643, \qquad 12/x_3 = 3\cdot46390,32, \qquad x_4 = 3\cdot46410,16,$$
$$x_4 = 3\cdot46410,16, \quad 12/x_4 = 3\cdot46410,16303, \quad x_5 = 3\cdot46410,16151.$$

Notes: (i) For the first two or three iterations it may be easiest to work with the numbers in the form of exact fractions; later it is more convenient to work with them in decimal form.

(ii) In this example, an unnecessarily bad approximation has been taken as a starting-point to illustrate the convergence of the process from even a very poor value of x_0. A more important application is the improvement of an already fairly good approximation such as x_3. From Barlow's tables a square root correct to four figures can always be obtained without any interpolation; then one application of Newton's process will give eight figures, and another will give fifteen figures at least.

Newton's process is not the only second-order one for a square root: another is given by
$$x_{n+1} = x_n(3b - x_n^2)/2b = x_n[1 + (b - x_n^2)/2b]. \tag{9.4}$$
This process does not converge as fast as Newton's, since for a given value of b, the value of a_2 in the series (9.3) is greater. But it has one feature which may be an advantage, namely that the divisor in (9.4) is constant instead of being different at each stage of the iteration process as it is in Newton's process.

O

(b) *The Newton–Raphson process*

A general second-order process for the solution of $f(x) = 0$, at a point not in the neighbourhood of a maximum or minimum of $f(x)$, is one given by

$$x_{n+1} = x_n - f(x_n)/f'(x_n). \tag{9.5}$$

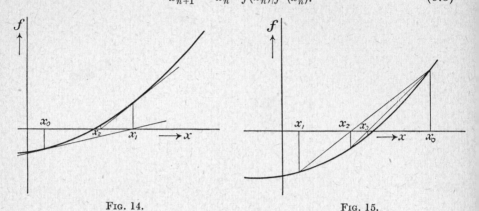

FIG. 14.   FIG. 15.

This is known as the Newton–Raphson process; Newton's process for a square root is the special case of it for the function $f(x) = x^2 - b$, and (9.4) is the special case of it for $f(x) = 1 - b/x^2$. For the general Newton–Raphson process,

$$F(x) = x - f(x)/f'(x), \qquad F'(x) = -f(x)f''(x)/[f'(x)]^2,$$

and since $f(X) = 0$, **it** follows that $F'(X) = 0$, so the process is second order.

Expressed in terms of the graph of $f(x)$, the Newton–Raphson process is equivalent to linear interpolation along the tangent to the curve $y = f(x)$ at x_n (see Fig. 14).

(c) *The 'rule of false position'*

Another iterative process is equivalent to linear interpolation along the chord joining $[x_0, f(x_0)]$ to $[x_n, f(x_n)]$ (see Fig. 15). This gives

$$x_{n+1} = x_0 - (x_n - x_0)f_0/(f_n - f_0) = (x_0 f_n - x_n f_0)/(f_n - f_0).$$

This method, however, is only first order, though if x_0 is a fair approximation to X, the coefficient a_1 in (9.3) is small; successive errors ξ_n are related by

$$\xi_{n+1} = \tfrac{1}{2}(x_0 - X)f''(X)\xi_n/f'(X),$$

approximately. It has the advantage that it does not require the evaluation of $f'(x)$.

A disadvantage of methods such as the Newton–Raphson and the method of false position is that they involve the evaluation of $f(x)$ and $f'(x)$ at a number of values of x which, though systematic in the sense that each is calculated from the previous one by the same formula such as (9.5), are irregularly spaced, and such a set of numbers is difficult to check adequately. An advantage is that a mistake in an intermediate value of x_n does not affect the final result; it is just equivalent to starting a new iteration with this erroneous value of x_n as x_0. But this does not eliminate the possibility of a mistake in the last repetition of the iterative process. Tabulation of $f(x)$ at equal intervals of x followed by a process of inverse interpolation is a process which provides more, and simpler, checks against occasional mistakes.

Example: To find the root of $x \tan x = \frac{1}{2}$ which lies between $x = 0 \cdot 6$ and $0 \cdot 7$.

(a) *By the Newton–Raphson process*

There are several forms in which this equation can be written, for example:

$$f(x) \equiv x \tan x - \tfrac{1}{2} = 0; \qquad f(x) \equiv 2x - \cot x = 0;$$
$$f(x) \equiv 2x \sin x - \cos x = 0.$$

The third of these will be adopted, as it gives the most convenient formula for $f'(x)$, namely
$$f'(x) = 2x \cos x + 3 \sin x.$$

Starting with $x_0 = 0 \cdot 6$, $\sin x_0 = 0 \cdot 5646$, $\cos x_0 = 0 \cdot 8253$, we have

$$\left. \begin{aligned} f(x_0) &= 2x_0 \sin x_0 - \cos x_0 = -0 \cdot 1478 \\ f'(x_0) &= 2x_0 \cos x_0 + 3 \sin x_0 = +2 \cdot 6842 \end{aligned} \right\}, \qquad \begin{aligned} f(x_0)/f'(x_0) &= -0 \cdot 0551, \\ x_1 &= 0 \cdot 6 + 0 \cdot 0551 \\ &= 0 \cdot 6551, \end{aligned}$$

$x_1 = 0 \cdot 655$, $\sin x_1 = 0 \cdot 609159$, $\cos x_1 = 0 \cdot 793048$

$$\left. \begin{aligned} f(x_1) &= 2x_1 \sin x_1 - \cos x_1 = +0 \cdot 004950 \\ f'(x_1) &= 2x_1 \cos x_1 + 3 \sin x_1 = 2 \cdot 86637 \end{aligned} \right\}, \qquad \begin{aligned} f(x_1)/f'(x_1) &= +0 \cdot 001727, \\ x_2 &= 0 \cdot 655 - 0 \cdot 001727 \\ &= 0 \cdot 653273, \end{aligned}$$

$x_2 = 0 \cdot 653273$, $\sin x_2 = 0 \cdot 607788$, $\cos x_2 = 0 \cdot 794099$

$$\left. \begin{aligned} f(x_2) &= 2x_2 \sin x_2 - \cos x_2 = +0 \cdot 000007_7 \\ f'(x_2) &= 2x_2 \cos x_2 + 3 \sin x_2 = 2 \cdot 86097 \end{aligned} \right\}, \qquad \begin{aligned} f(x_2)/f'(x_2) &= +0 \cdot 000002_7, \\ x_3 &= 0 \cdot 653270. \end{aligned}$$

Notes: (i) The first approximation $x_0 = 0 \cdot 6$ is a rough one and four-figure values of $\sin x$, $\cos x$ are adequate at this stage; more figures are used later when the accuracy of x_n has been improved.

(ii) For the second stage of the iteration, x_1 is taken as $0 \cdot 655$ instead of the value $0 \cdot 6551$ obtained from the first stage. It is not to be expected that the fourth decimal of this value will be correct, and the rounded value $x_1 = 0 \cdot 655$ enables tables with interval $\delta x = 0 \cdot 001$† to be used without interpolation. For the third stage, however, interpolation in the tables is necessary.

(iii) For the third stage (and later stages, if any) it would be adequate to use $f'(x_1)$ instead of recalculating $f'(x_n)$ for each new value of x_n. This makes the method formally only first order, but the coefficient a_1 in (9.3) is so small in such a case that the convergence of the first-order process is adequate for practical work.

(b) *By inverse interpolation*

To solve the equation by inverse interpolation, it is most convenient to take it in the form
$$f(x) \equiv 2x - \cot x = 0$$

† *Chambers's 6-Figure Tables*, vol. 2 (1949), for example.

as this avoids the calculation of any products and involves the least reference to tables. Evaluation of $f(x)$ to two or three decimals at intervals 0·05 or 0·02 in the range $x = 0·6$ to $0·7$, as might be used for a rough plot, locates the root as lying between $x = 0·65$ and $0·66$, and taking $0·01$ intervals we have the following table:

	$\cot x$	$f(x) = 2x - \cot x$	$\delta^2 f$
0·64	1·343104	−0·063104	
		47668	
0·65	1·315436	−0·015436	−718
		46950	
0·66	1·288486	+0·031514	−685
		46265	
0·67	1·262221	+0·077779	

Inverse interpolation for $f(x) = 0$ at $x = 0·65 + \theta(0·01)$ gives

$$\theta = \tfrac{15436}{46950} - B^{(ii)}(\theta) . \tfrac{1403}{46950}$$

$$\theta = 0·32878 - B^{(ii)}(\theta) . (0·02988),$$

and iterative solution of this equation gives $\theta = 0·32715$, $x = 0·653271_5$.

Alternatively, $0·002$ or $0·001$ intervals could be taken between $x = 0·65$ and $0·66$; for example

	$\cot x$	$f(x) = 2x - \cot x$	
0·650	1·315436	−0·015436	
		9447	
0·652	1·309989	−0·005989	−29
		9418	
0·654	1·304571	+0·003429	−29
		9389	
0·656	1·299182	+0·012818	

and linear interpolation is now adequate to give five decimals in x.

Note: The two methods may be combined; for example after obtaining the approximation x_1 by the Newton–Raphson method, the approximation to the root may be improved by tabulation at $0·001$ intervals in the neighbourhood of $x = 0·655$, followed by inverse interpolation. This avoids the interpolation in tables which has to be done if the Newton–Raphson process is continued.

9.32. Derivation of a second-order process from a first-order process

If it is known that an iterative process is first order, this knowledge enables a better approximation to the solution to be obtained by an application of the process of 'exponential extrapolation' (see § 3.4 (a)). If the first term in the expansion (9.3) were the only term, then we would have
$$\xi_2/\xi_1 = \xi_1/\xi_0 = a_1, \quad \text{that is, } \xi_0 \xi_2 = \xi_1^2$$
exactly, so that X would be given by

$$(x_2 - X)(x_0 - X) = (x_1 - X)^2.$$

Unless the higher terms in (9.3) are negligible, this will not give exactly the value of X, but an approximation, say X^*, to it:

$$X^* = \frac{x_2 x_0 - x_1^2}{x_2 - 2x_1 + x_0} = x_2 - \frac{(x_2 - x_1)^2}{x_2 - 2x_1 + x_0} \tag{9.6}$$

(see eq. 3.12), which will usually be a substantially better approximation than x_2. We can then repeat the process starting with $x_0 = X^*$.

In general, let X_{n+1}^* be the result of this process, starting with $x_0 = X_n^*$. Then it can be shown that the process of forming the successive values of X^* is second order.†

Example: To solve the equation $x^2 - 6x + 2 = 0$ by writing it in the form
$$x = 6 - (2/x)$$
and using an iterative process.

In this case the function $F(x)$ of §9.3 is $F(x) = 6 - (2/x)$, $F'(x) = 2/x^2$ and though the solution $x = X$ is not yet known, we can be sure that $F'(x)$ is not zero there, hence the iterative process $x_{n+1} = 6 - (2/x_n)$ is first order.

Starting with $X_0^* = 3$ we have
$$x_0 = 3, \qquad x_1 = \tfrac{16}{3}, \qquad x_2 = \tfrac{45}{8}.$$
Then, from formula (9.6),
$$x_2 - x_1 = \tfrac{7}{24}, \qquad x_2 - 2x_1 + x_0 = -\tfrac{49}{24},$$
$$X_1^* = \frac{45}{8} - \frac{(7/24)^2}{-49/24} = \frac{17}{3} = 5 \cdot 66667.$$

Then with $x_0 = X_1^* = \tfrac{17}{3}$, we have
$$x_1 = 6 - 2.3/17 = 5 \cdot 64706, \qquad x_2 = 6 - 2/5 \cdot 64706 = 5 \cdot 64584;$$
then from formula (9.6) again,
$$x_2 - x_1 = -0 \cdot 00122; \qquad x_2 - 2x_1 + x_0 = 0 \cdot 01839;$$
$$X_2^* = 5 \cdot 64584 - \frac{(0 \cdot 00122)^2}{0 \cdot 01839} = 5 \cdot 64584 - 0 \cdot 00008 = 5 \cdot 64576$$

which is already correct to six significant figures.

9.4. Multiple roots and neighbouring roots

Particular care is necessary when the coefficients in the equation are in the neighbourhood of values for which the equation has multiple roots. The values of the roots are then particularly sensitive to the values of the coefficients and to rounding errors. To take a simple example, the equation

$$x^2 - 8x + 16 \cdot 00 = 0 \text{ has a double root } x = 4,$$
$$x^2 - 8x + 16 \cdot 01 = 0 \text{ has no real root,}$$
$$x^2 - 8x + 15 \cdot 99 = 0 \text{ has roots } 3 \cdot 9, \ 4 \cdot 1,$$

so that a change of less than one part in 1000 in the constant term affects the roots by one part in 40. The situation is clear here, but may not be when the equation has other roots or involves transcendental functions. If a repeated root is suspected, either from the results of this process or from the graph, then careful numerical evaluation of the function should be carried out in the neighbourhood of the suspected repeated root.

† See D. R. Hartree, *Proc. Camb. Phil. Soc.* **45** (1948), 230.

Two (or more) close but not equal roots may be more troublesome than a true repeated root. If two close roots are suspected from examination of a graph or on other evidence, there will certainly be a root of $f'(x)$ in this neighbourhood, say $x = x_m$, and it is best to determine this first, and to evaluate $f(x_m)$. If this has the same sign as $f(x)$ at neighbouring values of x, then there is no real root; if $f(x_m)$ has the opposite sign to $f(x)$ at neighbouring values of x, then there are two real roots. Since $f'(x_m) = 0$, Taylor's series for $f(x)$ in the neighbourhood of x_m begins

$$f(x) = f(x_m) + \tfrac{1}{2}(x - x_m)^2 f''(x_m),$$

and if $(x - x_m)$ is sufficiently small (and $f''(x_m)$ is not too small)

$$x - x_m = \pm [2\{f(x) - f(x_m)\}/f''(x_m)]^{\frac{1}{2}}. \tag{9.7}$$

This, if not already accurate enough, will provide starting values for a further approximation to these roots.

The calculated values of these roots will be very sensitive to rounding errors; if $f(x)$ is given by a formula which can be evaluated to any degree of numerical accuracy (for example, by a polynomial), the roots can be evaluated to any accuracy required; but if the evaluation of $f(x)$ involves reference to tables, the accuracy of the calculated values of the roots may be small.

Example: To find the smallest positive root of $x \cos^2 x = 0.4115$.

A graph shows that $f(x) = x \cos^2 x$ has a maximum of about 0.41 in the neighbourhood of $x = 0.65$.

For this function, $f'(x) = -\cos x(2x \sin x - \cos x)$, and this has a zero at $x_m = 0.65327$ (see § 9.31, example), where $f(x) = 0.411949$; also

$$f''(x_m) = -\cos x_m(2x_m \cos x_m + 3 \sin x_m) = -2.272.$$

So $f(x) - f(x_m) = 0.4115 - 0.411949 = -0.000449,$

and the smallest root of $x \cos^2 x = 0.4115$ is approximately

$$0.65327 - [2(-0.000449)/(-2.272)]^{\frac{1}{2}} = 0.65327 - 0.01988$$

$$= 0.63339.$$

Note: The fifth decimal of this value of x is not determined to ± 1 by the sixth decimal of $f(x)$ or $f(x_m)$.

9.5. Special processes for special types of equations

The methods so far considered have been general methods applicable to any kind of algebraic equation, in the sense explained in § 9.1. For some special kinds of equations $f(x) = 0$, and particularly for those in which $f(x)$ is a polynomial in x, there are special methods.

Polynomial equations, like linear simultaneous equations, are met in contexts of two kinds. In one the coefficients are all known exactly and are usually integral; in the other they are only known to within a certain tolerance because they are results either of observations subject to experimental errors or of other calculations which are subject to rounding errors.

In the latter case it may be important to know the range of uncertainty of the solution arising from the tolerance in one or more of the coefficients. If the polynomial is

$$f(x) \equiv a_0 x^n + a_1 x^{n-1} + a_2 x^{n-2} + \dots + a_{n-1} x + a_n = 0 \qquad (9.8)$$

consider the first-order variation of a root $x = X$ with one of the coefficients, a_k. If the root X changes by ΔX when a_k changes by Δa_k, then

$$f'(X)\Delta X + X^{n-k}\Delta a_k = 0,$$

that is, $\qquad\qquad \Delta X = -[X^{n-k}/f'(X)]\Delta a_k,$

and for changes (not necessarily equal) in all the coefficients

$$\Delta X = -\Big[\sum_k (X^{n-k}\Delta a_k)\Big]\Big/f'(X). \qquad (9.9)$$

This shows that the roots are particularly sensitive to the values of the coefficients in the neighbourhood of a stationary value of the function.

9.51. Quadratic equations

It has already been pointed out that direct evaluation of the standard text-book formula for the roots of a quadratic equation $ax^2 + bx + c = 0$, namely $\qquad\qquad x = [-b \pm (b^2 - 4ac)^{\frac{1}{2}}]/2a,$

is *not* always the best way of determining numerical values of the roots of a quadratic and particularly not if the ratio of the roots is large $(b^2 \gg 4ac)$.

A better practical method in many cases is an iterative process based on use of the relations

$$x_1 + x_2 = -b/a, \qquad x_1 x_2 = c/a,$$

where x_1 and x_2 are the two roots. If x_1 is the root of greater modulus, then successive approximations to the roots can be evaluated by using the formulae $\qquad x_1 = -(b/a) - x_2, \qquad x_2 = (c/a)/x_1 \qquad (9.10)$

alternately, starting from the approximation $x_2 = 0$ if no other is easily available.

This process, though only first order, can be carried out so easily, and when $b^2 \gg 4ac$ it converges so quickly, that it is unnecessary to refine it further. If b^2 is not considerably larger than $4ac$, it may be convenient to use a second-order process derived from this first-order process as

explained in § 9.32. Elimination of x_2 between the two equations (9.10) gives
$$x_1 = -(b/a)-(c/a)/x_1$$
which is the general expression of which the example given in § 9.32 is a special case.

9.52. Cubic and quartic equations

A cubic equation with real coefficients has at least one real root, say x_1; if it is determined, division of the cubic by $(x-x_1)$ gives a quadratic which can then be solved by the standard formula or by iteration. For determination of the real root or roots the general methods of the previous sections will often be best.

There are also special methods available which depend on reducing the cubic to a standard form. If the cubic is
$$ax^3+bx^2+cx+d = 0$$
then the substitution $y = \beta(x+b/3a)$ reduces it to a cubic in y without a y^2 term; then either the coefficient of the term in y is zero, or a real value of β can be chosen so that the ratio of the coefficients of the terms in y and in y^3 is either $+1$ or -1. Thus any cubic can be reduced to one of the forms
$$y^3+D = 0, \qquad y^3+y+D = 0, \qquad y^3-y+D = 0;$$
the solution to an equation of the first of these forms can be found directly from a table of cube roots, and tables of the roots of the equations of the other two forms have been evaluated (for details, see the *Index of Mathematical Tables*).

If in the substitution $y = \beta(x+b/3a)$, β is chosen so as to reduce the equation to the form
$$4y^3\pm3y-D = 0$$
the further substitution $y = \sinh u$ (if the sign of the middle term is $+$), $y = \cosh u$ (if the sign of the middle term is $-$, and $D > 1$) or $y = \cos u$ (if the sign of the middle term is $-$, and $D < 1$) can be used to reduce it further to
$$\sinh 3u = D, \quad \cosh 3u = D, \quad \text{or} \quad \cos 3u = D$$
respectively and the solution found from tables of hyperbolic or circular functions.

The solution of a quartic equation can be reduced to the solution of a cubic equation, but in most cases it is better to use more direct methods.

9.53. Polynomial equations

For solving polynomial equations there are available a number of special methods.[†] Various theorems in the theory of equations can be used to determine how many roots lie in various ranges of x, and various special methods are available such as Horner's method or a method known as 'root-squaring' which depends on forming an equation whose roots are some high power of the roots of the equation to be solved.

The root-squaring method, however, only gives the magnitudes of the roots and not their signs, and some evaluation of $f(x)$ is necessary in order to determine their signs. Also both methods, as usually presented,

† For a survey, with particular reference to equations of high degree, see F. W. J. Olver, *Phil. Trans. Roy. Soc.* A, **244** (1952), 385.

are deficient or lacking in current checks, and their results should always be verified either by substitution in $f(x)$ or by evaluating $f(x)$ at a numerically convenient set of values in the neighbourhood of each root followed by interpolation. The root-squaring method in particular offers too many opportunities for mistakes for any alleged root to be accepted without such investigation.

Some evaluation of $f(x)$ is therefore required in any case, and it seems better for most practical purposes to use the general methods already considered, namely the use of graphs for approximate location of the roots followed either by evaluation in the neighbourhood of each root and inverse interpolation, or by an iterative process,† rather than to use the special methods available for polynomial equations.

9.54. Repeated roots

Repeated roots of polynomial equations can be located by finding the highest common factor of $f(x)$ and $f'(x)$. If the coefficients in the equations are known exactly (when they will usually be integral), repeated roots can be identified with certainty if the H.C.F. process is carried out exactly without any rounding off. Otherwise there can generally be no certainty whether the equation has a repeated root or two (or more) very nearly equal roots. However the H.C.F. process may well establish the absence of a repeated root.

With polynomial equations repeated roots should be removed by dividing $f(x)$ by the appropriate product of repeated factors before the determination of the remaining roots is started.

9.55. Division of a polynomial by a quadratic

A convenient way of finding the complex roots of a real polynomial equation with no real roots is to express the polynomial as a product of real quadratic factors. In one process for doing this it is necessary to carry out a number of divisions by successive approximations to a real quadratic factor, and it will be convenient first to consider a numerical process for carrying out this division.

Let $$a_0 x^n + a_1 x^{n-1} + a_2 x^{n-2} + \ldots + a_{n-1} x + a_n$$
be the dividend polynomial, and
$$x^2 + d_1 x + d_2$$
the divisor quadratic. Then we want to find a quotient polynomial
$$q_0 x^{n-2} + q_1 x^{n-3} + q_2 x^{n-4} + \ldots + q_{n-3} x + q_{n-2}$$

† For an iterative process for complex roots of polynomial equations, see P. A. Samuelson, *Journ. Math. and Phys.* **28** (1949), 259.

and a remainder $r_1 x + r_2$, such that

$$a_0 x^n + a_1 x^{n-1} + \ldots + a_n$$
$$\equiv (x^2 + d_1 x + d_2)(q_0 x^{n-2} + q_1 x^{n-3} + \ldots + q_{n-2}) + r_1 x + r_2.$$

Multiplying out, comparing coefficients, and solving for $q_0, q_1, \ldots, q_{n-2}, r_1, r_2$ in succession we have

$$
\begin{aligned}
a_0 &= q_0, & q_0 &= a_0, \\
a_1 &= q_1 + d_1 q_0, & q_1 &= a_1 - d_1 q_0, \\
a_2 &= q_2 + d_1 q_1 + d_2 q_0, & q_2 &= a_2 - d_1 q_1 - d_2 q_0, \\
a_3 &= q_3 + d_1 q_2 + d_2 q_1, & q_3 &= a_3 - d_1 q_2 - d_2 q_1,
\end{aligned}
$$

$$
\begin{aligned}
a_{n-2} &= q_{n-2} + d_1 q_{n-3} + d_2 q_{n-4}, & q_{n-2} &= a_{n-2} - d_1 q_{n-3} - d_2 q_{n-4}, \\
a_{n-1} &= r_1 + d_1 q_{n-2} + d_2 q_{n-3}, & r_1 &= a_{n-1} - d_1 q_{n-2} - d_2 q_{n-3}, \\
a_n &= r_2 + d_2 q_{n-2}, & r_2 &= a_n - d_2 q_{n-2}.
\end{aligned}
$$

The numerical work can conveniently be arranged in the following scheme:

Coefficient of	x^n	x^{n-1}	x^{n-2}	. . .	x^4	x	1
1,	a_0	a_1	a_2	. . .	a_{n-2}	a_{n-1}	a_n
$-d_1$		$-d_1 q_0$	$-d_1 q_1$	. . .	$-d_1 q_{n-3}$	$-d_1 q_{n-2}$	
$-d_2$			$-d_2 q_0$	. . .	$-d_2 q_{n-4}$	$-d_2 q_{n-3}$	$-d_2 q_{n-2}$
Sum	q_0	q_1	q_2	. .	q_{n-2}	r_1	r_2

On the left the numbers $1, -d_1, -d_2$ are written in three successive lines. In the first row are written the coefficients of the dividend polynomial. As each coefficient q_j in the quotient polynomial is determined, it is multiplied by $-d_1$ and $-d_2$, the product $-d_1 q_j$ being written in the second line in the column next to that containing q_j, and $-d_2 q_j$ in the third line of the column next but one, as shown by the arrows. The sum of the entries in the column containing a_j is the corresponding q_j.

This process, in which the division is started at the *highest* power of x and the remainder is of the form $r_1 x + r_2$, will be called 'forward division'. A similar process can be carried out starting at the term independent of x and proceeding from lower to higher powers of x, with a remainder $R_1 x^{n-1} + R_0 x^n$. This will be called 'backward division'. In this process it is convenient to take the divisor as $1 + D_1 x + D_2 x^2$, and to place $1, -D_1, -D_2$ on the right and work from right to left, thus:

Coefficient of	x^n	x^{n-1}	x^{n-2}	. . .	x^2	x	1	
	a_0	a_1	a_2	. . .	a_{n-2}	a_{n-1}	a_n	1
		$-D_1 Q_2$	$-D_1 Q_3$	. . .	$-D_1 Q_{n-1}$	$-D_1 Q_n$		$-D_1$
	$-D_2 Q_2$	$-D_2 Q_3$	$-D_2 Q_4$	. . .	$-D_2 Q_n$			$-D_2$
	R_0	R_1	Q_2	. . .	Q_{n-2}	Q_{n-1}	Q_n	Sum

Example: To divide $x^4+5x^3+12x^2+14x+8$ by x^2+2x+4 and by $1+\frac{3}{2}x+\frac{1}{2}x^2$.

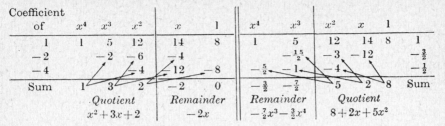

Coefficient of	x^4	x^3	x^2	x	1	x^4	x^3	x^2	x	1	
	1	5	12	14	8	1	5	12	14	8	1
-2		-2	-6	-4			$-\frac{15}{2}$	-3	-12		$-\frac{3}{2}$
-4			-4	12	-8	$-\frac{5}{2}$	-1	-4			$-\frac{1}{2}$
Sum	1	3	2	-2	0	$-\frac{3}{2}$	$-\frac{7}{2}$	5	2	8	Sum

Quotient	Remainder	Remainder	Quotient
x^2+3x+2	$-2x$	$-\frac{7}{2}x^3-\frac{3}{2}x^4$	$8+2x+5x^2$

9.56. Real quadratic factors of a polynomial

If some of the roots of a real polynomial equation $f(x)=0$, are complex, it is best first to determine the real roots $x_1, x_2,..., x_k$ by the methods already considered, and remove them by dividing $f(x)$ by $(x-x_1)(x-x_2)...(x-x_k)$; repeated roots, if any, should be identified as explained in § 9.54, and taken out with the corresponding multiplicity. This process provides a good check on these roots, since if the remainder in the division differs from zero by a greater amount than the tolerance for rounding errors, one of the roots must be in error.

The quotient will be a polynomial $F(x)$ with no real zeros, and its complex zeros can be determined by finding its real quadratic factors. We take a trial quadratic $D_0 = x^2+b_0x+c_0$ and find the quotient Q_0 on *forward* division of $F(x)$ by D_0 (the remainder is irrelevant). Then we find the quotient Q_0^* on *backward* division of $F(x)$ by Q_0 (or a multiple of it), write

$$D_1 = Q_0^*/(\text{coeff. of } x^2 \text{ in } Q_0^*) = x^2+b_1x+c_1,$$

and repeat the process with D_1 in place of D_0. This provides an iterative process† in which the successive quadratics

$$D_0 = x^2+b_0x+c_0,$$
$$D_1 = x^2+b_1x+c_1,$$
$$D_2 = x^2+b_2x+c_2$$

converge to the quadratic factor corresponding to the roots of smallest modulus of the equation $F(x)=0$. The condition for convergence is that these roots should be of smaller modulus than any other roots of the equation; one of the reasons for removing the real roots is to ensure that there shall be no real root of smaller modulus than any of the complex

† B. Friedman, *Commun. on Pure and Appl. Math.* **2** (1949), 195. For another iterative process see A. C. Aitken, *Proc. Roy. Soc. Edin.* **63** (1951), 174.

roots as the presence of such a root would make the results of this iterative process oscillate instead of converging.

Example: To find the real quadratic factor of

$$x^4 + 5x^3 + 12x^2 + 14x + 8.$$

The first steps, starting from $x^2 + 2x + 4$ as trial quadratic factor, have already been carried out in the example of the last section. The quotient of the first forward division is $x^2 + 3x + 2 = 2(1 + \frac{3}{2}x + \frac{1}{2}x^2)$; the factor 2 is taken out in order that the constant term in this divisor should be unity, and $1 + \frac{3}{2}x + \frac{1}{2}x^2$ used as the divisor in the backward division. For the present purpose the remainders are irrelevant, and the two pairs of columns in the centre can be omitted, so that thus far the working could be written

Coefficient of	x^4	x^3	x^2	x^2	x	1	
1	1	5	12	12	14	8	1
-2		-2	-6	-3	-12		$-\frac{3}{2}$
-4			-4	-4			$-\frac{1}{2}$
	1	3	2	5	2	8	
	$= 2(\frac{1}{2}$	$\frac{3}{2}$	1)	$= 5(1$	0·4	1·6)	

The calculation proceeds as follows:—

Coefficient of	x^4	x^3	x^2	x^2	x	1	
1	1	5	12	12	14	8	1
$-0·4$		$-0·4$	$-1·84$	-5	-4		$-0·5$
$-1·6$			$-1·6$	$-0·8$			$-0·1$
	1	4·6	8·56	6·2	10	8	
	$= 8·56(0·1$	0·5	1)	$= 6·2(1$	1·6	1·3)	

Coefficient of	x^4	x^3	x^2	x^2	x	1	
1	1	5	12	12	14	8	1
$-1·6$		$-1·6$	$-5·44$	$-5·72$	$-5·20$		$-0·65$
$-1·3$			$-1·3$	$-1·52$			$-0·19$
	1	3·4	5·26	4·76	8·80	8	
	$= 5·26(0·19$	0·65	1)	$= 4·76(1$	1·85	1·68)	

Coefficient of	x^4	x^3	x^2	x^2	x	1	
1	1	5	12	12	14	8	1
$-1·85$		$-1·85$	$-5·83$	$-5·88$	$-5·62$		$-0·702$
$-1·68$			$-1·68$	$-1·78$			$-0·223$
	1	3·15	4·49	4·34	8·38	8	
	$= 4·49(0·223$	0·702	1)	$= 4·34(1$	1·931	1·843)	

The last three approximations to a quadratic factor are

$$x^2 + 1·6x + 1·3,$$
$$x^2 + 1·85x + 1·68,$$
$$x^2 + 1·931x + 1·843.$$

The process is first order, so we can use the method of 'exponential extrapolation' (see §§ 3.4 (a) and 9.32) to estimate a better approximation from these. If we write the quadratic x^2+bx+c, with suffixes 0, 1, 2 for these approximations, and use formula (9.6), we have

$$b_2-b_1 = 0 \cdot 081, \qquad b_2-2b_1+b_0 = -0 \cdot 169,$$

$$\text{extrapolated } b = 1 \cdot 931 + \frac{(0 \cdot 081)^2}{0 \cdot 169} = 1 \cdot 970;$$

$$c_2-c_1 = 0 \cdot 163, \qquad c_2-2c_1+c_0 = -0 \cdot 217,$$

$$\text{extrapolated } c = 1 \cdot 843 + \frac{(0 \cdot 163)^2}{0 \cdot 217} = 1 \cdot 965;$$

and the calculation can be continued from these values in a similar way. An alternative method of improving the approximation to a real quadratic factor will be considered in the following section.

Notes: (i) As illustrated in the working of this example, only a few significant figures need be kept at first when the approximation to a quadratic factor is still only rough, and more kept as the calculation proceeds.

(ii) When applied to a $2n$th degree polynomial, the quotient of the forward division is a polynomial of the $(2n-2)$th degree and in the backward division we have to divide by this quotient. But the quotient of the backward division is a quadratic and is determined by the leading three terms in the divisor in this backward division, so that the above process for division by a quadratic can still be used.

(iii) There is no accumulation of rounding errors, since at each stage the *original polynomial* is divided by the current trial quadratic factor.

9.57. Second-order process for improving the approximation to a quadratic factor

The following is an extension of the Newton-Raphson process to the improvement of an approximation to a real quadratic factor of a real polynomial $f(x)$.

Let (x^2+bx+c) be an approximate quadratic factor and let

$$f(x) = (x^2+bx+c)q(x)+rx+s, \qquad (9.11)$$

where $q(x)$ is the quotient polynomial on division of $f(x)$ by (x^2+bx+c), and $(rx+s)$ is the remainder. These can be found by the method of §9.55. Differentiation of (9.11) with respect to b, for constant x and c, gives the variation of the coefficients r and s in the remainder with variation of the coefficient b in the trial quadratic factor:

$$0 = (x^2+bx+c)\left(\frac{\partial q(x)}{\partial b}\right)+xq(x)+\left(\frac{\partial r}{\partial b}\right)x+\left(\frac{\partial s}{\partial b}\right),$$

so that $-(\partial r/\partial b)x-(\partial s/\partial b)$ is the remainder when $xq(x)$ is divided by (x^2+bx+c). Similarly differentiation with respect to c gives

$$0 = (x^2+bx+c)\left(\frac{\partial q(x)}{\partial c}\right)+q(x)+\left(\frac{\partial r}{\partial c}\right)x+\left(\frac{\partial s}{\partial c}\right),$$

so that $-(\partial r/\partial c)x-(\partial s/\partial c)$ is the remainder when $q(x)$ is divided by (x^2+bx+c). These remainders can be found by the method of §9.55 (the quotients are also found, but are irrelevant) so the partial derivatives of r and s with respect to b and c can be determined.

If now changes Δb and Δc are made in b and c, the first-order changes in r and s are

$$\left(\frac{\partial r}{\partial b}\right)\Delta b+\left(\frac{\partial r}{\partial c}\right)\Delta c, \qquad \left(\frac{\partial s}{\partial b}\right)\Delta b+\left(\frac{\partial s}{\partial c}\right)\Delta c,$$

and we want to chose $\Delta b, \Delta c$ so as to reduce r and s to zero, that is, to make

$$r+\left(\frac{\partial r}{\partial b}\right)\Delta b+\left(\frac{\partial r}{\partial c}\right)\Delta c = 0, \qquad s+\left(\frac{\partial s}{\partial b}\right)\Delta b+\left(\frac{\partial s}{\partial c}\right)\Delta c = 0.$$

These determine $\Delta b, \Delta c$ and hence a better approximation

$$x^2+(b+\Delta b)x+(c+\Delta c)$$

to the quadratic factor sought. The process can be repeated, and is second-order.

Example: To improve the approximation $x^2+1\cdot970x+1\cdot965$ to a quadratic factor of $x^4+5x^3+12x^2+14x+8$ (see example in previous section).

Coefficient of	x^4	x^3	x^2	x	1
1	1	5	12	14	8
$-1\cdot970$		$-1\cdot970$	$-5\cdot9691$	$-8\cdot0098$	
$-1\cdot965$			$-1\cdot965$	$-5\cdot9540$	$-7\cdot9895$
	1	$3\cdot030$	$4\cdot0659$	$0\cdot0362$	$0\cdot0105$
Quotient	$q(x) = x^2+3\cdot030x+4\cdot0659$			r	s

Coefficient of	x^3	x^2	x	1	x^2	x	1
1	$xq(x) = 1$	$3\cdot030$	$4\cdot066$	0	$q(x) = 1$	$3\cdot030$	$4\cdot066$
$-1\cdot970$		$-1\cdot970$	$-2\cdot088$			$-1\cdot970$	
$-1\cdot965$			$-1\cdot965$	$-2\cdot083$			$-1\cdot965$
	1	$1\cdot060$	$0\cdot013$	$-2\cdot083$	1	$1\cdot060$	$2\cdot101$
		$-\left(\frac{\partial r}{\partial b}\right)$	$-\left(\frac{\partial s}{\partial b}\right)$			$-\left(\frac{\partial r}{\partial c}\right)$	$-\left(\frac{\partial s}{\partial c}\right)$

Hence $\Delta b, \Delta c$ are given by

$$0\cdot013\Delta b+1\cdot060\Delta c = 0\cdot0362,$$

$$-2\cdot083\Delta b+2\cdot101\Delta c = 0\cdot0105,$$

and solution of these equations gives $\Delta b = 0\cdot0291$, $\Delta c = 0\cdot0337$, whence

$$b = 1\cdot970+0\cdot0291 = 1\cdot9991,$$

$$c = 1\cdot965+0\cdot0337 = 1\cdot9987,$$

so that $x^2+1\cdot9991x+1\cdot9987$ is a better approximation to a quadratic factor.

Actually the quadratic factors in this case are x^2+2x+2 and x^2+3x+4 exactly. One application of this method has improved the approximation to the factor x^2+2x+2 by a factor of about 30.

9.6. Simultaneous non-linear equations

For simultaneous equations in two variables the same general procedure as for equations in one variable can be used, namely a graphical process for locating the roots approximately, followed by a numerical process for improving the approximation.

Let the equations be

$$f_1(x,y) = 0, \qquad f_2(x,y) = 0. \tag{9.12}$$

If both of these can be solved formally for y as a function of x, or x as a function of y, then it is easy to draw graphs of y against x for each equation, and the intersections of the two graphs give an approximation to the solutions. If one or both of the equations can be solved formally for y as a function of x or vice versa, then one of the variables can be eliminated and the equations reduced to an equation in one variable; for example if the second of equations (9.12) can be solved in the form $y = \phi_2(x)$, substitution of this in the first equation gives

$$F_1(x) \equiv f_1(x, \phi_2(x)) = 0.$$

There is no need to carry out the elimination explicitly in such a way as to exhibit $F_1(x)$ formally as a function of x; all that is wanted is that $y = \phi_2(x)$ should be evaluated for a set of values of x, and that these should be substituted into the formula for $f_1(x,y)$ for the corresponding values of x. This process carries out the elimination numerically without its having to be expressed formally.

Example:
$$\sin x + 2\sin y = 1,$$
$$2\sin 3x + 3\sin 3y = 0{\cdot}3.$$

It is most convenient here to solve the first equation for $\sin y$, then from this to calculate $\sin 3y$ either from the formula

$$\sin 3y = \sin y(3 - 4\sin^2 y)$$

or by use of inverse sine and sine tables, and then to evaluate

$$f_2(x) = 2\sin 3x + 3\sin 3y - 0{\cdot}3$$

for these values of $\sin 3y$ and the corresponding values of $\sin 3x$. The work is conveniently arranged in tabular form.

	$\sin y$ $= \frac{1}{2}(1-\sin x)$	$\sin 3y$	$\sin 3x$	$f_2(x)$
0	0·5	+1	0	+2·70
$1(\frac{1}{6}\pi) = 30°$	0·25	0·688	1	3·76
$2(\frac{1}{6}\pi) = 60°$	0·067	0·200	0	+0·30
$3(\frac{1}{6}\pi) = 90°$	0	0	−1	−2·30
$4(\frac{1}{6}\pi) = 120°$	0·067	0·200	0	+0·30
$5(\frac{1}{6}\pi) = 150°$	0·25	0·688	1	3·76
$6(\frac{1}{6}\pi) = 180°$	0·5	1	0	+2·70
$7(\frac{1}{6}\pi) = 210°$	0·75	+0·562	−1	−0·61
$8(\frac{1}{6}\pi) = 240°$	0·933	−0·450	0	−1·65
$9(\frac{1}{6}\pi) = 270°$	1	−1	1	−1·30
$10(\frac{1}{6}\pi) = 300°$	0·933	−0·450	0	−1·65
$11(\frac{1}{6}\pi) = 330°$	0·75	+0·562	−1	−0·61
$12(\frac{1}{6}\pi) = 360°$	0·5	1	0	+2·70

Two decimals are adequate to locate the roots approximately. A graph drawn from these values, or even inspection of the table without actually drawing a graph, shows that there are roots in the neighbourhood of $x/(\frac{1}{6}\pi) = 2\cdot1, 3\cdot9, 6\cdot8,$ and $11\cdot2$.

The approximate solutions so determined can be improved by tabulation at smaller intervals and inverse interpolation, or by an iterative process. If both the equations can be solved for one variable in terms of the other, say for y in terms of x:

$$y = \phi_1(x) \text{ for the first equation,}$$

$$y = \phi_2(x) \text{ for the second equation,}$$

then it may be more convenient to evaluate $\phi_1(x)-\phi_2(x)$ as a function of x and interpolate for the zero of this function.

Example: To find more exactly the root of

$$\sin x + 2\sin y = 1, \qquad 2\sin 3x + 3\sin 3y = 0\cdot3$$

in the neighbourhood of $x/(\frac{1}{6}\pi) = 2\cdot1$

$x/(\frac{1}{6}\pi)$	$x°$	$\sin y$ $= \frac{1}{2}(1-\sin x)$	$y = \phi_1(x)$	$\sin 3y$ $= 0\cdot1 - \frac{2}{3}\sin 3x$	$y = \phi_2(x)$	$\phi_2(x)-\phi_1(x)$	
2·0	60°	·0670	·0671	·1	·0334	−·0337	
							240
2·05	61½°	·0606	·0607	·1523	·0510	−·0097	−2
							238
2·1	63°	·0545	·0545	·2043	·0686	+·0141	−5
							233
2·15	64½°	·0487	·0487	·2556	·0862	+·0374	−2
							231
2·2	66°	·0432	·0432	·3060	·1037	+·0605	

and inverse interpolation then gives the required solution, approximately $x = 2\cdot140(\frac{1}{6}\pi)$.

When neither of the equations can be solved formally for x or y, the same processes can be used, one or both of the functions $\phi_1(x)$, $\phi_2(x)$ being determined roughly graphically, or more accurately numerically, by solution of the equation $f_1(x, y) = 0$ or $f_2(x, y) = 0$ for y in terms of x. For example, if a set of graphs of $f_1(x, y)$ against y for a set of constant values of x is constructed, the intersections of these graphs with the y-axis give the function $y = \phi_1(x)$ which can then be used to substitute for y in the second equation.

Another process is to evaluate $f_1(x, y)$ and $f_2(x, y)$ for a set of points on a coarse grid in the (x, y) plane, and on a piece of squared paper to mark at each (x, y) point the values of $f_1(x, y)$ and $f_2(x, y)$ there. The loci $f_1(x, y) = 0$ and $f_2(x, y) = 0$ can then be sketched roughly, and the intersections of the curves thus sketched then indicate the regions of the plane in which a closer examination is necessary in order to determine the roots more accurately.

Example: To locate approximately the real solutions of

$$xy(2x^2 - y^2) + 16(x+y) = 48, \tag{9.13}$$

$$x^2 + y^2 = 16. \tag{9.14}$$

The second equation shows that x and y lie between ± 4, so evaluate

$$xy(2x^2 - y^2) + 16(x+y)$$

on a square grid of mesh side unity in the (x, y) plane for $|x| \leqslant 4$, $|y| \leqslant 4$ (see Fig. 16). Although this grid is a coarse one, it enables the contour $f_1(x, y) = 0$, that is,

$$xy(2x^2 - y^2) + 16(x+y) = 48,$$

to be sketched roughly. In this particular case the contour $f_2(x, y) = 0$, that is, $x^2 + y^2 = 16$, could be drawn accurately; but in the figure it has been sketched freehand from the values of $x^2 + y^2$ at the mesh points, as would have to be done in general.

The intersections of the two contours show that there are four real solutions, approximately:

$$x = -2 \cdot 0 \qquad x = 0 \cdot 4 \qquad x = 1 \cdot 8 \qquad x = 4 \cdot 0$$
$$y = 3 \cdot 5 \qquad y = 4 \cdot 0 \qquad y = 3 \cdot 6 \qquad y = -0 \cdot 2$$

and probably two in the neighbourhood of $x = -3 \cdot 5$, $y = -0 \cdot 9$, though calculation of function values on a finer grid would be necessary in order to make certain whether the contours intersect in this region.

Notes: (i) The values recorded in the figure are not those of $f_1(x, y)$ and $f_2(x, y)$ themselves, but are those of the left-hand sides of equations (9.13), (9.14).

(ii) Since $f_1(x, y)$ in this case is a cubic in x for fixed y, and a cubic in y for fixed x, the table of its values can be checked both very easily and very thoroughly by differencing in both directions. Alternatively, these values could be built up from the differences in the y direction and checked by differencing in the x direction (or vice versa).

(iii) Since this method involves evaluating the function on a twofold array of points, it should in general be avoided when it is possible formally to use either

P

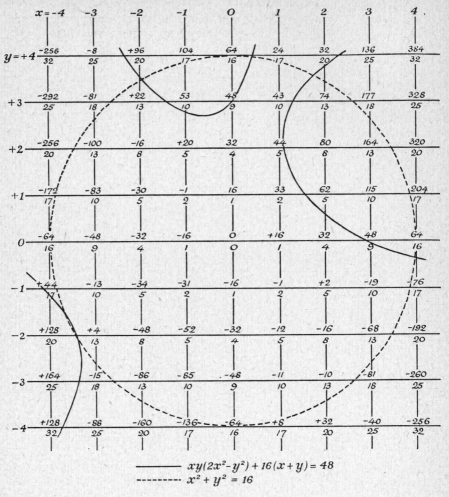

$$\text{———} \quad xy(2x^2-y^2) + 16(x+y) = 48$$
$$\text{- - - - -} \quad x^2 + y^2 = 16$$

Fig. 16

of the equations to solve for one or other variable in terms of the other, and so to reduce the problem to one in a single variable. It is used in this example to provide the possibility of comparing this method, and the results of using it and of improving the solutions, with others.

A convenient alternative method for these equations is to use the substitution $x = 4\cos\theta$, $y = 4\sin\theta$, which ensures that the equation (9.14) is satisfied, and then to treat equation (9.13) as an equation in θ. Another alternative is to use equation (9.14) to substitute for y^2 in (9.13), which then becomes

$$[(3x^2 - 16)x + 16]y = 48 - 16x, \tag{9.15}$$

and then treat equations (9.14) and (9.15) as two equations of the form $y = \phi(x)$.

(iv) The best method of improving the approximate solutions will depend on the equation and may be different for the different solutions. In the present example an iterative process is most convenient for the solutions near $x = 0.4$, $y = 4.0$, and $x = 4.0$, $y = -0.2$. Consider the latter. We use equations (9.14) and (9.15) alternately, the first to determine x from an approximate value of y, and the second to determine y from an approximate value of x. Since $|y/x|$ is small for this solution, the value of x obtained from (9.14) is insensitive to the value of y taken, and is not much altered when an improved approximation to y, derived from (9.15) with this value of x, is used. The iterative process, though only first order, converges rapidly.

A similar treatment, using an equation obtained by substituting for x^2 instead of for y^2 in (9.13), is similarly effective for the solution near $x = 0.4$, $y = 4.0$.

The following is a general process for improving the approximate values of a solution, when neither equation can be solved formally for either variable in terms of the other. The functions $f_1(x, y), f_2(x, y)$ are evaluated on a finer grid of points (x, y) in the neighbourhood of the solution. But instead of the function values being recorded in the (x, y) plane, the value of $f_2(x, y)$ is plotted against $f_1(x, y)$ for each pair of values (x, y), and curves of constant x (x-contours) and of constant y (y-contours) are drawn in the (f_1, f_2) plane. The advantage of this method of representing the behaviour of the two functions of x and y is that each curve is drawn *through plotted points* instead of being interpolated 'by eye' among an array of function values.

Such a plot of f_2 against f_1 is made for such values of x and y that the point $f_1 = f_2 = 0$ is enclosed between two x-contours and two y-contours. Within a small enough region not containing more than one solution, the x-contours and y-contours will usually be nearly equally spaced and not very curved, and if this is the case, it is possible to estimate fairly closely what contours pass through the point $f_1 = f_2 = 0$. A calculation of (f_1, f_2) for this approximation to the solution then suggests for what further values of (x, y) the function should be evaluated in order to enclose the point $f_1 = f_2 = 0$ still more closely. The process is illustrated by the following example.

Example: To find more accurately the solution of the equations

$$xy(2x^2-y^2)+16(x+y) = 48, \qquad x^2+y^2 = 16,$$

in the neighbourhood of $x = 1.8$, $y = 3.6$.

From Fig. 16 it is estimated that the solution lies between $x = 1.7$ and 1.9, and between $y = 3.5$ and 3.7. The improvement of this solution can be carried out by the following procedure. A set of values of f_1 and f_2 is first evaluated for $y = 3.5$, 3.6, and 3.7, $x = 1.6$ to 2.0, this range of x being taken in order to provide enough values to check by differences. The x-contours and y-contours drawn using these points are shown in Fig. 17; those for $y = 3.5$ and 3.6 already enclose the point $f_1 = f_2 = 0$; but some points for $y = 3.7$ have been calculated to check the spacing of the y-contours and to show the curvature of the x-contours. The (f_1, f_2) point for $x = 1\cdot85$, $y = 3\cdot55$ is also shown. The solution estimated from these contours was $x = 1\cdot84$, $y = 3\cdot55$.

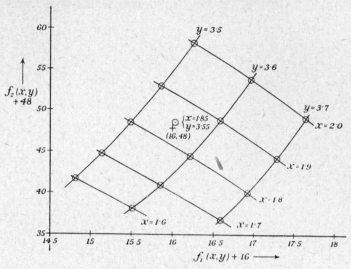

FIG. 17.

Values of (f_1, f_2) are now calculated for these four sets of values $x = 1\cdot83$, $1\cdot84$ and $y = 3\cdot55$, $3\cdot56$, and the results plotted on a larger scale. For this small range of x and y, the contours can be taken as straight and equally spaced to the accuracy of the plot. Inverse interpolation in x and y is required to determine the values of x and y to give $f_1 = f_2 = 0$, and this is most easily done by measurement. The values obtained can be checked by calculating f_1 and f_2 for them.

Notes: (i) As in Fig. 16, the functions plotted in Fig. 17 are the left-hand sides of the two equations, namely $f_1(x, y) + 48$ and $f_2(x, y) + 16$.

(ii) A convenient way of carrying out the final interpolation is as follows. Consider the interpolation between the two x-contours, say $x = x_0$ and x_1, and let $x = x_0 + \theta(x_1 - x_0)$ be the interpolated value required. Lay a ruler on the (f_1, f_2) diagram so that its edge passes through the point $f_1 = f_2 = 0$; rotate it about this point and move it in the direction of its length until it cuts both x-contours at exact graduations on the scale, at a convenient interval (say 5, 10, or 20 units of the scale graduation); then the value of the fraction θ of the x-interval between the contours can be read off directly.

(iii) This method of plotting is *not* satisfactory for the preliminary location of roots, since (x, y) is not in general a single-valued function of (f_1, f_2), so that two or more x-contours and two or more y-contours may pass through each point in a region of the (f_1, f_2) plane. If this occurs, and it will occur if the equations have more than one solution, the (f_1, f_2) diagram becomes complicated and its interpretation needs considerable care.

9.7. Three or more variables

There is no satisfactory practical method, graphical or tabular, of displaying the behaviour of functions of three or more variables, and the approximate location of solutions of such equations is therefore difficult.

In some cases the solutions can be regarded as representing the asymptotic steady-state values of the solutions of a system of differential equations, and then they may be determined approximately by integrating this system of differential equations. If the equations arise from some scientific problem, this may suggest the appropriate differential equations to use. For example, in the chemical equilibrium of a system of a number of gaseous components, the relations between the concentrations of the components are given by a set of non-linear equations involving the equilibrium constants of the various reactions. If, for example, one of the reactions was $2CO + O_2 \rightleftharpoons 2CO_2$ and $\mathscr{C}(X)$ stands for the concentration of the molecular species X, one equation would be

$$[\mathscr{C}(CO)]^2 \mathscr{C}(O_2) = K_1 [\mathscr{C}(CO_2)]^2. \tag{9.16}$$

But the equilibrium is attained through a non-steady process in which the concentrations of the components change with time, that of oxygen, for example, being given by an equation

$$\frac{d}{dt} \mathscr{C}(O_2) = \beta_1 [K_1 \{\mathscr{C}(CO_2)\}^2 - \mathscr{C}(O_2) \{\mathscr{C}(CO)\}^2], \tag{9.17}$$

and similarly for other components. We can try to make the calculations approach a steady state by following out such a time-varying process. However, since the purpose of the differential equation (9.17) is solely to provide a means for approaching a solution of the equation (9.16), there is no need to take experimental values of the reaction rate coefficients like β_1 in (9.17) even if these are known; an artificial set can be taken, convenient for the numerical work, and they need not even be taken to be constant.

X

FUNCTIONS OF TWO OR MORE VARIABLES

10.1. Functions of a complex variable and functions of two variables

THERE are two rather distinct contexts in which functions of two or more variables may arise in numerical work. One is concerned with complex numbers and functions of a complex variable. In numerical work it is usually best to treat a complex number as a pair of real numbers, either (x, y) in the Cartesian form $(z = x+iy)$ or (r, θ) in the polar form $(z = re^{i\theta})$ of the complex number as is most convenient for the calculation concerned. In this context a particularly important feature is the property of any analytical function $f(z) = g(z)+ih(z)$ of a complex variable z, that its real and imaginary parts both satisfy Laplace's equation in two dimensions. For this reason, the finite difference form of the two-dimensional Laplacian operator $(\partial^2/\partial x^2)+(\partial^2/\partial y^2)$ plays a particularly important part in such contexts.

The other is the general case of functions of two or more real variables other than those arising from formal expressions involving complex numbers. Here, too, the finite difference form of the Laplacian operator is important, particularly in two dimensions, and in three dimensions with some degree of spatial symmetry.

10.11. Numerical calculations with complex numbers

The details of numerical calculations with complex numbers will be carried out almost entirely with pairs of real numbers, since there is no standard calculating machine which deals directly with complex numbers. For addition and subtraction the Cartesian form $z = x+iy$ is clearly the more convenient. For multiplication and division the polar form $z = |z|e^{i\theta}$ seems preferable to the Cartesian form since although the Cartesian formulae

$$(x_1+iy_1)(x_2+iy_2) = x_1 x_2 - y_1 y_2 + i(x_1 y_2 + x_2 y_1),$$

$$(x_1+iy_1)/(x_2+iy_2) = [x_1 x_2 + y_1 y_2 + i(-x_1 y_2 + x_2 y_1)]/(x_2^2+y_2^2)$$

are not difficult to evaluate, it is also not difficult to make a mistake of sign in this evaluation, particularly when x_1, x_2, y_1, and y_2 are not all positive. Use of the polar form will probably involve some conversion from Cartesian to polar form; various good modern books of tables†

† For example, *Chambers's 6-Figure Tables*, vol. 2 (1949).

include tables for simplifying this conversion. Whether, and at what stages of a calculation, it is advisable to make a conversion from Cartesian to polar form or vice versa will depend so much on the calculation, and also perhaps on the individual worker and on whether Cartesian–polar conversion tables are available, that no general rule can be laid down.

For finding powers (other than squares and perhaps fourth powers) or roots of complex numbers, the polar form is usually the most convenient. But square roots can be found directly from the Cartesian form as follows. Let

$$(x+iy)^{\frac{1}{2}} = \xi+i\eta,$$

where ξ, η are real. On squaring and separating real and imaginary parts this gives

$$\xi^2-\eta^2 = x, \qquad 2\xi\eta = y. \tag{10.1}$$

Elimination of η gives a quadratic for ξ^2, of which only the positive root is significant since ξ is real; this root is

$$\xi^2 = \tfrac{1}{2}\{x+|(x^2+y^2)^{\frac{1}{2}}|\},$$

whence

$$\xi = [\tfrac{1}{2}\{x+|(x^2+y^2)^{\frac{1}{2}}|\}]^{\frac{1}{2}}, \qquad \eta = [\tfrac{1}{2}\{-x+|(x^2+y^2)^{\frac{1}{2}}|\}]^{\frac{1}{2}}, \tag{10.2}$$

the signs of these square roots being taken so that $2\xi\eta = y$. If x is positive it may be best to use the first of formulae (10.2) to determine ξ, and then to find η from $\eta = y/2\xi$; and similarly if x is negative to use the second of formulae (10.2) to determine η, and then find ξ from $\xi = y/2\eta$. The result can be checked by squaring the value of $(\xi+i\eta)$ obtained.

10.2. Finite differences in two dimensions; square grid

Just as for functions of one variable x we often have to consider functions as specified by a table at discrete values of x, usually at equal intervals, so for a function of two or more independent variables we are often concerned with a function specified at discrete, equally spaced, values of all the independent variables. In particular, with two independent variables (x, y) it is very often most convenient to take these discrete values of x and y in such a way that they form a grid of square mesh in the (x, y) plane, such as

$$(x, y) = (x_0+j\,\delta x, y_0+k\,\delta y); \qquad \delta x = \delta y = \delta s \tag{10.3}$$

with integral values of (j, k). The values of a function f at such a point will be written $f_{j,k}$.

Such a function can be differenced in the x direction and in the y

direction; δ_x, δ_y will be used for central difference operators in the x and y directions, so that

$$\delta_x f_{j,k} = f_{j+\frac{1}{2},k} - f_{j-\frac{1}{2},k}, \qquad \delta_y f_{j,k} = f_{j,k+\frac{1}{2}} - f_{j,k-\frac{1}{2}};$$
$$\delta_x^2 f_{j,k} = f_{j+1,k} - 2f_{j,k} + f_{j-1,k}, \qquad \delta_y^2 f_{j,k} = f_{j,k+1} - 2f_{j,k} + f_{j,k-1}.$$

A particularly important relation is

$$(\delta_x^2 + \delta_y^2) f_{j,k} = f_{j+1,k} + f_{j,k+1} + f_{j-1,k} + f_{j,k-1} - 4f_{j,k}. \tag{10.4}$$

The operators $\delta x(\partial/\partial x)$ and $\delta y(\partial/\partial y)$ will be written U_x, U_y, the notation being an obvious extension of that of §4.7. Then, as in §4.7,

$$\delta_x = 2\sinh\tfrac{1}{2}U_x, \qquad \delta_y = 2\sinh\tfrac{1}{2}U_y,$$

and

$$\delta_x^2 + \delta_y^2 = 2(\cosh U_x + \cosh U_y) - 4. \tag{10.5}$$

It is convenient to represent formulae such as (10.4), which represent

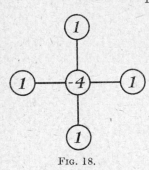

FIG. 18.

linear combinations of values of f at a set of neighbouring points in the (x, y) plane, in a diagrammatic form in which the way in which the different function values enter is more immediately evident. Bickley† uses diagrams in which the set of coefficients in formula (10.4) would be represented by Fig. 18. A similar diagram, however, is used by Southwell in a different sense (see §10.61, Fig. 19), and its use to represent the coefficients in formula (10.4) might be confusing. A more convenient form for printing is the following diagrammatic representation of formula (10.4):

$$(\delta_x^2 + \delta_y^2) f_{j,k} = \begin{array}{|ccc|} 0 & 1 & 0 \\ 1 & -4 & 1 \\ 0 & 1 & 0 \end{array} f_{j,k},$$

the set of coefficients being enclosed in a 'box' to distinguish it from a matrix. Another formula which will be needed, and which can be written in a similar form, is

$$\delta_x^2 \delta_y^2 f_{j,k} = \begin{array}{|ccc|} 1 & -2 & 1 \end{array} \delta_y^2 f_{j,k} = \begin{array}{|ccc|} 1 & -2 & 1 \\ -2 & 4 & -2 \\ 1 & -2 & 1 \end{array} f_{j,k}. \tag{10.6}$$

The quantity $(\delta_x^2 + \delta_y^2) f_{j,k}$ is four times the difference between the arithmetic mean of the values of f at the corners of a square centred on the point (j, k) and the value of f at the centre, the corners of the square

† W. G. Bickley, *Quart. J. Mech. and Applied Math.* **1** (1948), 35.

being the grid points which are the nearest neighbours of (j, k) (the side of the square is $\sqrt{2}(\delta s)$, not δs). A similar quantity involving next-nearest neighbours is

$$\begin{vmatrix} 1 & 0 & 1 \\ 0 & -4 & 0 \\ 1 & 0 & 1 \end{vmatrix} f_{j,k} = f_{j+1,k+1} + f_{j-1,k+1} + f_{j-1,k-1} + f_{j+1,k-1} - 4f_{j,k}.$$

In terms of the operators U_x, U_y this is

$$[e^{U_x+U_y} + e^{-U_x+U_y} + e^{-U_x-U_y} + e^{U_x-U_y} - 4]f_{j,k}$$
$$= [2\cosh(U_x+U_y) + 2\cosh(U_x-U_y) - 4]f_{j,k}$$
$$= 4[\cosh U_x \cosh U_y - 1]f_{j,k}.$$

In terms of the differences of f it can be written:

$$\begin{vmatrix} 1 & 0 & 1 \\ 0 & -4 & 0 \\ 1 & 0 & 1 \end{vmatrix} f_{j,k} = \left\{ \begin{vmatrix} 1 & -2 & 1 \\ -2 & 4 & -2 \\ 1 & -2 & 1 \end{vmatrix} + \begin{vmatrix} 0 & 2 & 0 \\ 2 & -8 & 2 \\ 0 & 2 & 0 \end{vmatrix} \right\} f_{j,k}$$
$$= [\delta_x^2 \delta_y^2 + 2(\delta_x^2 + \delta_y^2)]f_{j,k},$$

so that

$$\delta_x^2 \delta_y^2 f_{j,k} = \begin{vmatrix} 1 & 0 & 1 \\ 0 & -4 & 0 \\ 1 & 0 & 1 \end{vmatrix} f_{j,k} - 2(\delta_x^2 + \delta_y^2)f_{j,k}. \tag{10.7}$$

10.3. The operator $\partial^2/\partial x^2 + \partial^2/\partial y^2$

The particular importance of the Laplacian operator in two dimensions has already been noted in § 10.1. On a grid of square mesh of side δs we have

$$(\delta s)^2 (\partial^2/\partial x^2 + \partial^2/\partial y^2) = U_x^2 + U_y^2,$$

and are therefore concerned with finite-difference approximations to $U_x^2 + U_y^2$. Using the approximations of § 4.7 we can express this in terms of the operators δ_x^2 and δ_y^2 as follows:

$$U_x^2 + U_y^2 = \delta_x^2 [(\sinh^{-1} \tfrac{1}{2}\delta_x)/\tfrac{1}{2}\delta_x]^2 + \delta_y^2 [(\sinh^{-1} \tfrac{1}{2}\delta_y)/\tfrac{1}{2}\delta_y]^2$$
$$= \delta_x^2 - \tfrac{1}{12}\delta_x^4 + O(\delta x)^6 + \delta_y^2 - \tfrac{1}{12}\delta_y^4 + O(\delta y)^6$$
$$= \delta_x^2 + \delta_y^2 - \tfrac{1}{12}(\delta_x^4 + \delta_y^4) + O(\delta s)^6. \tag{10.8}$$

Thus the simplest approximation to $U_x^2 + U_y^2$ is

$$U_x^2 + U_y^2 = \delta_x^2 + \delta_y^2 + O(\delta s)^4,$$

which gives

$$\left(\frac{\partial^2 f}{\partial x^2} + \frac{\partial^2 f}{\partial y^2}\right)_{j,k} = \frac{1}{(\delta s)^2} \begin{vmatrix} 0 & 1 & 0 \\ 1 & -4 & 1 \\ 0 & 1 & 0 \end{vmatrix} f_{j,k} \tag{10.9}$$

with an error term of order $(\delta s)^2$. This approximation is widely used in numerical work. In particular it gives

$$\begin{array}{|ccc|} 0 & 1 & 0 \\ 1 & -4 & 1 \\ 0 & 1 & 0 \end{array} f_{j,k} = 0 \qquad (10.10)$$

as a finite-difference form of $\partial^2 f/\partial x^2 + \partial^2 f/\partial y^2 = 0$.

10.31. Special relations when $\partial^2 f/\partial x^2 + \partial^2 f/\partial y^2 = 0$

In many contexts in which the operator $(\partial^2/\partial x^2 + \partial^2/\partial y^2)$ arises, its importance comes from the fact that one or more of the functions $f(x, y)$ concerned satisfy the relation

$$\partial^2 f/\partial x^2 + \partial^2 f/\partial y^2 = 0.$$

This is always the case when we are concerned with analytic functions of a complex variable, and is often the case in calculations not directly concerned with complex variables. If the operands are restricted to such functions, we have
$$U_x^2 + U_y^2 = 0,$$

and this can be used to obtain some special formulae for use in such contexts; but it must be remembered that they are restricted to such operands.

One of the most important can be derived as follows:

Since $U_x^2 + U_y^2 = 0$ it follows that
$$U_x^4 = U_y^4 = -U_x^2 U_y^2. \qquad (10.11)$$
Hence
$$\delta_x^4 + \delta_y^4 = -2\delta_x^2\delta_y^2 + O(\delta s)^6,$$
so that formula (10.8) can be written
$$0 = \delta_x^2 + \delta_y^2 + \tfrac{1}{6}\delta_x^2\delta_y^2 + O(\delta s)^6,$$
and substitution from (10.7) gives

$$4(\delta_x^2 + \delta_y^2)f_{j,k} + \begin{array}{|ccc|} 1 & 0 & 1 \\ 0 & -4 & 0 \\ 1 & 0 & 1 \end{array} f_{j,k} = O(\delta s)^6$$

that is,

$$\begin{array}{|ccc|} 1 & 4 & 1 \\ 4 & -20 & 4 \\ 1 & 4 & 1 \end{array} f_{j,k} = 0 \qquad (10.12)$$

with an error term of order $(\delta s)^6$. This is an improvement on the simplest finite-difference form (10.10) of the equation $\partial^2 f/\partial x^2 + \partial^2 f/\partial y^2 = 0$, for which the error is of order $(\delta s)^4$.

Another consequence of the relations (10.8) and (10.11) is that

$$\delta_x^4 = 6(\delta_x^2 + \delta_y^2) + O(\delta s)^6, \tag{10.13}$$

and this can, if convenient, be used in integration or interpolation formulae to substitute for fourth differences in the x direction in terms of the second differences. For example, one formula for integration in the x direction is

$$\int_{x_0-\delta x}^{x_0+\delta x} f\,dx = 2(\delta x)[f_0 + \tfrac{1}{6}\delta^2 f_0 - \tfrac{1}{180}\delta^4 f_0] + O(\delta x)^7 \tag{10.14}$$

(this is equivalent to Simpson's rule improved by the inclusion of the leading correcting term; see §6.3). Expressed in diagrammatic form in terms of function values, this is

$$\int_{x_{j-1}}^{x_{j+1}} f(x, y_k)\,dx = \tfrac{1}{90}(\delta x)[-1 \quad 34 \quad 114 \quad 34 \quad -1]f_{j,k} + O(\delta x)^7. \tag{10.15}$$

Substitution for $\delta_x^4 f$ from (10.13) in (10.14) gives

$$\int_{x_0-\delta x}^{x_0+\delta x} f\,dx = 2(\delta x)[f_0 + \tfrac{2}{15}\delta_x^2 f_0 - \tfrac{1}{30}\delta_y^2 f_0] + O(\delta x)^7,$$

that is,†
$$\int_{x_{j-1}}^{x_{j+1}} f(x, y_k)\,dx = \tfrac{1}{15}(\delta x) \begin{vmatrix} 0 & -1 & 0 \\ 4 & 24 & 4 \\ 0 & -1 & 0 \end{vmatrix} f_{j,k} + O(\delta x)^7. \tag{10.16}$$

The coefficients are simpler in (10.16) than in (10.15) and the coefficient in the error term is smaller, as might be expected from the fact that the values of f involved in formula (10.16) lie nearer the range through which the integration is being carried than do the function values in (10.15).‡

10.4. Finite differences in cylindrical coordinates

It is occasionally convenient to use finite differences at equal intervals in polar coordinates (r, θ) in a plane, or in cylindrical polar coordinates, rather than in Cartesian coordinates. Plane polar coordinates would be the natural ones to use, for example, in a calculation concerned with a solution of Laplace's equation in two dimensions with boundary conditions given on a circular boundary; and cylindrical polar coordinates would be the natural ones to use in a three-dimensional problem

† This formula was first derived by another method by G. Birkhoff and D. M. Young, see *Journ. of Math. and Phys.* **29** (1950), 217.

‡ For a similar use of the relation $U_x^2 + U_y^2 = 0$ in the interpolation of functions of a complex variable, see P. M. and A. M. Woodward, *Phil. Mag.* (7) **37** (1946), 236; **39** (1948), 594.

with axial symmetry and boundary conditions on the surface of a circular cylinder. These cases can be considered together, the case of plane polar coordinates being given by putting $\partial/\partial z = 0$ in the equations for cylindrical polar coordinates.

One way of dealing with such calculations is to make the conformal transformation to $(\log r, \theta)$ and to work on a rectangular or square grid in the $(\log r, \theta)$ plane. But this is often not convenient when the point (or axis) $r = 0$ is in the domain to be covered by the integration, and it is then better to use the (r, θ) coordinates without modification.

Consider first the case of axial symmetry. Then the Laplacian operator in cylindrical polar coordinates is

$$\frac{\partial^2}{\partial r^2} + \frac{1}{r}\frac{\partial}{\partial r} + \frac{\partial^2}{\partial z^2}.$$

The finite-difference approximation to $\partial^2/\partial z^2$ is the same as in Cartesian coordinates; only the r-derivatives need special treatment. Let f_j stand for $f(j\,\delta r)$. Then

$$\left(\frac{\partial^2 f}{\partial r^2}\right)_j = (f_{j+1} - 2f_j + f_{j-1})/(\delta r)^2 + O(\delta r)^2.$$

An approximation to $(\partial f/\partial r)_j$, with an error term of the same order, is

$$\left(\frac{\partial f}{\partial r}\right)_j = (f_{j+1} - f_{j-1})/2(\delta r) + O(\delta r)^2,$$

so that for $j \neq 0$

$$\left(\frac{\partial^2 f}{\partial r^2} + \frac{1}{r}\frac{\partial f}{\partial r}\right)_j = \left[\left(1 - \frac{1}{2j}\right)f_{j-1} - 2f_j + \left(1 + \frac{1}{2j}\right)f_{j+1}\right]\Big/(\delta r)^2 + O(\delta r)^2$$

$$= [(2j-1)f_{j-1} - 4jf_j + (2j+1)f_{j+1}]/2j(\delta r)^2 + O(\delta r)^2. \qquad (10.17)$$

For axial symmetry, either there is a singularity at $r = 0$ or $\partial f/\partial r$ is zero there. If there is a singularity, further analytical investigation is required before numerical methods are applied. If $\partial f/\partial r = 0$ at $r = 0$, then

$$\left(\frac{\partial^2 f}{\partial r^2} + \frac{1}{r}\frac{\partial f}{\partial r}\right)_0 = 4(f_1 - f_0)/(\delta r)^2 + O(\delta r)^2, \qquad (10.18)$$

a relation which can also be obtained from (10.9), since for axial symmetry each of the values of f with coefficient unity in (10.9) is f_1.

If there is not axial symmetry, then there is an additional term $r^{-2}\partial^2/\partial\theta^2$ in the Laplacian operator, and if $f_{j,k}$ stands for $f(j\,\delta r, k\,\delta\theta)$, we have for $j \neq 0$,

$$\left(\frac{1}{r^2}\frac{\partial^2 f}{\partial\theta^2}\right)_{j,k} = \frac{1}{(j\,\delta r)^2}\left[\frac{f_{j,k+1} - 2f_{j,k} + f_{j,k-1}}{(\delta\theta)^2}\right] + O(\delta\theta)^2. \qquad (10.19)$$

For the equation for $j = 0$, let $\bar{f}_1$ be the arithmetic mean of the values $f_{1,k}$ of f on the circle $r = \delta r$. Then

$$\left(\frac{\partial^2 f}{\partial r^2} + \frac{1}{r}\frac{\partial f}{\partial r} + \frac{1}{r^2}\frac{\partial^2 f}{\partial \theta^2}\right)_0 = 4(\bar{f}_1 - f_0)/(\delta r)^2 + O(\delta r)^2. \tag{10.20}$$

If f varies in the z direction, then to give $\nabla^2 f$, a finite-difference approximation to $\partial^2 f / \partial z^2$ has to be added to whichever of formulae (10.17) to (10.20) is the appropriate one to use for the variations in the (r, θ) plane.

10.5. Partial differential equations

Solutions of partial differential equations can sometimes be obtained by a separation of variables, by which the partial differential equation is reduced to a number of separate ordinary equations, one in each of the independent variables. Such a separation, if possible, is part of the preliminary analytical treatment of the problem before numerical methods come to be applied, and will not be considered here. The following sections are concerned with the numerical treatment of partial differential equations as such. It will mainly be concerned with partial differential equations in two independent variables, as the numerical solution of equations with three or more independent variables is usually a problem on too large a scale to handle without special equipment.

Most partial differential equations which arise in contexts in which numerical solutions are required are second order in at least one of the independent variables, and, moreover, are linear in the second-order derivatives. Simple examples are Poisson's equation in two dimensions

$$\frac{\partial^2 f}{\partial x^2} + \frac{\partial^2 f}{\partial y^2} = g(x, y), \tag{10.21}$$

where $g(x, y)$ is given; the equation of heat conduction or diffusion in one dimension

$$\frac{\partial f}{\partial t} = D\frac{\partial^2 f}{\partial x^2} \tag{10.22}$$

in which the diffusivity D may depend on f (this would make the equation as a whole non-linear, but the second derivative enters linearly); and the wave equation

$$\frac{\partial^2 f}{\partial t^2} = \alpha^2\frac{\partial^2 f}{\partial x^2}. \tag{10.23}$$

Just as the nature of the problem of numerical solution of ordinary differential equations depends on whether the conditions the solution has to satisfy are of the one-point or two-point type, so the nature of the problem of the numerical solution of partial differential equations depends on whether the boundary conditions are given on a boundary completely enclosing the domain of the variables over which a solution is required, or whether this domain is unbounded in one or more directions. There is a classification of second-order equations in two variables as 'elliptic', 'parabolic', or 'hyperbolic' which is closely related to the different characters of boundary conditions usually associated with such equations, and the character of the problem of numerical integration is correspondingly different in the three cases.

The general second-order equation in two variables, linear in the second derivatives, is

$$H \frac{\partial^2 f}{\partial x^2} + 2K \frac{\partial^2 f}{\partial x \partial y} + L \frac{\partial^2 f}{\partial y^2} + M = 0, \qquad (10.24)$$

where H, K, L, M may be functions of any one or more of the variables x, y, f, $\partial f/\partial x$, $\partial f/\partial y$. The classification depends on the sign of $K^2 - HL$; the reason for this will be explained in §10.8. If this quantity is negative, the equation is termed 'elliptic'; if it is zero, the equation is termed 'parabolic'; and if it is positive, the equation is termed 'hyperbolic'. Poisson's equation (10.21) is a simple example of an 'elliptic' equation, the diffusion equation (10.22) is one of a 'parabolic' equation, and the wave equation (10.23) is one of a 'hyperbolic' equation. 'Elliptic' equations are usually associated with a domain completely bounded by closed curves (one of which may be the circle at infinity) on which boundary conditions are given. 'Parabolic' and 'hyperbolic' equations are usually associated with a domain which is open in the direction of one variable, which physically is often the time variable. For example we may require a solution of the heat conduction equation (10.22) from given *initial* conditions in time (f given as a function of x at $t = 0$) and with given *terminal* conditions in space (f given as a function of t at $x = a, x = b$) but with no condition to be satisfied at a later time $t = T$; the initial and terminal conditions are enough to define a solution, and such an independent condition at a later time could not generally be satisfied. It is not, however, *necessary* that the boundary conditions should be of this type; we might alternatively have no initial conditions, but given terminal conditions and a condition of periodicity in time, that is, a condition that f should be the same function of x at a given time T as at time $t = 0$.

If H, K, and L are not all constants, then the equation may be of different type in different parts of the domain in which the solution is required. But in many of the simpler partial differential equations, such as (10.21), (10.22), and (10.23), including many practically important ones for which numerical work is likely to be needed, the equation remains of the same type throughout the whole domain, and only such cases will be considered here.

10.6. Elliptic equations

Poisson's equation (10.21) in two dimensions will be taken as a typical example of an elliptic equation for whose solution we require a numerical process. This process will cover as special cases Laplace's equation ($g(x, y) = 0$ in (10.21)) and the torsion equation ($g(x, y) = $ const.). The first step is to replace the partial differential equation by a finite-difference relation on a convenient grid of discrete points. A Cartesian or polar grid will usually be most convenient, and for the present only a Cartesian grid of square mesh with mesh side h will be considered. It is clearly most convenient if the boundaries are of such a form that a grid can be chosen so that the boundaries lie along the sides or diagonals of the grid squares, and it will be supposed for the present that this is the case and that the grid is so chosen.

Using the simplest approximation (10.9) to $[(\partial^2/\partial x^2) + (\partial^2/\partial y^2)]$ we then have a set of equations

$$\begin{array}{|ccc|} 0 & 1 & 0 \\ 1 & -4 & 1 \\ 0 & 1 & 0 \end{array} f_{j,k} = h^2 g_{j,k}, \tag{10.25}$$

one for each mesh point. These are linear simultaneous algebraic equations, so that we have formally reduced the numerical problem to one of the kind already considered in Chapter VIII. The solution of the set of equations (10.25) is not, of course, the solution of the partial differential equation on account of the truncation error of the approximation (10.9). The approximation can be improved by taking a finer mesh or by using the better approximation (10.8) to $\partial^2 f/\partial^2 x + \partial^2 f/\partial y^2$. If the latter process is used, a convenient procedure is to write the finite-difference equation

$$\begin{array}{|ccc|} 0 & 1 & 0 \\ 1 & -4 & 1 \\ 0 & 1 & 0 \end{array} f_{j,k} = h^2 g_{j,k} + \tfrac{1}{12}(\delta_x^4 + \delta_y^4) f_{j,k} \tag{10.26}$$

and to solve this by an iterative process, using in the nth stage of the iterative process values of $(\delta_x^4 + \delta_y^4)f$ obtained from the results of the $(n-1)$th stage.†

10.61. Relaxation process

A 'relaxation' process (§ 8.5) is very convenient for carrying out the numerical solution of the set of equations (10.25) or (10.26), and is commonly used for this purpose. This common association of the relaxation procedure with the approximate equations (10.25) seems to have given the impression that the relaxation process itself is approximate, and the errors of the approximation (10.25) are sometimes referred to as 'errors of the relaxation process'. But this is a misunderstanding; the approximation is not in the relaxation process itself but in the equations (10.25) whose solution is evaluated by this process. Regarded as a solution of the partial differential equation, the solution of equations (10.25) is equally in error whether it is evaluated by the relaxation process or by any other (such as elimination or inversion of the matrix of the coefficients of equations (10.25)) and the errors have nothing to do with the relaxation process used to obtain a solution of these finite-difference equations.

The approximation to the solution of the partial differential equations can be improved by reducing the mesh size of the grid on which the finite differences are taken. In practice it is advisable to start with a very coarse mesh so that the number of grid points is quite small, and then to break down the grid to one of smaller mesh size when an approximate solution on the coarse mesh has been reached. Then the relaxation process on the finer grid starts from a set of values which is already a fair approximation to the solution.

It is convenient to carry out the relaxation process on a diagram representing the domain in which the solution is required, with the finite-difference grid drawn on it. The usual convention is to write the function values and their *changes* to the left of each grid point, and *values* of the residuals to the right. For the simplest finite-difference approximation (10.25) to Poisson's equation, the residual $R_{j,k}$ at the point (j, k) is

$$R_{j,k} = \begin{vmatrix} 0 & 1 & 0 \\ 1 & -4 & 1 \\ 0 & 1 & 0 \end{vmatrix} f_{j,k} - h^2 g_{j,k}. \tag{10.27}$$

If a relaxation Δf is made at one point, the residual at that point is changed by $-4\,\Delta f$, and that at each nearest neighbour, other than a

† See, for example, L. Fox, *Proc. Roy. Soc.* A, **190** (1947), 31.

boundary point, is changed by $+\Delta f$, so that the pattern of the *changes in the residuals* is as represented diagrammatically in Fig. 19. The entries here are the coefficients of a *single* Δf value.

Example: To find approximately the solution of Laplace's equation

$$\frac{\partial^2 V}{\partial x^2} + \frac{\partial^2 V}{\partial y^2} = 0$$

for the system shown in Fig. 20, with equipotentials $V = 0$ and $V = 80$ as indicated.

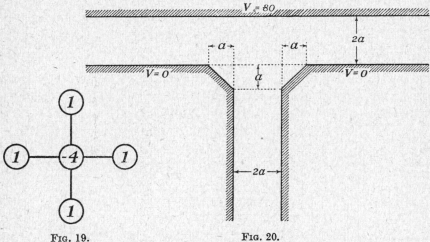

FIG. 19.   FIG. 20.

The first, coarse, grid can be taken as shown in Fig. 21. It might seem at first sight that this grid is too coarse for the results to be of any value. But we shall see that this rough approximation is in fact useful, and is obtained much more easily and quickly than results on a finer grid. By symmetry, only half of the diagram need be shown, but it must be remembered that each relaxation ΔV at a point one interval from the centre line is accompanied by an equal one at the image point, so that the contribution to the residual on the centre line is $2\Delta V$.

A set of values of V from which to start the relaxation process can be written in as if the equipotential $V = 0$ were the straight line AB. Then the residuals are zero except on AB. These values of V and the residuals are entered on Fig. 21.

We could start the relaxation process by making such a relaxation as to reduce the residual at C (for example) to zero; this would require a relaxation $\Delta V = +10$ at C (and at its image in the centre line). But clearly a positive relaxation ΔV is going to be required at D, which will make a positive contribution to the residual at C, and a further positive relaxation ΔV at C will be needed to remove it. We can anticipate this by deliberately taking a larger relaxation ΔV at C than is required to reduce the residual there to zero; this is called 'over-relaxing'. Experience is the only way of learning when and by how much to over-relax; the beginner will probably be inclined not to over-relax enough. As a rough rule it may be suggested that when there are several residuals of the same sign together, over-relaxation by a factor 2 will not be excessive.

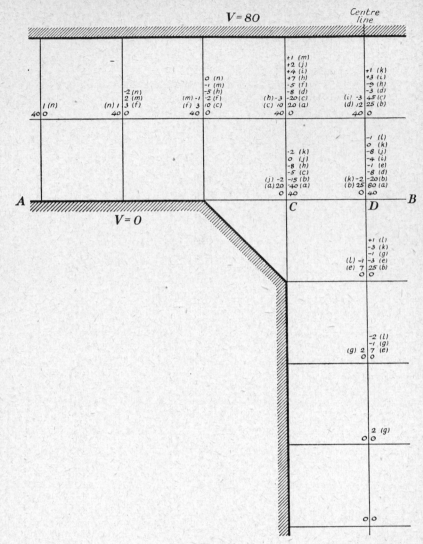

FIG. 21.

Let us start, therefore, with a relaxation $\Delta V = +20$ at C; this leaves a considerable positive residual at D, flanked now by large negative residuals at C and its image point, so that a smaller degree of over-relaxation is now required. Let us therefore take next a relaxation $\Delta V = +25$ at D.

The further process of the calculation is indicated in Fig. 21, the relaxations and the values of the residuals resulting from them being indicated by (a), (b), (c),... in succession. At some convenient stage in the work, it is advisable to collect together the values of ΔV and write down a new set of V's at the mesh points, and to recalculate the residuals from these values of V in case any mistake has been made in the relaxation process. The calculation can then be continued from these values of V and the corresponding residuals. This check should normally be made before the accuracy of the numerical work is increased by taking an extra significant figure (compare the examples in §§ 8.51 and 8.53) and always before changing from a coarser to a finer grid.

Notes: (i) The individual numerical steps of the relaxation process are very simple and are carried out with small numbers, usually of one or two significant figures; they can therefore be carried out rapidly and easily.

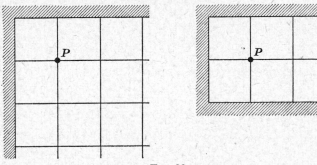

FIG. 22.

(ii) When the value of V at a point *not* at a distance δs from a boundary is changed, the sum of the residuals remains unchanged; all that is changed is the distribution of this total among the grid points. But if a relaxation ΔV is made at a grid point P adjacent to a boundary, the sum of the residuals is reduced by ΔV, or by $2\Delta V$ or $3\Delta V$ if two or three of the nearest neighbours of P are on the boundary (see Fig. 22).

(iii) A physical analogue of the relaxation process, as applied to the finite-difference form of Laplace's equation, can be given by considering Poisson's equation for the potential of two-dimensional distribution of electrical charge, namely

$$\frac{\partial^2 V}{\partial x^2} + \frac{\partial^2 V}{\partial y^2} = -4\pi\rho.$$

The finite-difference approximation (10.10) to the left-hand side gives

$$R_{j,k} = \begin{vmatrix} 0 & 1 & 0 \\ 1 & -4 & 1 \\ 0 & 1 & 0 \end{vmatrix} V_{j,k} = h^2 \left[\frac{\partial^2 V}{\partial x^2} + \frac{\partial^2 V}{\partial y^2} \right] = -4\pi h^2 \rho_{j,k}, \qquad (10.28)$$

and $h^2 \rho_{j,k}$ is (to this approximation) the charge on a square of side h centred on the point (j,k). Thus for any assigned set of values of $V_{j,k}$, the residuals $R_{j,k}$ are a measure of the charge distribution required to give the assigned potential distribution. The relaxation process can be regarded as a process of shifting this charge distribution about until it is ultimately all in the form of surface charge on conductors forming the given equipotential boundaries and none is left as space charge in the domain over which the integration is carried.

The constancy of the sum of the residuals when a relaxation is made at a grid point *not* adjacent to a boundary corresponds to the constancy of the total space charge in the domain when some charge is taken from one grid point and distributed among its four nearest neighbours. The change in the sum of the residuals when a relaxation is made at a point adjacent to a boundary corresponds to the transfer of some of the space charge to surface charge on the boundary.

This analogy suggests that the aim of the relaxation process should be not only to make the residuals small but to make them not all of the same sign, so that their sum, represented by the total residual space charge in this analogy, is small. It will not in general be possible to reduce all residuals to zero in the least significant digital position; a sprinkling of values ± 1 with occasional values ± 2 is the best that can be expected, and such a set of residuals, with mean value perhaps $0 \cdot 1$ or $0 \cdot 2$, probably indicates a better approximation to a solution than a set of residuals $+1$ over the whole field.

(iv) A set of residuals of magnitude not greater than 2 does not necessarily mean that the values of V are correct to a unit. It is advisable to reduce the residuals on the final grid to ± 2 in the next figure beyond the last figure in V required in the final results.

(v) No indications such as the letters (a), (b), (c),... in Fig. 21 are required in actual working; they are only given in this figure to help the reader to follow the details of the calculation. As soon as one value of a residual is replaced by another, the earlier one can be crossed out or erased as being of no further interest.

(vi) If the grid is drawn in ink and the working is done lightly in pencil, then old values of V and old residuals can be erased without losing the pattern of the grid. This erasing of old values need not be done at every relaxation, but only when the space for values of residuals gets filled up.

(vii) In this example the over-relaxation by a factor of 2 in the first relaxation has been a little too much, and a small relaxation of the opposite sign has had to be made later. But this step of over-relaxation has speeded the approach to a solution of the finite-difference equation. Only fourteen steps of relaxation have been needed to reduce the greatest value of $|R_{j,k}|$ from 40 to 2.

(viii) With the very coarse grid used here, there is no point in trying to improve the approximation to the solution of the finite-difference equations by taking an extra figure in the V-values. The next step is to reduce the truncation errors by taking a finer grid.

10.62. Reducing the mesh size

At some stage in the calculation it will usually be necessary, as in the above example, to change from a coarse to a finer grid. Let h_1 be the mesh size of the coarser grid. A convenient first step is to take the diagonals of the squares of the old grid as forming a new grid of mesh size $h_2 = h_1/\surd 2$ (see Fig. 23). The new grid points are the centres of the squares of the old grid. For Poisson's equation we have on the new grid, with the finite-difference approximation adopted

$$\begin{bmatrix} 0 & 1 & 0 \\ 1 & -4 & 1 \\ 0 & 1 & 0 \end{bmatrix} f_{j,k} = h_2^2 g_{j,k} = \tfrac{1}{2}h_1^2 g_{j,k},$$

and hence $\qquad f_{j,k} = \tfrac{1}{4}\left\{ \begin{bmatrix} 0 & 1 & 0 \\ 1 & 0 & 1 \\ 0 & 1 & 0 \end{bmatrix} f_{j,k} - h_2^2 g_{j,k} \right\}.$ $\qquad\qquad$ (10.29)

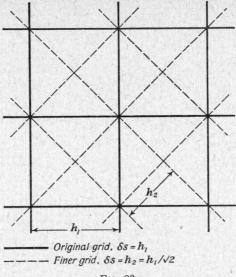

Original grid, $\delta s = h_1$
— — — Finer grid, $\delta s = h_2 = h_1/\sqrt{2}$

FIG. 23.

This gives a set of values of f at the centres of the squares of the old grid, which are the new grid points of the new grid. In particular for Laplace's equation we have, in this approximation

$$f_{j,k} = \tfrac{1}{4} \begin{vmatrix} 0 & 1 & 0 \\ 1 & 0 & 1 \\ 0 & 1 & 0 \end{vmatrix} f_{j,k}; \qquad (10.30)$$

that is to say, the value of f at the centre of a square is the arithmetic mean of its values at the corners. A further relaxation may be carried out on this grid, or this process may be repeated immediately, giving a grid of mesh size $h_3 = \tfrac{1}{2}h_1$, whose grid points are the corners, centres, and mid-points of the sides of the original grid (see Fig. 24).

Example: The example of the previous section continued. Fig. 25 shows the process of breaking down the grid in two stages. The numbers in squares are the values of V obtained in the calculation shown in Fig. 21. The numbers in circles, at the centres of the squares of the original grid, are obtained by the application of formula (10.30) to the intermediate grid formed by the diagonals of the original grid. The numbers at the other grid points of Fig. 25 are then obtained by the application of formula (10.30) to the grid formed by the diagonals of the intermediate grid.

The residuals are shown on the right of the grid points, and only a single step of relaxation is then required to reduce the greatest $|R_{j,k}|$ to 2. At this stage another significant figure can be taken in V and the relaxation process continued.

Note: The advantage of starting with a very coarse grid will now be apparent. The number of grid points varies as $1/h^2$ and the number of relaxations at each grid point probably varies roughly as $1/h$, so that if the finer grid of Fig. 25 had been used from the beginning, something like eight times as much work would be required to reach the stage represented by the results in Fig. 25. In terms of the analogy explained in note (iii) of the previous section, despite the coarse grid of Fig. 21, relaxation on this grid has carried out the bulk of the transfer of charge from the inter-electrode space to the electrodes, and what has to be done on the finer grid is mainly a minor rearrangement of the residual charges.

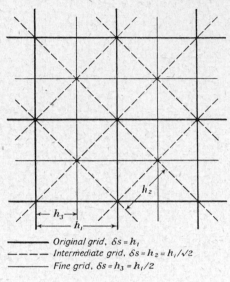

——————— Original grid, $\delta s = h_1$
- - - - - - Intermediate grid, $\delta s = h_2 = h_1/\sqrt{2}$
——————— Fine grid, $\delta s = h_3 = h_1/2$

Fig. 24.

10.63. Further notes on the relaxation process

We have only been concerned here with the simplest case in which (i) the boundary of the domain of integration does not cut the side of any of the grid squares, (ii) the boundary condition is that V is given, and (iii) the equation to be solved is the simplest example of an elliptic equation. For extensions of the procedure to deal with boundaries which cut the sides of some of the grid squares, with boundary conditions involving the normal derivative of V, and with less simple equations, for further practical hints on carrying out the relaxation process in this context, and for examples, reference should be made to Southwell's *Relaxation Methods in Theoretical Physics* and papers referred to in the bibliography in that book.†

† See also E. Stiefel, *Zeit. f. angew. Math. und Phys.* **3** (1952), 1.

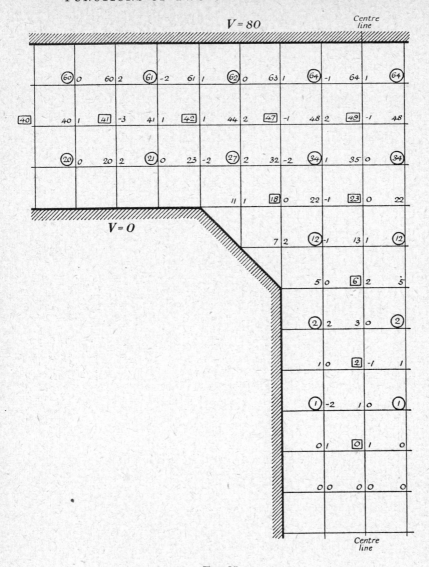

FIG. 25.

The method can be adapted to characteristic value problems such as the determination of the values—or at least the smallest value—of λ for which the equation

$$\frac{\partial^2 f}{\partial x^2} + \frac{\partial^2 f}{\partial y^2} = -\lambda f$$

with boundary conditions $f = 0$ on a closed curve, has a non-trivial solution. Use of the finite-difference approximation (10.9) on the left-hand side gives the set of simultaneous equations

$$\begin{array}{|ccc|} 0 & 1 & 0 \\ 1 & -(4-\lambda h^2) & 1 \\ 0 & 1 & 0 \end{array} f_{j,k} = 0,$$

and the determination of λ by a relaxation process follows the general lines of § 8.7.

10.64. Richardson–Liebmann process for Laplace's equation

There is another process of successive approximation for solving the set of equations (10.10) which form the simplest finite-difference approximation to

$$\frac{\partial^2 f}{\partial x^2} + \frac{\partial^2 f}{\partial y^2} = 0.$$

In its simplest form, given by Liebmann,[†] this process consists of repeated use of formula (10.30), working systematically over the grid, replacing f at each grid point by the arithmetic mean of the value of f at its four nearest neighbours.

In another form, given by L. F. Richardson,[‡] each value of $f_{j,k}$ in a trial solution is increased by a multiple α of the residual $R_{j,k}$ at that point, and the result is taken as the next trial solution. Richardson proposed the use of a set of different values of α in the construction of successive trial solutions. Liebmann's process is equivalent to a special case of Richardson's in which α is kept fixed.

Compared with the more recently devised relaxation process, the Richardson–Liebmann process has three disadvantages. First, all the work is done with large numbers, the values of f themselves, whereas in the relaxation process the bulk of the work is done with relatively small and simple numbers, the *relaxations* of f and the residuals. Secondly, a lot of time and work is spent on calculation in regions where the residuals are small, whereas in the relaxation process attention is first directed to the region where the residuals are large and the rest of the domain is left untouched until the larger residuals have been removed. And, thirdly, it is not so easy to modify so as to take into account the higher differences in the replacement of derivatives by finite differences.

10.7. Parabolic equations

Processes for the numerical solution of parabolic and hyperbolic equations have been much less explored than those for elliptic equations,

---

† H. Liebmann, *Sitzungsber. Bayer. Akad. München* (1918), 385.
‡ L. F. Richardson, *Phil. Trans. Roy. Soc.* A, **210** (1910), 307.

though several practicable methods have been devised; some of these are indicated in the following sections (§§ 10.71–10.73).

As a simple case of a parabolic equation we will consider the equation of heat conduction in one dimension

$$\frac{\partial f}{\partial t} = \frac{\partial^2 f}{\partial x^2}, \tag{10.31}$$

with given initial and terminal conditions.

One way of dealing with this equation is first to replace only one of the derivatives by a finite difference; this replaces the partial differential equation by a set of ordinary equations which can then be treated by one of the methods of Chapter VII. The form of this set of ordinary equations and the process for their solution differ considerably according as it is the first-order (time) derivative or the second-order (space) derivative which is replaced by a finite difference.

10.71. Replacement of the second-order (space) derivative by a finite difference

Let $f_j(t)$ be written for the value of f at $x = j\,\delta x$ and at time t. Then replacement of the second derivative by a finite difference gives

$$\frac{df_j(t)}{dt} = [f_{j+1}(t) - 2f_j(t) + f_{j-1}(t)]/(\delta x)^2 + O(\delta x)^2. \tag{10.32}$$

This is a set of simultaneous first-order equations for the different functions $f_j(t)$ and these can be solved numerically without difficulty. The initial values of each f_j is given by the initial conditions. The truncation errors are of order $(\delta x)^2$; they can be estimated, and the leading term in the corrections applied, by Richardson's h^2-extrapolation process (see § 7.51). This method is not restricted to one space variable and the time variable, and it is practicable to use it for the numerical solution of the equation of heat conduction in two space variables and, moreover, for a substance of which the thermal properties vary with temperature.†

10.72. Replacement of the first-order (time) derivative by a finite difference

For a time interval δt, the time derivative at any value of x can be replaced by a finite difference as follows:

$$\left(\frac{\partial f}{\partial t}\right)_{x,\,t+\frac{1}{2}\delta t} = [f(x,\,t+\delta t) - f(x,\,t)]/(\delta t) + O(\delta t)^2,$$

and, with an error term of the same order, $\partial^2 f/\partial x^2$ at time $t + \frac{1}{2}\delta t$ can be

† See N. R. Eyres and others, *Phil. Trans. Roy. Soc.* **240** (1946), 1.

replaced by the arithmetic mean of its values at the beginning and end of the time interval:

$$\left(\frac{\partial^2 f}{\partial x^2}\right)_{x,t+\frac{1}{2}\delta t} = \frac{1}{2}\left[\frac{\partial^2}{\partial x^2}\{f(x,t+\delta t)+f(x,t)\}\right]+O(\delta t)^2.$$

If the right-hand sides of these are equated and the error terms neglected, we have

$$\frac{\partial^2}{\partial x^2}[f(x,t+\delta t)+f(x,t)] = (2/\delta t)[f(x,t+\delta t)+f(x,t)]-(4/\delta t)f(x,t).$$

$$(10.33)$$

Given f as a function of x at time t, this is an *ordinary* differential equation for f as a function of x at time $t+\delta t$. There is a set of equations (10.33), one for each time interval. But they can be integrated *successively*, and do not have to be treated simultaneously as equations (10.32) do; the calculation proceeds interval by interval in t, the results $f(x,t+\delta t)$ for the end of one interval being the given function $f(x,t)$ for the beginning of the next.

In the integration of equation (10.33) it is not necessary to know the values of $\partial^2 f/\partial x^2$ at the beginning of the interval; the best procedure is to carry out the numerical solution regarding equation (10.33) as an equation for $[f(x,t+\delta t)+f(x,t)]$ and then to subtract the known $f(x,t)$ to give $f(x,t+\delta t)$.

If two separate integrations covering the same range in t are carried out, with different time intervals δt, the leading term in the truncation error can be eliminated by Richardson's h^2-extrapolation process (see § 7.51), and in many cases this will also correct for the next term in the truncation error.[†]

Although in this method we carry out successive integrations of a single equation (10.33) instead of simultaneous integrations of a set of equations, and, moreover, equation (10.33) is a second-order equation with the first derivative absent, which as mentioned in § 7.2 is the most convenient form of all for numerical treatment, the method has the great disadvantage that the solution of this equation has to satisfy two-point boundary conditions in x, and a step-by-step integration is often difficult because of the extreme sensitiveness of the solution to the initial conditions and to rounding errors. This sensitiveness is more marked the smaller the value taken for the time interval δt, so that while a small value of δt would be preferred in order to keep down the truncation errors, it may make the integration process impracticable.

[†] See D. R. Hartree and J. R. Womersley, *Proc. Roy. Soc.* A, **161** (1937), 363.

The two-point character of the boundary conditions and the sensitiveness of the solution makes the method less simple and straightforward than it may appear at first sight, and in its application to less simple equations other precautions may be necessary in using the finite-difference approximations to derivatives.†

10.73. Replacement of both derivatives by finite differences

In the notation of § 10.71

$$\left(\frac{\partial f}{\partial t}\right)_{x_j,t} = [f_j(t+\delta t)-f_j(t-\delta t)]/2\delta t+O(\delta t)^2$$

and

$$\left(\frac{\partial^2 f}{\partial x^2}\right)_{x_j,t} = [f_{j+1}(t)-2f_j(t)+f_{j-1}(t)]/(\delta x)^2+O(\delta x)^2.$$

These approximations invite us to equate the right-hand sides and so obtain (neglecting the error terms)

$$f_j(t+\delta t) = f_j(t-\delta t)-\{2\delta t/(\delta x)^2\}[f_{j+1}(t)-2f_j(t)+f_{j-1}(t)].$$

This looks a very attractive formula, since if the solution has been carried to any value of t, it gives directly each value of $f_j(t+\delta t)$ separately in terms of known quantities, and a process of using this formula to integrate through successive intervals δt looks simple and straightforward. Unfortunately, however, such a process is unstable, and effects of rounding errors build up rapidly and uncontrollably.‡

However, there is another way of using similar approximations which leads to a stable numerical process which is practicable but not quite so simple.‡ This is based on equating approximations to $\partial f/\partial t$ and $\partial^2 f/\partial x^2$ not at grid points in the (x,t) plane but at points half-way in t between grid points. We have

$$\left(\frac{\partial f}{\partial t}\right)_{x_j,t+\frac{1}{2}\delta t} = [f_j(t+\delta t)-f_j(t)]/\delta t+O(\delta t)^2,$$

$$\left(\frac{\partial^2 f}{\partial x^2}\right)_{x_j,t+\frac{1}{2}\delta t} = \frac{1}{2}\left[\left(\frac{\partial^2 f}{\partial x^2}\right)_{x_j,t+\delta t}+\left(\frac{\partial^2 f}{\partial x^2}\right)_{x_j,t}\right]+O(\delta t)^2$$

$$= \{1/2(\delta x)^2\}[f_{j+1}(t+\delta t)-2f_j(t+\delta t)+f_{j-1}(t+\delta t)+$$
$$+f_{j+1}(t)-2f_j(t)+f_{j-1}(t)]+O(\delta t)^2+O(\delta x)^2.$$

If we equate the right-hand sides of these expressions and neglect the error terms, we have

$$f_{j+1}(t+\delta t)-2\{1+(\delta x)^2/2(\delta t)\}f_j(t+\delta t)+f_{j-1}(t+\delta t)$$
$$= -[f_{j+1}(t)-2\{1-(\delta x)^2/2\delta t\}f_j(t)+f_{j-1}(t)]. \quad (10.34)$$

† For examples and further discussion, see D. R. Hartree, *Rep. and Mem. A.R.C.*, Nos. 2426, 2427 (1939).

‡ See J. Crank and P. Nicolson, *Proc. Camb. Phil. Soc.* **43** (1947), 50.

This is a set of simultaneous algebraic equations for $f_j(t+\delta t)$ as a function of x_j with boundary conditions of the two-point type in x_j; they can be solved by an application of the relaxation process or by some other process of successive approximation.

10.74. Note on methods for parabolic equations

In all three of the methods considered in §§ 10.71 to 10.73 the process of evaluating an approximate solution is carried out in the direction of t increasing, t being in the conduction equation (10.31) the time variable, and in general that independent variable which does not occur in any second derivatives. All three methods are practicable only if the domain of integration is open in the direction of this variable, so that the whole solution does not have to satisfy any conditions at some later time in the course of the process of solution. As already mentioned in § 10.5 this is the most common situation with parabolic equations.

10.8. Hyperbolic equations. Characteristics

For hyperbolic equations methods similar to those for parabolic equations can

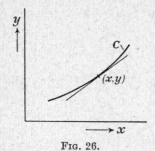

FIG. 26.

be used, and in addition there is another class of methods peculiar to hyperbolic equations. These depend on the properties of sets of curves called 'characteristics' of a hyperbolic equation. As in § 10.5, let the equation be

$$H \frac{\partial^2 f}{\partial x^2} + 2K \frac{\partial^2 f}{\partial x \partial y} + L \frac{\partial^2 f}{\partial y^2} + M = 0, \quad (10.35)$$

where H, K, L, and M may be functions of any one or more of $x, y, f, \partial f/\partial x, \partial f/\partial y$, and consider the integration of the equation along a curve C in the (x, y) plane. Let dy/dx be the gradient of C at (x, y) (see Fig. 26). Then for an element of arc ds of C

$$d\left(\frac{\partial f}{\partial x}\right) = \left(\frac{\partial^2 f}{\partial x^2}\frac{dx}{ds} + \frac{\partial^2 f}{\partial x \partial y}\frac{dy}{ds}\right) ds, \qquad d\left(\frac{\partial f}{\partial y}\right) = \left(\frac{\partial^2 f}{\partial x \partial y}\frac{dx}{ds} + \frac{\partial^2 f}{\partial y^2}\frac{dy}{ds}\right) ds,$$

and hence

$$H \frac{dy}{ds} d\left(\frac{\partial f}{\partial x}\right) + L \frac{dx}{ds} d\left(\frac{\partial f}{\partial y}\right) = \left[\left(H \frac{\partial^2 f}{\partial x^2} + L \frac{\partial^2 f}{\partial y^2}\right)\frac{dx}{ds}\frac{dy}{ds} + \frac{\partial^2 f}{\partial x \partial y}\left\{H\left(\frac{dy}{ds}\right)^2 + L\left(\frac{dx}{ds}\right)^2\right\}\right] ds.$$

On substitution from the differential equation (10.35) this becomes

$$H \frac{dy}{ds} d\left(\frac{\partial f}{\partial x}\right) + L \frac{dx}{ds} d\left(\frac{\partial f}{\partial y}\right) = \left[-M \frac{dx}{ds}\frac{dy}{ds} + \frac{\partial^2 f}{\partial x \partial y}\left\{H\left(\frac{dy}{ds}\right)^2 - 2K \frac{dx}{ds}\frac{dy}{ds} + L\left(\frac{dx}{ds}\right)^2\right\}\right] ds.$$

If now the curve C is chosen so that

$$H\left(\frac{dy}{ds}\right)^2 - 2K \frac{dx}{ds}\frac{dy}{ds} + L\left(\frac{dx}{ds}\right)^2 = 0, \quad\quad\quad (10.36)$$

then

$$H \frac{dy}{ds} d\left(\frac{\partial f}{\partial x}\right) + L \frac{dx}{ds} d\left(\frac{\partial f}{\partial y}\right) + M \frac{dx}{ds}\frac{dy}{ds} ds = 0. \quad\quad (10.37)$$

Unless $dx/ds = 0$, these equations can be written

$$H\left(\frac{dy}{dx}\right)^2 - 2K\frac{dy}{dx} + L = 0, \tag{10.38}$$

$$H\frac{dy}{dx}\,d\left(\frac{\partial f}{\partial x}\right) + L\,d\left(\frac{\partial f}{\partial y}\right) + M\,dy = 0. \tag{10.39}$$

A curve in the (x, y) plane such that equation (10.38) is satisfied at each point of it is called a *characteristic*. If $K^2 > HL$ (and only then), the roots of equation (10.38) at any point (x, y) are real and different, so that the characteristics are real; it is for this reason that the sign of $K^2 - HL$ is taken as the defining property to distinguish the classes of 'elliptic', 'parabolic', and 'hyperbolic' equations. Since for hyperbolic equations the roots of (10.38) are distinct it follows that through each point of the (x, y) plane there pass two characteristics. Thus there are two sets of characteristics covering the (x, y) plane, one member of each set passing through each point (x, y). These two sets will be called 'set 1' and 'set 2'.

If H, K, and L do not depend on f, $\partial f/\partial x$, or $\partial f/\partial y$ (though they may depend on (x, y)), the characteristics are independent of the particular solution, and can be evaluated over the whole relevant domain of the (x, y) plane before the evaluation of a solution is started. But when one or more of H, K, and L depend on f, $\partial f/\partial x$, or $\partial f/\partial y$, the characteristics depend on the solution and the evaluation of the characteristics has to proceed simultaneously with that of the solution.

It is convenient to write μ_1, μ_2 for the roots dy/dx of (10.38), the value of μ_1 at any point referring to the characteristic of set 1 through that point, and the value of μ_2 to the characteristic of set 2. Then

$$\mu_1 + \mu_2 = 2K/H, \qquad \mu_1\mu_2 = L/H.$$

On a characteristic of set 1 we have

$$\frac{dy}{dx} = \mu_1, \tag{10.40}$$

and from (10.39),
$$d\left(\frac{\partial f}{\partial x}\right) + \mu_2\,d\left(\frac{\partial f}{\partial y}\right) = -(M/H)\,dx; \tag{10.41}$$

on a characteristic of set 2
$$\frac{dy}{dx} = \mu_2, \tag{10.42}$$

and
$$d\left(\frac{\partial f}{\partial x}\right) + \mu_1\,d\left(\frac{\partial f}{\partial y}\right) = -(M/H)\,dx. \tag{10.43}$$

It sometimes happens that the derivatives $\partial f/\partial x$ and $\partial f/\partial y$, rather than f itself, are the quantities required in the solution, and further that H, K, L, M do not depend on f, though they may depend on $\partial f/\partial y$ and $\partial f/\partial x$; this is the case, for example, if f is the velocity potential of a fluid flow, when $\partial f/\partial x$ and $\partial f/\partial y$, the components of the velocity, are the quantities really required. Then it is convenient to write u, v for $\partial f/\partial x$, $\partial f/\partial y$ respectively, and (10.41), (10.43) become

$$du + \mu_2\,dv = -(M/H)\,dx \tag{10.44}$$

on a characteristic of set 1, and

$$du + \mu_1\,dv = -(M/H)\,dx \tag{10.45}$$

on a characteristic of set 2.

10.81. Finite differences between characteristics

One way of adapting these equations for numerical work is, in effect, to use members of the two sets of characteristics as defining a finite-difference grid in the (x, y) plane and to work in terms of finite differences between neighbouring characteristics. In Fig. 27 the two sets of curves represent the two sets of characteristics; the heavy portions represent the portions on which the solution has been carried out, and we want to determine the solution on the set of intersections of which A is typical.

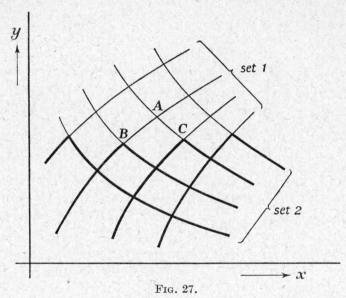

FIG. 27.

On the characteristic AB of set 1, a finite-difference approximation to (10.40) is

$$y_A - y_B = \tfrac{1}{2}(\mu_{1A} + \mu_{1B})(x_A - x_B),$$

and similarly on AC
$$y_A - y_C = \tfrac{1}{2}(\mu_{2A} + \mu_{2B})(x_A - x_C).$$

Also on AB a finite-difference approximation to (10.44) is

$$(u_A - u_B) + \tfrac{1}{2}(\mu_{2A} + \mu_{2B})(v_A - v_B) = -\tfrac{1}{2}[(M/H)_A + (M/H)_B](x_A - x_B),$$

and similarly on AC

$$(u_A - u_C) + \tfrac{1}{2}(\mu_{1A} + \mu_{1C})(v_A - v_C) = -\tfrac{1}{2}[(M/H)_A + (M/H)_C](x_A - x_C).$$

The quantities u, v, x, y being known at B and C, this is a set of four equations for u, v, x, y at A.

If H, K, L, and so μ_1 and μ_2, are independent of f, $\partial f/\partial x$, and $\partial f/\partial y$, then the first two equations give the position of A independently of the particular solution, and further, the coefficients on the left-hand sides of the second two equations are known in advance of the solutions of these equations. The evaluation of a solution is then relatively simple. But if one or more of H, K, and L depend on f, $\partial f/\partial x$, or $\partial f/\partial y$ these four equations have to be solved as a set of simultaneous equations for u_A, v_A, x_A, y_A; they are non-linear and can only be solved by trial and successive approximation. This makes the evaluation of a solution of the partial differential equation in such a case a long and often troublesome and tedious process.

XI

MISCELLANEOUS PROCESSES

11.1. Summation of series

IN practical applications of numerical analysis, as distinct from artificial examples constructed for the purpose, it is comparatively seldom that the original formulation of a problem is the summation of a series, though summation of a series is sometimes a useful method of dealing with a problem originally formulated in some other terms.

For example, the properties of the Airy function $Ai(x)$ which make it important in applications are these:

(i) it is a solution of $y'' = xy$ which tends to zero as x tends to infinity; this defines it except for a constant multiplying factor;

(ii) it is $\int_0^\infty \cos(xt + \tfrac{1}{3}t^3)\, dt$.

It can be evaluated from either of these properties without the use of a series expansion. Its power series expansion is a further property which happens to be useful in the evaluation of $Ai(x)$ for small values of x, but it is not the primary reason for the importance of this function, nor a property which need be used at all in its evaluation.

A series is useful in numerical work only if the sum of the first few terms is an adequate approximation to the sum of the series, or to the function represented by the series—just what a 'few' terms and an 'adequate approximation' mean will depend on the context. Suppose we have a numerical problem originally formulated in some other way than the summation of a series, and in trying to evaluate results by summing a series we find that the convergence of the first few terms is not rapid enough for them to be useful. Then this is a strong hint that evaluation of the series is not the best process for getting the results required, and the possibilities of other processes should be investigated.

But sometimes we may be concerned with the summation of slowly convergent series either in calculations originally formulated in such terms, or through the reduction of a more complicated situation to such a summation. In such cases we need processes for transforming slowly convergent series into more rapidly convergent ones. The simplest such transformation is one due to Euler for a series of terms of alternating signs.

11.11. Euler's transformation for a slowly convergent series of terms of alternate signs

This transformation can be derived by an application of finite-difference operators, and is one of the few cases in which the use of forward differences gives the most convenient form for results.

Let the *magnitudes* of the terms be $u_0, u_1, u_2, \ldots$, in general u_n, so that the series which we wish to sum is

$$S = u_0 - u_1 + u_2 - u_3 + \ldots = \sum_n (-1)^n u_n. \tag{11.1}$$

Let us take the successive differences of the terms u_n, regarded as a function of n. Then in the notation of § 4.6,

$$u_n = E^n u_0, \qquad E = 1 + \Delta,$$

where Δ is the forward-difference operator with respect to n, defined by $\Delta u_n = u_{n+1} - u_n$. Then

$$S = (1 - E + E^2 - E^3 + \ldots)u_0 = \frac{1}{1+E}u_0 = \frac{1}{2+\Delta}u_0 = \tfrac{1}{2}(1 + \tfrac{1}{2}\Delta)^{-1}u_0$$

$$= \tfrac{1}{2}[u_0 - \tfrac{1}{2}\Delta u_0 + \tfrac{1}{4}\Delta^2 u_0 - \tfrac{1}{8}\Delta^3 u_0 + \ldots]. \tag{11.2}$$

The differences involved here are the *forward* differences from the first entry of the table of u_n, and are all available.

If the series (11.1) is slowly convergent, then the successive differences of the u_n's usually decrease rapidly and the series (11.2) converges much more rapidly than the series (11.1) It will often be best not to carry the transformation back to the beginning of the series to be evaluated, but to calculate separately the sum of the first N terms ($N = 6$ or 8, perhaps) and apply the Euler transformation to the remainder. A good check on the results can be obtained by carrying out this process with two different values of N.

Example: To calculate $S(x) = \sum\limits_{m=0}^{\infty} (-1)^m/(x+m)^2$ for $x = 10$.

A table of the function $10^7/(x+m)^2$ for $x = 10$, $m = 0(1)10$ and its differences up to the sixth order is given opposite; the effects of rounding errors are becoming marked in the sixth differences. The value of $S(x)$ is the sum of *alternate* first differences of $-1/(x+n)^2$. If we take the first of these first differences (that is, the first two terms of the series) and apply the Euler transformation to the remainder of the series, we obtain

$$10^7 S(10) = 17355 + \tfrac{1}{2}[69444 + \tfrac{1}{2}(10272) + \tfrac{1}{4}(2120) + \tfrac{1}{8}(544) + \tfrac{1}{16}(162) +$$
$$+ \tfrac{1}{32}(52) + \tfrac{1}{64}(14) + \ldots]$$
$$= 17355 + 37595 = 54950.$$

The values of differences used are those underlined in the table.

m	$10^7/(x+m)^2$					
0	100000					
		−17355				
1	82645		4154			
		−13201		−1225		
2	69444		2929		416	
		−10272		−809		−151
3	59172		2120		265		48
		−8152		−544		−103
4	51020		1576		162		51
		−6576		−382		−52
5	44444		1194		110		14
		−5382		−272		−38
6	39062		922		72		19
		−4460		−200		−19
7	34602		722		53		0
		−3738		−147		−19
8	30864		575		34	
		−3163		−113		
9	27701		462			
		−2701				
10	25000					

If we take the first four terms of the series and apply the Euler transformation to the remainder, we obtain

$$10^7 S(10) = 17355 + 10272 +$$
$$+ \tfrac{1}{2}[51020 + \tfrac{1}{2}(6576) + \tfrac{1}{4}(1194) + \tfrac{1}{8}(272) + \tfrac{1}{16}(72) + \tfrac{1}{32}(19) + \ldots]$$
$$= 27627 + 27323 = 54950.$$

This agrees with the value already calculated, and we obtain the result $S(10) = 0 \cdot 005495$ to six decimals.

If the ratios of successive terms u_{n+1}/u_n are nearly constant, a modified form of the Euler transformation can be used effectively. Let

$$v_n = \beta^n u_n,$$

β being a number chosen so that the variation of v_n with n is small. Then

$$S = v_0 - \beta^{-1} v_1 + \beta^{-2} v_2 - \beta^{-3} v_3 + \ldots$$
$$= [1 - (E/\beta) + (E/\beta)^2 - (E/\beta)^3 + \ldots]v_0$$
$$= \frac{1}{1 + (E/\beta)} v_0 = \frac{\beta}{(\beta+1) + \Delta} v_0 = \frac{\beta}{\beta+1}\left(1 + \frac{\Delta}{\beta+1}\right)^{-1} v_0$$
$$= \frac{\beta}{\beta+1}\left[v_0 - \frac{1}{\beta+1}\Delta v_0 + \frac{1}{(\beta+1)^2}\Delta^2 v_0 - \frac{1}{(\beta+1)^3}\Delta^3 v_0 + \ldots\right]. \quad (11.3)$$

11.12. Use of the Euler–Maclaurin integration formula in the summation of series

When $f(x)$ is a function such that $\int f(x)\,dx$ can be integrated formally, the Euler–Maclaurin formula (6.22) can often be used effectively for evaluating sums of the type $\sum\limits_{m} f(m)$ over a set of integral values of m. From formula (6.22) with $x_0 = 0$ and interval $(\delta x) = 1$, we have

$$f_0 + f_1 + \cdots + f_n$$

$$= \int_0^{x_n} f(x)\,dx + \tfrac{1}{2}(f_0 + f_n) + \tfrac{1}{12}(f'_n - f'_0) - \tfrac{1}{720}(f'''_n - f'''_0) + \tfrac{1}{30240}(f^v_n - f^v_0) - \cdots$$

$$\text{(11.4)}$$

and in particular, if $f(x)$ and all its derivatives tend to 0 as x tends to ∞,

$$\sum_{m=0}^{\infty} f_m = \int_0^{\infty} f(x)\,dx + \tfrac{1}{2}f_0 - \tfrac{1}{12}f'_0 + \tfrac{1}{720}f'''_0 - \tfrac{1}{30240}f^v_0 + \cdots. \qquad \text{(11.5)}$$

As in the previous section, the result of using this formula can be checked by applying it to the series formed by omitting the first few terms from the series to be summed.

Example: To evaluate $\sum\limits_{m=0}^{\infty} 1/(8+m)^2$.

For $\qquad f(x) = 1/(a+x)^2$, we have $\int_0^{\infty} f(x)\,dx = 1/a$,

and $\qquad f'(0) = -2/a^3, \qquad f'''(0) = -24/a^5, \qquad f^v(0) = -720/a^7$,

so evaluation of formula (11.5) for $a = 8$ gives

$$\sum_{m=0}^{\infty} 1/(8+m)^2 = \frac{1}{8} + \frac{1}{2}\frac{1}{64} + \frac{1}{12}\frac{2}{8^3} - \frac{1}{720}\frac{24}{8^5} + \cdots$$

$$= \cdot 125 + \cdot 00781\ 25 + \cdot 00032\ 55 - \cdot 00000\ 10 + \cdots$$

$$= \cdot 133{,}137 \text{ to six decimals.}$$

Also $\qquad \sum\limits_{m=0}^{\infty} 1/(8+m)^2 = \tfrac{1}{64} + \tfrac{1}{81} + \sum\limits_{m=0}^{\infty} 1/(10+m)^2$

and evaluation of formula (11.5) for $a = 10$ gives

$$\sum_{m=0}^{\infty} 1/(10+m)^2 = \frac{1}{10} + \frac{1}{2}\frac{1}{100} + \frac{1}{12}\frac{2}{10^3} - \frac{1}{720}\frac{24}{10^5}$$

$$= \cdot 1 + \cdot 005 + \cdot 00016\ 67 - \cdot 00000\ 03$$

$$= \cdot 10516\ 64$$

so $\qquad \sum\limits_{m=0}^{\infty} 1/(8+m)^2 = \cdot 01562\ 5 + \cdot 01234\ 57 + \cdot 10516\ 64$

$$= \cdot 13313\ 7 \text{ to six decimals}$$

verifying the value obtained by evaluating formula (11.5) with $a = 8$.

Slowly convergent series of positive terms which cannot be handled by this application of the Euler–Maclaurin formula are often difficult to deal with numerically. If the terms are given by an algebraical formula, then it may be possible to find an analytical transformation which con-verts the series into a more rapidly convergent one, but this procedure is not usually available unless each term is of a relatively simple form.†

11.2. Harmonic analysis

Harmonic analysis is concerned with the representation of a function $f(x)$, over a finite range of x which will be taken as 2π, as a series of circular functions of x:

$$f(x) = \tfrac{1}{2}A_0 + A_1\cos x + A_2\cos 2x + \dots + B_1\sin x + B_2\sin 2x + \dots.$$

$$(11.6)$$

The most important applications are to cases in which $f(x)$ is periodic in x with period 2π, or in which $f(x)$, although not periodic, or not defined outside a range $x_0 \leqslant x \leqslant (x_0+2\pi)$, satisfies the conditions

$$f^{(k)}(x_0+2\pi) = f^{(k)}(x_0).$$

$$(11.7)$$

If $f(x)$ does not satisfy such conditions, or if it has discontinuities in magnitude or in a differential coefficient of low order, then harmonic analysis is usually of formal rather than numerical interest, since in numerical work only a finite number of coefficients in the series (11.4) can be evaluated, and the sum of any finite number of terms gives a function which satisfies the conditions (11.7) and has no discontinuity in any derivative. If f itself has a discontinuity or does not satisfy

$$f(x_0+2\pi) = f(x_0),$$

then the behaviour of the sum of a finite number of terms, in the neighbourhood of the discontinuity (or of x_0 and $x_0+2\pi$) differs con-siderably from the behaviour of $f(x)$; as n increases, the behaviour of f remains of the character shown in Fig. 28, the scale of x, but *not* the scale of the oscillations in f, becoming smaller as n increases. This is known as the 'Gibbs phenomenon' and illustrates the need for caution in regarding a finite number of terms of the series (11.6) as an adequate representation of the function unless it is free from discontinuities and the conditions (11.7) are satisfied.

The most usual applications of harmonic analysis are in connexion with the analysis of results of experiment or observation. Occasionally,

† For other methods of treatment of such series, see J. C. P. Miller, *Phil. Mag.* (7) **22** (1936), 754; T. M. Cherry, *Proc. Camb. Phil. Soc.* **46** (1950) 436; G. G. Macfarlane, *Phil. Mag.* (7) **40** (1949), 188. See also O. Szász, *Journ. Math. and Phys.* **28** (1949), 272.

however, it may be required in purely analytical or numerical contexts. For example, in the solution of Laplace's equation in two dimensions,

$$\frac{\partial^2 V}{\partial x^2} + \frac{\partial^2 V}{\partial y^2} = 0$$

in the interior of the unit circle, it may be convenient to use the result that V can be written

$$V = V_0 + r(A_1 \cos\theta + B_1 \sin\theta) + r^2(A_2 \cos 2\theta + B_2 \sin 2\theta) + \dots.$$

Harmonic analysis of V as a function of θ on the unit circle gives V_0 and the coefficients A_n and B_n directly, and hence the solution V, without requiring numerical integration over the whole interior of the unit circle.

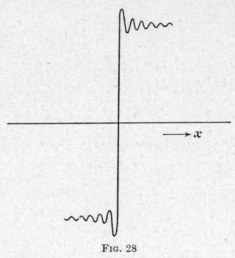

FIG. 28

The coefficients in the series (11.6) are given by

$$\pi A_n = \int_0^{2\pi} f(x)\cos nx\, dx, \qquad \pi B_n = \int_0^{2\pi} f(x)\sin nx\, dx. \qquad (11.8)$$

If $f(x)$ satisfies the conditions (11.7) it follows that, in each of these integrals, each derivative of the integrand has the same value at the upper limit as at the lower limit. Hence in the Euler–Maclaurin formula (6.25) for each of the integrals the correcting terms from the two ends of the range cancel identically, and if the integrals can be evaluated from a set of values of $f(x)$ at equal intervals on x, the appropriate integration formula is the trapezium rule without corrections. Hence if the range 2π in x is divided into K equal intervals, we have

$$\tfrac{1}{2}K A_n = \sum_{k=0}^{K-1} f(x_k)\cos nx_k, \qquad \tfrac{1}{2}K B_n = \sum_{k=0}^{K-1} f(x_k)\sin nx_k, \qquad (11.9)$$

where $x_k = 2\pi k/K$.

These expressions for the coefficients are not significant for $n > \frac{1}{2}K$. This can be seen as follows. Let n_0 be a value of n less than $\frac{1}{2}K$, and m any positive integer. Then at the points $x_k = 2\pi k/K$ we have

$$\cos(mK \pm n_0)x_k = \cos(2\pi mk \pm n_0 x_k) = \cos n_0 x_k,$$
$$\sin(mK \pm n_0)x_k = \sin(2\pi mk \pm n_0 x_k) = \pm \sin n_0 x_k.$$

Hence at these points the contributions from the terms with $n = mK \pm n_0$ have exactly the same variation with k as contributions from the term with $n = n_0$, and no analysis using only the values of f at these points can distinguish the contributions from the values $n = mK \pm n_0$ with different values of m. The first of the sums (11.9) gives the same values for each A_n ($n = mK \pm n_0$); but the values of the A_n's are independent, so these values given by (11.9) cannot all be significant.

The point is that for values of n greater than $\frac{1}{2}K$ the values of x_k are not closely enough spaced, relative to the period of $\sin nx$, for the formulae (11.9) for the integrals to be valid. For $n = \frac{1}{2}K$ the values of the integrand $f(x)\cos nx$ at successive values of x_k are

$$+f(x_0), \quad -f(x_1), \quad +f(x_2), \quad -f(x_3), \quad \ldots$$

and for most functions f these values are too irregular to give any confidence that they represent the behaviour of the integrand well enough to justify any numerical work on it at all. Their differences diverge and the situation is similar to that considered in § 6.54, where also we were concerned with an integral for which the correction to the trapezium rule vanished at both ends of the range of integration, but an incorrect value was obtained if too great an interval of integration was taken. To define an oscillating function adequately it is advisable to have at least six points per period, and this suggests that the series (11.9) should not be regarded as adequate approximations to the integrals (11.8) for $n > \frac{1}{6}K$.

Another aspect of these results can be illustrated by considering an alternative way in which the coefficients A_n, B_n might be determined numerically, not as values of the integrals (11.8) but by fitting the series (11.6) to $f(x)$ at the discrete set of values x_k of x. If this is done, then we have

$$\left.\begin{array}{l} \displaystyle\sum_{k=0}^{K-1} f(x_k)\cos nx_k = \tfrac{1}{2}K[A_n + A_{K-n} + A_{K+n} + A_{2K-n} + \ldots] \\[2mm] \displaystyle\sum_{k=0}^{K-1} f(x_k)\sin nx_k = \tfrac{1}{2}K[B_n - B_{K-n} + B_{K+n} - B_{2K-n} + \ldots] \end{array}\right\} \quad (11.10)$$

It is clear that with the restriction to K values of x, it is not possible to determine more than K relations between the coefficients, namely the first of relations (11.9) for $n = 0$ to $\tfrac{1}{2}K$ and the second for $n = 1$ to $(\tfrac{1}{2}K-1)$; the terms $B_n \sin nx_k$ for $n = (m+\tfrac{1}{2})K$ make no contribution to the sum (11.6) at any of the points $x = x_k$. The smoothest function with the assigned values of $f(x_k)$ will be that for which $A_n = B_n = 0$ for $n > \tfrac{1}{2}K$, and then A_n, B_n for $n \leqslant \tfrac{1}{2}K$ are given by (11.9).

If $f(x)$ is a continuous function, then a good test of the significance of the values of A_n, B_n calculated from (11.9) is given by making two analyses with values of K which are relatively prime or have only a small common factor, such as $K = 30$ and 32, or 48 and 50; this process also provides a good overall check on the results.

11.3. Recurrence relations for a sequence of functions

The Bessel functions of integral order $J_n(x)$ form an example of a set of functions of one variable (x) and one parameter (n) which have a number of properties in common, such as the form of the differential equation satisfied by them and their asymptotic behaviour. They are connected by relations between the functions of different orders n, such as

$$J_{n+1}(x) - J_{n-1}(x) = -2J'_n(x), \qquad (11.11)$$

$$J_{n-1}(x) + J_{n+1}(x) = (2n/x)J_n(x). \qquad (11.12)$$

Such relations are called recurrence relations. Other examples of such sets of function are the Legendre functions $P_n(x)$, the confluent hypergeometric functions $W_{k,m}(x)$ of Whittaker,[†] and the Weber functions $D_n(x)$[‡].

It is often convenient to use such recurrence relations to evaluate functions, for some value of the parameter for which there may be no tables available, from tabulated values of the functions for other parameter values. Such a process must be used with care or it may lead to quite spurious results. This can be seen by considering, as an example, the evaluation of $J_n(x)$ for a given value of x and for large values of n from $J_0(x)$ and $J_1(x)$ by repeated use of the relation (11.12).

For $J_n(x)$ we require that solution of (11.11) which tends to zero as n tends to infinity. But if we evaluate $J_n(x), J_{n+1}(x), J_{n+2}(x),...$ in succession by using (11.12) in the form

$$J_{n+1}(x) = (2n/x)J_n(x) - J_{n-1}(x), \qquad (11.13)$$

the rounding errors introduce a small multiple of the second solution

† E. T. Whittaker and G. N. Watson, *Modern Analysis* (C.U.P. 1927), ch. 16.
‡ Ibid., § 16.2.

$Y_n(x)$ of this recurrence relation. For $n < x$ this remains small, but for $n > x$ it behaves roughly as an increasing exponential, and increases without limit as n tends to infinity.

Thus this way of using the recurrence relation is not satisfactory for calculating Bessel functions $J_n(x)$ for $n > x$, though it is satisfactory for $n < x$. It would, however, be satisfactory for calculating $Y_n(x)$, since in this case the unwanted solution, of which a small multiple may be introduced by rounding errors, is one which decreases indefinitely, relative to the wanted solution $Y_n(x)$, as n increases.

On the other hand, the range over which $(n/x) > 1$ is just the range over which relaxation methods can be used effectively for the solution of (11.12), provided the solution has to satisfy two-point boundary conditions in n. This is the case for the Bessel function $J_n(x)$, since up to $n = x$ these can be built up satisfactorily by successive use of formula (11.13). This gives $J_n(n)$ as one terminal condition in n, and the other is given by $J_n(x) \to 0$ as $n \to \infty$.

This example shows how quite different results can be obtained by different ways of using the same simple formula; one way of using the recurrence relation (11.12) may lead to quite spurious results although no mistakes have been made in the calculation, whereas another way of using the same formula can be used to give results accurate to any assigned degree.

11.4. Smoothing

'Smoothness', either of a continuous function or of a set of discrete values, is a property of which it is difficult to give a quantitative definition. For a continuous function it implies smallness of high-order derivatives, and for a table of function values it implies smallness of the higher orders of differences; this implies also regularity of the differences, since if the nth differences are irregular, the $(n+10)$th differences will not be small.

By 'smoothing' a set of function values is meant a process of replacing them by another set which differ only slightly from them but are 'smoother' in this sense. If each member of a set of function values has been obtained by an independent calculation, and each is subject to a rounding error, then the accuracy of the values may be increased somewhat by a smoothing process. But this improvement should not be relied on, and cannot be estimated. It should not be relied on because it is always possible that the rounding errors in a number of consecutive function values may be of the same sign and similar in magnitude, and then smoothing will not improve them. Further, as we have already seen in Chapter IV, an incorrect set of function values may have smooth differences, and a set of correctly rounded-off function values may be less smooth than a set obtained by rounding off incorrectly. Also without knowing in some other way a more accurate set of function values, there is no criterion by which the improvement of the function values can be assessed; and if these more accurate function values were known, there would be no point in carrying out the smoothing process. If a set of function values is too much affected by rounding errors, the only reliable way of getting more accurate values is to carry out the calculation of the function values to greater numerical accuracy.

The main purpose in carrying out a process of smoothing must therefore be to achieve smoothness, not accuracy. The contexts in numerical analysis in which smoothness is a prime requirement are not many, so that such a process is not often required. But occasionally it is difficult to make satisfactory progress without one.

Consider, for example, the evaluation of a set of solutions of a differential equation involving a function $f(y)$ determined by experiment or by statistical sampling, the different solutions being distinguished by different initial conditions or different values of one or more parameters. For consistency between the various solutions, and also in order to use the differences of intermediate quantities for checking the integrations, it may be advisable to use in the numerical work a table of $f(y)$ which is smooth to a substantially greater degree of numerical accuracy than the accuracy of the experiments from which $f(y)$ is determined. This can sometimes be achieved by fitting an analytical formula to the experimentally determined values; when this has been done, the formula can be evaluated to any required numerical accuracy. But this process is inconvenient unless a relatively simple formula can be found to fit the experimental values within the experimental or sampling error, and it is also unnecessary. A more purely numerical smoothing process is often more useful and more effective.

Another example is provided by the process of § 10.72 for the integration of a parabolic partial differential equation. For one time interval of this process, as applied to the equation

$$\frac{\partial f}{\partial t} = \frac{\partial^2 f}{\partial x^2},$$

the equation

$$\frac{\delta^2}{\delta x^2}[f(x, t+\delta t)+f(x, t)] = (2/\delta t)[f(x, t+\delta t)+f(x, t)]-(4/\delta t)f(x, t)$$

is solved with two-point boundary conditions in x. In the processes of numerical integration and interpolation for the solution satisfying the two-point boundary conditions, random rounding errors may occur in $[f(x,t+\delta t)+f(x,t)]$ up to ± 2 in the last significant figure kept. If the rounding error in $f(t)$ may be $\pm p$, that in $f(x,t+\delta t)$ may be $\pm(p+2)$, that in $f(x,t+2\delta t)$ may be $\pm(p+4)$ and so on, and effects of rounding errors may be increased if Richardson's process of h^2-extrapolation is used to correct approximately for the truncation error. Thus, however many figures are kept, the last will become more and more irregular as the calculation proceeds. If two or three guarding figures are kept, this will not affect the final results significantly, but such irregularities make it difficult to use differences for checking, and may lead to time being wasted in trying to find a suspected mistake that is not there. For this reason it is advisable occasionally to smooth $f(x,t)$ as a function of x during the progress of the calculation.

11.41. Automatic methods of smoothing

A simple example of one class of methods of smoothing is the following: Replace each function value f_j by the mean $\bar{f}_j$ of five successive values of f centred on f_j, that is, take

$$\bar{f}_j = \tfrac{1}{5}(f_{j+2}+f_{j+1}+f_j+f_{j-1}+f_{j-2}).$$

This is sometimes called 'smoothing by fives', or 'smoothing by groups of five'. In this process, the irregularities get smoothed out by being distributed among neighbouring function values. This can be illustrated by the set of function values

$$f \quad 0 \quad 0 \quad 0 \quad 0 \quad 1 \quad 0 \quad 0 \quad 0 \quad 0, \qquad (11.14)$$

for which this process gives

$$\bar{f} \quad 0 \quad 0 \quad \tfrac{1}{5} \quad \tfrac{1}{5} \quad \tfrac{1}{5} \quad \tfrac{1}{5} \quad \tfrac{1}{5} \quad 0 \quad 0. \qquad (11.15)$$

The maximum value of $|\delta^2 \bar{f}|$ is $\tfrac{1}{5}$ whereas that of $|\delta^2 f|$ is 2: on the basis of this criterion, the set of values (11.15) is ten times as smooth as the set (11.14).

This process of smoothing by groups of $(2n+1)$ can be repeated. For example, two successive processes of smoothing by groups of three, starting from the set of values (11.14) gives

$$\bar{f} \quad 0 \quad 0 \quad \tfrac{1}{9} \quad \tfrac{2}{9} \quad \tfrac{3}{9} \quad \tfrac{2}{9} \quad \tfrac{1}{9} \quad 0 \quad 0. \qquad (11.16)$$

For this set of values, the maximum $|\delta^2 \bar{f}|$ is $\tfrac{2}{9}$.

These are two examples of a general method which consists of replacing each f_j by a linear combination

$$\bar{f}_j = \sum_{k=-n}^{n} a_k f_{j-k} \qquad (11.17)$$

of function values centred on f_j. The smoothest set of function values is simply f_j = constant, and in order that these should not be altered by the smoothing process, the coefficients must satisfy

$$\sum_{k=-n}^{n} a_k = 1;$$

and normally the coefficients will be symmetrical about $k = 0$. Different processes are given by different choices of the coefficients a_k in (11.17).

These methods are often unsatisfactory in practice for three reasons. First, once the particular smoothing formula to use has been decided, it is automatic in character in that the results are then determinate, and gives no opportunity for the exercise of judgement by the individual who is carrying out the calculation. This might at first sight seem an advantage, since the results will then be independent of the individual. But this apparent definiteness of the results is spurious since there is a good deal of latitude in the choice of what smoothing formula to adopt. And the smoothing process is in practice one in which it seems desirable to give the individual who is carrying it out some discretion on matters such as the degree of smoothing at which to aim and the degree to which changes $\bar{f}_j - f_j$ from the original function values are acceptable. Secondly, with methods depending on the use of formulae of the type (11.17), the smoothed values $\bar{f}_j$ cover a smaller range of j than the original values; in a method due to Spencer,[†] recommended by Whittaker and Robinson,[‡] ten values at each end of the range are lost, so that from 30 values of f_j only 10 smoothed values in the middle of the range of j are obtained. Such a loss of range is often unacceptable. Thirdly, a special procedure is needed if it happens that some value of $f(x)$ is known exactly, such as a value $f(x) = 0$ at $x = 0$, and is not to be modified by the smoothing process.

The dangers of a blind use of an automatic smoothing process are illustrated in Fig. 29. Here the full curve is representative of the behaviour of the function $f(v) = R/v^2$, where R is the resistance of the air to a body moving through it at a speed of v ft./sec. If $f(v)$ is tabulated at intervals of 50 ft./sec. the behaviour of the second and higher differences of $f(v)$ is rather violent, and can be mollified by the application of a

[†] J. Spencer, *J. Inst. Actuaries*, **38** (1904), 334.
[‡] *Calculus of Observations* (Blackie, 1940), p. 290.

smoothing process. Spencer's process, applied to these data, gives results represented by the squares and broken curve in Fig. 29. They are certainly smoother (the greatest value of $|\delta^2 f|$ has been reduced from 232 to 48 in terms of the third decimal place as unit). But it does

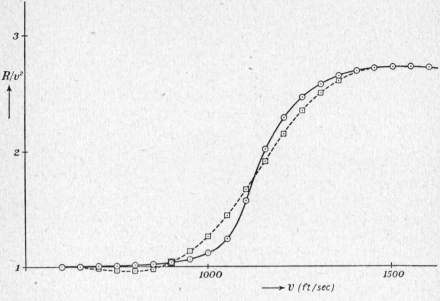

Fig. 29.

not follow that the smoothed values are a better representation of the actual behaviour of $f(v)$ than the unsmoothed values; they are almost certainly worse, and in particular the minimum about $v = 780$ ft./sec. is almost certainly spurious. But if one insists on using an automatic formula one has no control over the results it is going to give; if one believes the use of the formula to be significant at all, all that one can do is to accept the results of using it.

11.42. Smoothing by use of an auxiliary function

A less formal but more practical method is due to A. T. Doodson.†
It is based on the use of graphs.

Let $f(x)$ be the function which it is desired to smooth. Unless $f(x)$ is of only two or three figures, and sometimes even if it is of three figures, it will not generally be possible to smooth it directly by plotting and drawing a smooth curve 'through' the plotted points. But if $g(x)$ is a

† This method was devised in connexion with ballistic work during the First World War, but only published recently, in *Quart. J. Mech. and Applied Math.* **3** (1950), 217.

smooth function approximately equal to $f(x)$, it may be possible to plot the *difference* $f(x)-g(x)$ on a scale open enough to smooth it, to the degree of numerical accuracy required, by such a graphical process. Then $\bar{f}(x)$, the smoothed function by which $f(x)$ is replaced, is constructed as
$$\bar{f}(x) = g(x)+\text{smoothed}\{f(x)-g(x)\}.$$

The auxiliary function $g(x)$ can be formed in several ways. It may, for example, be taken to be given by an analytical formula, such as ax^2, $ax/(x^2+b^2)$, e^{ax}, be^{-ax^2}, if there is any theoretical reason or empirical indication that $f(x)$ is approximately of such a form. Another process is to build up $g(x)$ from a smooth set of differences. This is of more practical use in many cases, as it can be used equally well whether or not a good approximation to $f(x)$ can be obtained by a simple analytical formula, and it does not involve any selection and adjustment of parameters in an analytical formula so as to get a good overall fit to $f(x)$.

For simplicity suppose $f(x)$ to be given at equal intervals of x. And as an example of the general process, suppose this function, and the interval of tabulation, to be such that the range of the values of $\delta^2 f$ is not more than 200, so that they can be plotted on such a scale (1 mm. or $\frac{1}{20}$ in. to a unit) that they can be read off to a unit.

The process is then as follows. Plot $\delta^2 f(x)$ and draw 'through' the plotted points as smooth a curve as possible without smoothing away significant features of the behaviour of the second differences. This is one place at which discretion is required in judging what features of the behaviour of the second differences are significant. If the uncertainty of each value of $f(x)$ is known, the range of uncertainty of each second difference can be found and indicated on the plot, and this may help in distinguishing significant from non-significant features of the variation of the second differences. It is better to over-smooth at this stage rather than the reverse; significant variations which are smoothed out at this stage are replaced at a later stage.

Let $h(x)$ be these smoothed values of $\delta^2 f(x)$. It is not advisable to double-sum them directly to give the auxiliary function $g(x)$. A small systematic difference between two different ways of drawing the curve from which $h(x)$ is read off may build up, on double-summing, to a substantial amount, so that though one curve might give a $g(x)$ which differed little from $f(x)$, the other might give a $g(x)$ departing from it to such an extent that it would be difficult to plot $f(x)-g(x)$ on an adequate scale; and there can be no certainty that the curve from which $h(x)$ is read off is not of the latter kind. It is therefore best first to form the single sum $\sigma h(x)$ of the values of $h(x)$, and to modify this if necessary so as to get a general agreement with the first differences of $f(x)$, before forming an auxiliary function. The differences

$$\delta f(x) - \sigma h(x)$$

between the first differences of $f(x)$ and the first sum of $h(x)$ are therefore plotted and smoothed graphically. The smoothed values of

$$\delta f(x) - \sigma h(x)$$

are then added to the values of $\sigma h(x)$ to give the first differences of the auxiliary function $g(x)$ which is then built up from these differences. Thus $g(x)$ is given by

$$g = \sigma[\sigma h + \text{smoothed}(\delta f - \sigma h)].$$

Finally, $(f-g)$ is plotted and smoothed, and the smoothed function $\bar{f}(x)$ is given by

$$\bar{f}(x) = g(x) + \text{smoothed}\{f(x) - g(x)\}.$$

In this final stage discretion can again be exercised regarding the extent to which values of f may be modified by the smoothing process, and the significance of various features of the behaviour of f. The difference between the original and smoothed values of f at any value of f is

$$f(x) - \bar{f}(x) = \{f(x) - g(x)\} - \text{smoothed}\{f(x) - g(x)\},$$

and the right-hand side here is the departure of the smooth curve from the plotted point $(f-g)$ at each value of x. If the range of uncertainty of each value of f, or the maximum change in each value which would be acceptable, is known, this can be indicated on the plot, and the smooth curve drawn so that its departures from the plotted points do not exceed this range at any point. In particular, if at any point the value of $f(x)$ is known exactly, the curve of $(f-g)$ must be drawn to pass through the plotted point at that value of x. In Doodson's method of smoothing, particular features such as this can be taken into account quite easily and without departure from the regular procedure.

The differences of the final values of $\bar{f}(x)$ provide a check of the calculation and an indication of the degree of smoothness which has been obtained. An indication of the extent to which the final results depend on the details of the process of smoothing is given by carrying out the process twice using the same set of values of $f(x)$ but different smooth curves from which to read off the smoothed second differences of $h(x)$.

The process can be adapted to start from other orders of differences than the second. However, if $f(x)$ is at all seriously irregular, the higher differences of $f(x)$ probably vary so wildly that it is difficult to see any general trend in their values.

Examples of this process, and its extension to functions of two variables, can be found in Doodson's paper.

XII

ORGANIZATION OF CALCULATIONS FOR AN AUTOMATIC MACHINE

12.1. Automatic digital calculating machines

WHEN we write a number in the ordinary way, such as 1925, the symbols such as 1, 9, 2, 5 in this example stand for what we call the *digits* of a number, and a piece of equipment which operates directly with, and records, the discrete digits of each number is often called a *digital calculating machine*. Since about 1938 there has been a great development of such machines with two important features. First, they can carry out long and intricate numerical calculations quite automatically once they have been provided with a specification, in a suitable form, of the calculation to be carried out. And, secondly, they are very versatile, so that the same machine can be used for many quite different kinds of calculation; for example, for calculating values of a function from its power-series expansion, for solving large systems of linear simultaneous equations, for finding the characteristic values of matrices, and for the step-by-step integration of ordinary differential equations. To express these two features, such machines are sometimes called *general-purpose, automatic*, digital calculating machines.

The process of organizing calculations for such machines is a branch of numerical analysis which has only come into being with the machines, and this chapter is included here to give an introduction to the subject. It is concerned with the planning of calculations for such machines rather than with the machines themselves; it is only concerned with the machines in so far as their characteristics affect the process of organizing calculations for them.

We have already considered in §2.7 the general organization of a hand computation done with the assistance of a desk machine. An automatic machine must be capable of carrying out the same processes, and can be thought of as having a similar organization, as shown diagrammatically in Fig. 30. It must have an *arithmetical unit* in which arithmetical operations can be carried out, to take the place of the desk machine in a hand calculation; a *store* both for numbers and for operating instructions, to take the place of the work sheet and tables; and a *control system* to take the place of the human computer who controls the sequence of operations in a hand calculation. The machine also needs input and output equipment for receiving numerical data and operating instructions from the outside world and for delivering its results.

Whatever the physical form of the store, it must provide a number of identifiable *storage locations*, and it is convenient to think of these as numbered. The number which is the label of any storage location is often called its 'address', or the 'address' of its content. $C(n)$ will be used for 'the content of storage location n'. It is sometimes convenient to represent the address of the number which is the value of a quantity x by $L(x)$ or $A(x)$, or by $C^{-1}(x)$ if it is desired to emphasize that the relation $n = L(x)$ is the inverse of the relation $x = C(n)$.

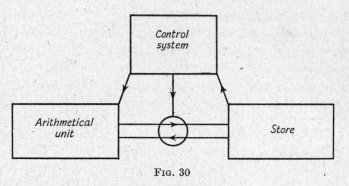

FIG. 30

The specification of an operation which the machine is required to carry out is called an 'instruction' or 'order' (sometimes a 'command'), and the ordered set of such instructions needed to carry out a calculation is called the 'program' for that calculation. An important feature of most recent and projected machines is that instructions are coded in such a way that they have the same form, within the machine, as numbers, the difference between numbers and instructions being in the way they are used. The content of a storage location is then usually called a 'word', whether it represents a number or an instruction; 'words' representing numbers are normally used by being transferred between the store and the arithmetical unit, and 'words' representing instructions are normally used by being transferred to the control system. But since there is no distinction, within the machine, between numbers and instructions, it is possible to use the arithmetical unit to build up, transfer, and modify the operating instructions themselves as the calculation proceeds.

The effect of this on the organization of a calculation is so profound that there may be little relation between the processes of organizing a calculation for machines which do and for those which do not provide this possibility. However, its importance is now well realized, and it is provided on several of the machines already (1951) in operation and is likely to be provided on all future machines. It will be assumed in the rest of this chapter.

There are two main forms for instructions; these can be illustrated by an example. Suppose we want the machine to form the sum of the contents of storage locations n_1 and n_2 and to put the result into location n_3. This could be done by a single instruction which could be written symbolically

$$C(n_1) + C(n_2) \text{ to } n_3. \tag{12.1}$$

An alternative is as follows. Suppose that the arithmetical unit is of a kind which includes as one of its components a register, usually called an 'accumulator', corresponding to the 'product register' or 'accumulator' of a desk machine, which accumulates the sum of numbers added into it until it is cleared; the content of the accumulator will be written $C(Acc)$. Then the required operation can be done by the three separate instructions:

$$C(n_1) \text{ to } Acc, \qquad C(n_2) \text{ to } Acc, \qquad C(Acc) \text{ to } n_3. \tag{12.2}$$

Each of the instructions of the form (12.1) specifies three addresses in the store, whereas each instruction of the form (12.2) specifies a single such address. These forms of instruction are consequently known as the 'three-address' and 'one-address' forms respectively.

An instruction specifies an operation to be carried out. But it is also necessary to specify the sequence in which such operations are to be carried out; that is to say, after carrying out one operation, the machine must be enabled to select the instruction for the next operation. In a machine in which instructions are contained in the same store as numbers this can be done in two ways. One is to include in each instruction the address from which the *next* instruction is to be taken; with a three-address specification of the operation to be carried out, this gives altogether a 'four-address' form of instruction. Another way is normally to store instructions at addresses numbered serially in the same order as the time-sequence in which they are to be carried out. This will be referred to as 'serial storage' of instructions. In this case the address of the instruction currently being carried out is recorded in a register whose content is normally increased by unity on the completion of this instruction, and the content of this register is used to control the selection of the next instruction. Then an explicit specification of the address of the next instruction is needed only when it is required to depart from the serial order in which the instructions are located in the store.

The control system of a machine will depend on the standard form adopted for instructions and the means adopted for selecting the next instruction, and once the machine is built, the instructions used must conform to the type for which the control system has been designed. These features, rather than the physical form of the store or of the arithmetical unit, are the essential features of a machine from the point of view of the user.

12.2. Preparation of calculations for an automatic digital calculating machine

The process of preparing a calculation for an automatic digital machine can be broken down into two parts, often called 'programming' and 'coding'.

By the 'program' for a calculation is meant the schedule of operating instructions which has to be provided to the machine in order that it shall carry out the calculation. 'Programming' is the process of planning the sequence of operating instructions required, and 'coding' is the process of translating these instructions into the particular form in which they are supplied to the machine. In simple calculations these are hardly two distinct processes, but in more elaborate calculations it is convenient to treat them as separate.

A process of programming is required in a hand calculation; before we can start doing any calculation we must decide just how we are going to do it. For work with an automatic machine, programming may involve breaking down the calculation to a sequence of the elementary operations, such as addition, multiplication, and selection of the next instruction, which the machine can carry out. But the machine and the process of providing it with instructions may be such that groups of operations for standard processes, such as evaluation of $\cos x$ given the value of x, or of $\int_a^b f(x)\,dx$ given the values of $f(x)$ at a set of values of x, can be programmed and coded once for all. If this can be done, each such process can be regarded as a unit in programming a calculation, and not analysed into elementary operations. The program for such a standard process will be called a 'sub-routine'. The possibility of using such sub-routines freely greatly lightens the work of preparing a calculation for a machine, and the machine and the form of its instructions should be planned to provide this facility. The use of the same form in the machine for instructions and for numbers, and the freedom which this gives to modify instructions by arithmetical and other operations on them, are important features in making it easy to provide and exploit the possibilities of using such sub-routines. To a potential user of an automatic machine, means of organizing calculations for it are as important as the provision of the machine itself, and the provision of a library of sub-routines for standard processes is an important step in this direction.

Although the various kinds of machines differ considerably from one another in their internal organization and operation, the general process of programming a calculation will be much the same for any of them, for it depends primarily on the structure of the sequence of operating instructions required to carry out the calculation. Some characteristic features on an individual machine may, however, affect the details of the programming. Such features are

(i) The standard form of operating instructions adopted; whether this is, for example, a one-address or four-address form.

(ii) The facilities provided by the standard instructions; for example, whether division can be carried out directly or has to be done by means of an iterative process which has to be programmed.

(iii) The criteria which it is possible to use for discrimination between possible alternative courses of procedure; for example, whether it is only possible to discriminate on the sign of a number or also on criteria such as the likeness or unlikeness of signs of two numbers.

The process of coding does, however, depend on the particular machine. It does not depend primarily on the physical form of the store or on the way in which numbers are represented in the machine, but on two features, namely the standard form of instructions and the means of selecting the next instruction, as explained at the end of § 12.1.

12.3. Flow diagrams

It is sometimes convenient to represent the general structure of the sequence of processes required in a calculation by a flow diagram. This can take the form of a block diagram, in which the blocks represent operations or groups of operations, and are joined by directed lines representing the sequence of these operations.

Suppose, for example, we want to carry out the numerical integration of an ordinary differential equation in the form

$$y'' + 2ky' + y(1+y^2) = C\cos x$$

through four periods of $\cos x$ starting from $x = 0$, using intervals

$\delta x = \pi/15 = 12°$, and printing the results at the end of every period in $\cos x$, that is to say, after every thirtieth interval; and we want to do this for twenty sets of initial conditions. The general organization of this calculation can be represented diagrammatically as in Fig. 31.

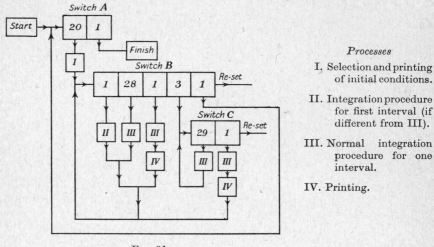

Processes

I. Selection and printing of initial conditions.

II. Integration procedure for first interval (if different from III).

III. Normal integration procedure for one interval.

IV. Printing.

FIG. 31.

Here the blocks containing roman numerals represent different processes required in the calculation, the processes being indicated in the table beside the diagram. The blocks divided into sections represent counting and switching processes, each of which has one input and a number of outputs. They do *not*, or anyway need not, represent actual switches in the sense of hardware, but they may be groups of machine operations—operations of addition for counting and of selection of the next instruction for switching—which altogether produce the same result as an actual switch would do. Each of the sections of one of these blocks represents a switch position, and the number n in it indicates that the switch moves to its next position to the right after n inputs to the switch in the position labelled n. 'Re-set' at the right-hand end means that the last input to the switch in its last position re-sets it to its first position.

For example, each of the first twenty-nine inputs to the switch labelled 'switch C' results in the integration being carried out through one interval of integration without printing; the thirtieth input to this switch results in the integration being carried through another interval, followed by a printing, and re-sets the switch; this group of operations controls the printing of the results once every period of $\cos x$. After this printing, the next input to switch C is through switch B, which controls the number of periods of $\cos x$ through which the calculation is taken. In some processes of numerical integration a special procedure is necessary for the first interval in order to start the integration, and then the procedure for the first period of $\cos x$ is different from that for subsequent periods, the special procedure for the first interval being followed by the standard integration procedure for twenty-eight intervals, without printing, and for a further interval followed by printing; switch B also controls the sequence of processes for this first period. At the end of an integration control is transferred to switch A for counting the number of integrations and for determining the initial conditions for the next integration, if there is to be one, and for stopping the machine if the work is complete.

A flow diagram of this kind may be helpful in showing the general structure of a calculation and how it can be built up from simpler processes for which sub-routines may already be available. For this example, standard sub-routines would probably be available for processes II and III, apart from the evaluation of y'' from y' and y according to the differential equation, for process IV and for the counting and switching processes, leaving only quite a small amount of detailed programming and coding to be done for this particular calculation.

It is also possible to draw more detailed flow diagrams showing the sequence of operations within a single process such as those represented by single blocks in Fig. 31; but it is simpler to program and code simple processes directly.

12.4. Coding

In discussing coding it is easiest and clearest to write in terms of one particular machine; the different kinds of instructions and different ways of selecting the next instruction make it difficult to generalize or to illustrate the different possibilities in a short account. Understanding of the methods of coding for one machine is a great help to understanding that of other machines, so that this account, though written in terms of one machine, will serve as an introduction to the subject in general. It is easiest to write in terms of the machine with which the writer is most familiar, and the following therefore refers mainly to the EDSAC at the Mathematical Laboratory at the University of Cambridge.[†]

The main features of it which we need for a discussion of coding are

(i) It uses a one-address form for instructions;

† M. V. Wilkes, *Nature*, **164** (1949), 557; *Journ. Sci. Insts.* **26** (1949), 385.

(ii) It uses serial storage of instructions; that is, instructions are normally stored at addresses numbered in the sequence in which the instructions themselves are to be carried out;

(iii) Numbers are stored in binary form ; negative numbers are stored as complements, the sign of a number being indicated by a 'sign digit' (0 for a positive number, 1 for a negative number) in the most significant digital position;

(iv) The system of storage is such that the content of a storage location remains unchanged until another 'word' is planted there ;

(v) Input is by five-hole teleprinter tape, numbers punched in decimal form on the tape being translated into their binary form in the machine during the process of reading the tape;

(vi) The machine does *not* proceed by reading an instruction from the tape, carrying it out, then reading the next, and so on; normally the *whole* set of entries on the tape are first transferred to the store, and *then* the machine starts doing the calculation.

An instruction is written in the form of a 'function letter' specifying the operation to be carried out (A for add, S for subtract, T for transfer, etc.) followed, in most cases, by an address to which that instruction refers. It is punched in the form of a row of holes representing the function letter, followed by rows of holes representing the decimal digits of the address, followed by a code letter whose purpose will be explained later ($\S 12.5\,(a)$). The following are the written forms of the instructions which are involved in the examples here considered:†

$A\ n$ add $C(n)$ into the accumulator.

$S\ n$ add $-C(n)$ into the accumulator.

$T\ n$ transfer $C(Acc)$ to storage location n and clear the accumulator.

$U\ n$ transfer $C(Acc)$ to storage location n and retain it in the accumulator.

$E\ n$ examine sign digit of $C(Acc)$; if this is 0 take $C(n)$ as the next instruction; if sign digit of $C(Acc) = 1$ proceed serially (that is, if this instruction has been taken from address m, take

† For the complete set of elementary operations and the form of the instructions for them, see M. V. Wilkes, *Journ. Sci. Insts.* **26** (1949), 217; M. V. Wilkes and W. Renwick, *M.T.A.C.* **4** (1950), 61; M. V. Wilkes, *Applied Scientific Research*, B, **1** (1950), 429; D. J. Wheeler, *Proc. Roy. Soc.* A, **202** (1950), 573.

The examples here considered have been chosen to use only some of the more important instructions, so that the reader will not have to memorize the whole instruction code in order to follow the examples. For a detailed account of programming for the EDSAC, see M. V. Wilkes, D. J. Wheeler, and S. Gill, *Preparation of Programs for an Electronic Digital Calculating Machine* (Addison-Wesley Press, Cambridge, Mass., 1951).

$C(m+1)$ as the next instruction); if the word standing in the accumulator represents a number, this gives a discrimination based on the sign of this number.

$G\ n$ examine sign digit of $C(Acc)$; if this is 1, take $C(n)$ as the next instruction; if this is 0, proceed serially.

Z stop.

The function letter of a written instruction is represented in the machine by a group of digits in the five most significant digital positions (including that of the sign digit) of the word which represents the instruction, and the address n referred to in the instruction, which is written and punched in decimal form, is translated into its binary form in the machine as part of the process of reading the tape and converting entries on the tape into contents of storage locations.

12.5. Examples of programming and coding

(a) *To place* $|C(6)|$ *in location* 4.

As a simple example of the use of instructions of this kind, consider a sequence of instructions for placing $|C(6)|$ in location 4, $C(6)$ being in complementary form; this process is to be considered as one component process in a larger calculation. The required result can be obtained in several ways. The following is one possibility; it is assumed that the accumulator is initially clear and that the first of these instructions is located at address m:

Address	Content		Resulting $C(Acc)$	Notes
m	A	6	$C(6)$	
$m+1$	E	$(m+4)$		test sign digit of $C(Acc)$
$m+2$	T	0	0	
$m+3$	S	0	$-C(6)$	
$m+4$	T	4	0	

$C(6)$ is first put into the store, then its sign digit is tested. The subsequent procedure depends on whether $C(6)$ is positive (including zero) or negative.

Consider first what happens if it is negative; then we want $-C(6)$ to be placed in location 4. In this case the next instruction after the test is taken from address $(m+2)$, and this and the two subsequent instructions have the effect of placing $-C(6)$ in location 4 as required.

If $C(6)$ is found to be positive, then we want it to be placed in location

4; it is in the accumulator at the stage at which the test of sign is made, we therefore want the next instruction to be T 4. We have already just such an instruction in location $(m+4)$ to deal with the case in which $C(6)$ is negative. Thus when $C(6)$ is positive we want the machine to take the instruction in location $(m+4)$ immediately after the test of sign. Hence the address specified in the E-instruction in location $(m+1)$ must be $(m+4)$.

The address specified in the instructions in locations $(m+2)$ and $(m+3)$ may be any address not at this stage containing a number or instruction required later in the calculation. Address 0 is often used, as in this example, as temporary storage for numbers which are wanted almost immediately in the course of the calculation; it is also a convenient 'rubbish-bin' to which contents of the accumulator which are no longer required can be sent in order to clear it.

The instruction in location $(m+3)$ could equally well be S 6 but then two instructions instead of one would have to be changed if we wanted to use a similar group of instructions to put into location 4 the modulus of the content of some storage location other than 6.

(b) *To add the contents of storage locations* 80 *to* 150 *inclusive and place the result in storage location* 4; *or symbolically*

$$\sum_{j=0}^{70} C(80+j) \text{ to } 4.$$

This is to be thought of as one process in a larger calculation in the course of which the contents of locations 80 to 150 inclusive are calculated, the sum being required in location 4 for use in a sub-routine which (for example) is drawn up in such a way as to find $\sin\{C(4)\}$.

The simplest and most straightforward way of programming this would be by the sequence of instructions:

$$A\ 80,\ A\ 81,\ A\ 82,...,\ A\ 149,\ A\ 150,\ T\ 4.$$

This supposes the accumulator to be initially clear as a result of previous instructions. If it is not, it is first cleared by the instruction T 0.

This sequence of instructions, however, is very extravagant of storage space, and as far as storage space for instructions is concerned the calculation can be done much more economically as follows. We take the group of instructions

$$A\ 4,\ A\ n,\ T\ 4$$

which result in $C(4)$ being increased by $C(n)$, and use this group of three instructions over and over again, with n having successively the values 80, 81,..., 150. This means that we have to increase the value of n, the address specified in the instruction $A\ n$, by unity every time this instruction $A\ n$ is used. This can be done by adding the instruction itself into the arithmetical unit and adding unity to it in the digital position corresponding to the unit in n. The number consisting of unity in this digital position is conventionally kept in storage location 2 for just this purpose.

These instructions may have to be preceded by preliminary instructions to clear the accumulator and location 4. Thus so far we have the following instructions, at addresses starting from, say, m:

Storage location	Content		Notes
m	T	0	to clear accumulator } preliminary
$m+1$	T	4	to clear $C(4)$ } preparation
$m+2$	A	4	the addition process; the instruction in location $(m+3)$
$m+3$	A	80	becomes successively A 80, A 81,..., A 150 as the result
$m+4$	T	4	of instructions in locations $(m+5)$ to $(m+7)$
$m+5$	A	$(m+3)$	these instructions increase by unity the address specified
$m+6$	A	2	in the instruction in location $(m+3)$
$m+7$	T	$(m+3)$	

Each time this set of operations is repeated, the address specified in the instruction in location $(m+3)$ is increased by unity. Before repeating it again, the machine must test that the addition is not yet complete. This could be done by keeping at a separate address, say location 6, a count of the number of numbers $C(n)$ added, and examining $C(6)$ after each addition to see if the requisite number of additions has been performed. In this case, however, the address specified in the instruction in location $(m+3)$ is increased by unity for each addition performed, so this instruction itself can be used as the counter. There are several ways in which it can be so used; the following is not the most elegant, but is straightforward and probably the easiest to follow.

If the last number added was $C(n)$, then after the instruction in address $(m+6)$ has been carried out, the content of the accumulator is $A\ (n+1)$. If the instruction in $(m+7)$ is replaced by $U\ (m+3)$, then $A\ (n+1)$ will be retained in the accumulator after being transferred to address $(m+3)$. If then A 151 is subtracted from the content of the accumulator, the result is $(n-150)$, which is negative if the addition is incomplete and zero if it is complete, and an E-order can then be used to discriminate between the procedure necessary to repeat the process of addition and that required if the addition is complete. Thus the process can be completed by the following instructions:

Storage location	Content		Notes
$m+7$	U	$(m+3)$	in place of T $(m+3)$ in first schedule
$m+8$	S	$(m+12)$	
$m+9$	E	$(m+13)$	if the addition is complete, $C(Acc) = 0$ and the next instruction is taken from address $(m+13)$; if it is incomplete, then $C(Acc)$ is negative, and the next instruction is taken from address $(m+10)$
$m+10$	T	0	clears accumulator
$m+11$	E	$(m+2)$	this instruction is only reached if the addition is incomplete; $C(Acc) = 0$ as the result of the previous instruction, so the next instruction is taken from address $(m+2)$ to repeat the addition process; and the accumulator has been cleared in preparation for this addition
$m+12$	A	151	
$m+13$			the next instruction after the addition is complete

The 'word' A 151 in location $(m+12)$ here does not represent an operation which is carried out by the machine in this calculation; it is only used for the purpose of comparison with the instruction A n constructed by the machine to test whether the addition is complete or not.

With the addition programmed in this way, and with this method of coding and operating on instructions, only thirteen instructions are necessary to carry out the addition; and this number of instructions is required for any similar addition, *however many numbers have to be added.* This illustrates, in a simple case, that when the machine can be programmed to alter its own instructions in the course of a calculation, the number of instructions which have to be programmed explicitly, and stored, does not necessarily increase with the total number of operations to be carried out.

Of the thirteen instructions in the above process, only three, namely those in locations $(m+2)$, $(m+3)$, and $(m+4)$ are directly concerned with arithmetical operations on the numbers to be added; the others are concerned with the organization of the calculation. This use of the machine to organize its own work is characteristic of programs for a machine which provides facilities for doing operations on the instructions themselves in the course of a calculation.

In using these instructions, the number 80, which is the address from which the first term in the sum is to be taken, is lost, since the content of location $(m+3)$ has been changed in the course of forming the sum. If this addition process has to be repeated in the course of a single calculation, the instruction A 80 must be replaced in location $(m+3)$; or better, it can be stored somewhere else where it can remain unaltered, and transferred to the appropriate address by instructions which form part of the preliminary preparation before the addition process itself is started. We thus obtain the instructions in the second column of the following table:†

Storage location	Content		Entry on tape GK		Notes control combination	
m	T	0	T	F		
$m+1$	T	4	T 4	F		preliminary
$m+2$	A	$(m+14)$	A 14	θ	to set $C(m+5)$	preparation
$m+3$	T	$(m+5)$	T 5	θ	$= A\,80$	
$m+4$	A	4	A 4	F		
$m+5$	A	n	Z	F	$C(m+5)$ is initially set by $(m+3)$, and later modified by $(m+9)$	the addition process
$m+6$	T	4	T 4	F		
$m+7$	A	$(m+5)$	A 5	θ	add 1 to the address specified in the instruction in location $(m+5)$	
$m+8$	A	2	A 2	F		
$m+9$	U	$(m+5)$	U 5	θ		
$m+10$	S	$(m+15)$	S 15	θ	test if addition complete	
$m+11$	E	$(m+16)$	E 16	θ		
$m+12$	T	0	T	F'	to repeat the addition process if the addition is not complete	
$m+13$	E	$(m+4)$	E 4	θ		
$m+14$	A	80	A 80	F	stored for use by instruction in $(m+2)$	
$m+15$	A	151	A 151	F	stored for use by instruction in $(m+10)$	
$m+16$					next instruction after addition complete	

In this program the address (80) of the first of the sequence of numbers to be added is stored, as part of an instruction, in location $(m+14)$. The instructions in locations $(m+2)$, $(m+3)$ transfer this instruction from $(m+14)$ to $(m+5)$ as part of the preliminary preparation for this calculation. The initial content of location $(m+5)$ is therefore irrelevant, since it is replaced by the instruction $A\,80$ from address $(m+14)$ before the machine reaches the address $(m+5)$ in carrying out its sequence of operations. The stop order Z is often used as the initial content of a location such as $(m+5)$ here, so that if by some mistake it is not replaced by another instruction, the machine will stop there, and by so doing will give an indication of the mistake.

12.6. Form of instructions on the input tape

In this schedule some of the instructions refer to addresses which depend on the value of m, which is determined by the position in the store in which these instructions themselves are placed, whereas others

† The entries in the third column are explained in § 12.6.

are independent of this position. But in drawing up the program of instructions, and punching them on the input tape, it is convenient to have them in a form which does not explicitly depend on the value of m. This can be done by including in each instruction, as punched on the tape, an additional symbol, which for the EDSAC takes the form of a code letter; F for an instruction in which the number is to be read as it stands as the address to which an instruction refers, and θ for one in which the number punched has to have the value of m added to it in order to give that address. That is to say, the terminal code letter θ indicates that the number in the instruction is an address relative to the address of the first of the group of instructions as zero; this can be expressed by saying that this number specifies a 'relative address'. To specify the address from which these relative addresses are counted, a special instruction, called a 'control combination', which is coded as the letters GK, is punched on the tape immediately before the first of the group of instructions. This is an instruction to the machine that in the process of taking in entries from the tape, the address m of the location in which the next instruction is placed is to be recorded so as to be available for constructing the addresses in those instructions which are punched on the tape with the code letter θ.

Thus on the tape the instructions for placing $|C(6)|$ in location 4 (§ 12.5 (a)) take the form shown in the fourth column of the following schedule:

Address	Content		Relative address	Entry on tape		
				GK		
m	A	6	0	A	6	F
$m+1$	E	$(m+4)$	1	E	4	θ
$m+2$	T	0	2	T		F
$m+3$	S	0	3	S		F
$m+4$	T	4	4	T	4	F

The first two columns are the same as in the schedule on p. 263; the fourth shows the way in which the instructions are written and punched. Similarly the instructions for the second example take the form shown in the third column of the schedule on p. 267. The code letters GK, F, and θ do not appear in the instructions in the form they take in the store; they are subsidiary instructions to the machine regarding the interpretation of the punchings on the tape and the formation of contents of storage locations from them in the course of the input process. The code letter F or θ also serves to identify the end of the number which specifies the address to which the instruction refers.

As thus coded on the tape, the instructions have the same form where-ever they are placed in the store, and once drawn up they can be copied as they stand whenever the calculation they carry out is required. This copying can be done and checked mechanically. An important extension of this use of code letters enables a set of instructions to be punched in such a form that they can be used for the calculation of

$$\sum_{j=j_1}^{j_2} C(j) \text{ to } j_3$$

for any predetermined values of the parameters j_1, j_2, and j_3, that is to say, values which are known before the calculation is started, and do not depend on the results obtained in the course of it.

Similar facilities could be provided in other ways if the control system of the machine were designed appropriately. For example, the operations called for by the code letters F and θ in the above example could be carried out not in the course of input of the instructions but by an auxiliary operation carried out on each instruction in the process of transferring it from the store to the control unit, immediately before the operation specified by it is carried out.

12.7. Sub-routines

There are two kinds of contexts in which sub-routines may be used. In the first, the sub-routine is either required only once in the course of a calculation, or it is always required at the same stage of a repetitive calculation, so that the instructions which immediately precede and follow the sub-routine are at definite addresses in the programme. A sub-routine suitable for such a context is called an 'open' sub-routine. The sequence of instructions considered in the previous section can be regarded as an open sub-routine for the process

$$\sum_{j=0}^{70} C(80+j) \text{ to } 4.$$

In operation, it is entered from an instruction in location $(m-1)$ and followed by one in location $(m+16)$. The instruction $E(m+16)$ in location $(m+11)$, which results in the next instruction being taken from location $(m+16)$ when the addition process of the sub-routine is complete, is usually called the 'link' between the end of the sub-routine and the main programme.

If, however, a sub-routine is to be used several times, and the instructions which immediately precede or (more particularly) follow it are located at different addresses on the different occasions on which it is used, then this form is not convenient, as the sub-routine cannot be placed in the store so that its first instruction is always next after the instruction which immediately precedes it in time; and, more important, the address to be used in the 'link' instruction, for return to the main program when the process carried out by the sub-routine is complete, cannot be punched on the input tape as it is different on the different occasions on which the sub-routine is used.

In these circumstances it is more convenient to use another form of sub-routine, called a 'closed' form, which can be placed in the store in any position, independently of the main program, and which includes instructions for forming the link instruction for return to the main program. How this is done depends on how the main program is planned and how the sub-routine is entered from the main program.

The standard method used with the EDSAC will be illustrated first by a simple example. The sequence of operations for placing $|C(6)|$ in location 4 (see § 12.5 example (a)) is too short to be worth coding by itself as a sub-routine, though it might well form part of a longer sub-routine; but for the purpose of illustration let us consider a closed sub-routine for this process.

Let n be the address of the beginning of the sub-routine; it is to be entered after the instruction in location $(m-1)$ has been carried out, the accumulator being then clear. It is entered as follows:

Address	Content		Entry on tape			Notes
m	A	m	A	m	F	accumulator initially clear
$m+1$	G	n	G	n	F	the function digits representing A have a 1 in the sign-digital position; hence the next instruction is taken from address n, the beginning of the sub-routine
$m+2$						next instruction after completion of sub-routine

The instruction $A\ m$ adds *itself* into the accumulator, so that when the sub-routine is entered, the accumulator contains a record of the point in the main programme from which it was entered. The link instruction for return to the main programme must be $E\ (m+2)$. This is obtained by adding to $A\ m$, which is the content of the accumulator on entering the sub-routine, such a group of digits, or 'word', that it converts the 'word' $A\ m$ into the 'word' $E\ (m+2)$. The 'word' which is required for this purpose is conventionally stored as the content of location 3 for use in just this context. Thus the instruction $A\ 3$ results in the link instruction being formed in the accumulator, from which it is transferred to the location immediately following the instruction for the last operation of the sub-routine, which is arranged to leave the accumulator clear.

Address	Content		Relative address	Entry on tape		Notes
				GK		control combination (on tape only)
n	A	3	0	A 3	F	entered with $C(Acc) = A\ m\ F$. This instruction results in the link instruction $E\ (m+2)$ being formed in the accumulator
$n+1$	T	$n+7$	1	T 7	θ	plants link in $(n+7)$
$n+2$	A	6	2	A 6	F	
$n+3$	E	$n+6$	3	E 6	θ	
$n+4$	T	0	4	T	F	$\|C(6)\|$ to location 4 (as in § 12.5, example (a))
$n+5$	S	0	5	S	F	
$n+6$	T	4	6	T 4	F	
$n+7$	Z		7	Z	F	$C(m+7)$ becomes $E\ (m+2)$ as the result of instruction in location $(n+1)$

The method here given for entering a closed sub-routine, forming the link instruction, and planting it at the appropriate place in the sub-routine, is a general one; the only change required is that the instruction $T\ 7\ \theta$ in this example is replaced by $T\ r\ \theta$, where r is the relative address, within the sub-routine, of the location for the link instruction.

This method of using closed sub-routines can be developed to include the possibility of modifying the instructions of the sub-routine itself in the course of the calculation,[†] so that, for example, a single sub-routine for the process $|C(j)|$ to location k could be used for different pairs of values of j and k at different stages in a single calculation, the appropriate values of these parameters being incorporated in the sub-routine on each occasion on which it is used. Similarly, a closed sub-routine based on the process of § 12.5, example (b), could be used for any calculation of the form

$$\sum_{j=a}^{b} C(j) \text{ to } c,$$

where a, b, and c may have different values for different uses of this same sub-routine within a single calculation.

12.8. Hand and automatic calculation

Almost any method for doing a calculation by hand, that is, with a desk machine but without the use of an automatic machine, can be programmed for an automatic machine. A possible exception is the

† See, for example, D. J. Wheeler, *Proc. Roy. Soc.* A, **202** (1950), 573.

relaxation process (§§ 8.5, 10.61) for which it would be difficult to formalize the judgements one uses in practice about when and by how much to over-relax, and when to use group relaxations, and to express these judgements in terms of operating instructions to an automatic machine. But it does not follow that the best method for a hand calculation is the best method for an automatic machine. There are three main reasons for this difference.

First, in most hand calculations of any magnitude, the time taken in carrying out the numerical work is substantially longer than the time taken in planning it, whereas with an automatic machine the time taken to carry it out may be shorter than the time taken to program and code it. Thus in a hand calculation it is worth spending some time in planning the calculation to save numerical work, whereas with an automatic machine it may be best to obtain the same results by a simple process involving a large number of steps to save the time that would be taken in planning, programming, and coding a less simple method using fewer numerical steps. For example, on an automatic machine a relatively large number of repetitions of a simple first-order iterative process (§ 9.3) may be preferable to a smaller number of repetitions of a more complicated second-order process. And in calculating an integral as a function of the upper limit, it might be best with an automatic machine to use a very simple integration formula, such as Simpson's rule or even the trapezium rule, with a large number of short intervals, $0 \cdot 01$, or $0 \cdot 005$, or even perhaps $0 \cdot 001$, when in a hand calculation one might prefer to use an integration formula to sixth or eighth differences of the integrand, with interval $0 \cdot 1$.

Secondly, the storage capacity of a machine is limited, whereas that of the working sheets of a hand calculation is practically unlimited. This has several reactions on programming for an automatic machine. For example: (i) use of many repetitions of a simple procedure which can be programmed in a few instructions is preferable to a few repetitions of a more elaborate procedure for which the longer program would take more storage space; (ii) a strictly repetitive procedure is to be preferred to a procedure which is mainly repetitive but for which special occasional processes have to be used in addition: for example, in some processes for the numerical integration of differential equations a special procedure is needed for the first interval of the integration; the instructions for this special procedure will take up some storage space but will be used once only for each solution, and a method which does not require a special starting process may be preferred; (iii) it may be preferable to calculate values of standard functions, such as circular and exponential functions and their inverses, as they are required, rather than to store tables and the instructions for entering them and interpolating in them.

And thirdly it is usually no shorter or easier to calculate with simple numbers than with numbers of many digits. For example, if e^y is calculated from a series, then in calculating, say, $\int_0^1 e^{x^2}\,dx$ by a Gauss formula (see § 6.55) the fact that e^{x^2} is required for values of x such as $0 \cdot 230765$ (x_2 for a five-point Gauss formula, see § 6.57) and not only for simple values is no drawback.

All these differences have considerable influence on the choice of methods for carrying out calculations by automatic machines. For example, for evaluating an integral between fixed limits formulae of the Gauss type are much more attractive for work with an automatic machine than for a hand computation. Also for evaluating an integral as a function of its upper limit it might even be better to do a number of independent integrations by means of a Gauss formula, with different values of the upper limit, rather than to build up the integral by accumulating a sequence of contributions to it. And for the solution of partial differential equations of elliptic type, a form of the Richardson–Liebmann process (§ 10.64) may be more convenient for an automatic machine than the relaxation process.

Some work has been done on the development of methods particularly suited to the capabilities and limitations of automatic machines, but the main developments of this branch of numerical analysis probably still lie in the future.

EXAMPLES

Note: Several of the following examples are specimens of types of which the reader can make up other examples for himself. For instance, in the first example $e^{0.1}$ could be replaced by some other number, and in Example 4, the series to be evaluated could be replaced by the series solution of some other second-order linear differential equation with the first derivative absent.

1. Given $e^{0.1} = 1.105171$ to six decimals:

(i) Calculate $y_n = e^{0.1n}$ up to $n = 10$ by successive multiplication and transfer.

(ii) Check the results by verifying the following relations between the y_n's:

$$y_6 \times y_4 = y_{10}, \qquad\qquad y_{10}/y_7 = y_3,$$
$$y_7 \times y_2 = y_9, \qquad\qquad y_9/y_5 = y_4,$$
$$y_5 \times y_3 = y_8, \qquad\qquad y_8/y_6 = y_2.$$

(iii) Check the results by differencing the values of y_n (including the value $y_0 = 1$) to second differences, and verifying that $(\delta^2 y_n)/y_n$ is constant.

(*Note*: The main purpose of this example is to give practice in the use of a desk machine; the method of checking in section (ii) of the example is not recommended as a standard procedure for regular use.)

2. Given $e^{0.125} = 1.133148$, evaluate $2[(\cosh 0.125) - 1]$ without writing down any intermediate results.

Prove the relation $\delta^2 e^x = 2[(\cosh \delta x) - 1]e^x$ and use it to build up $e^{0.125n}$ up to $n = 10$.

3. Given $\sin 10° = 0.1736482$, find $(1 - \cos 10°)$ to seven decimals by an iterative process based on the formula

$$1 - \cos x = \sin^2 x / [2 - (1 - \cos x)].$$

Prove the relation $\delta^2(\sin x) = -2(1 - \cos \delta x)\sin x$, and use it to build up a table of $\sin(n \cdot 10°)$ as far as $n = 9$.

4. Evaluate $\qquad y = \tfrac{1}{2}x^2 + \dfrac{1}{2.4.5}x^5 + \dfrac{1}{2.4.5.7.8}x^8 + \cdots$

to five decimals for $x = 0(0.2)2.0$, keeping seven decimals in the individual terms and rounding off the sums to five decimals.

Check the results by evaluating y'' from the differential equation $y'' = 1 + xy$ satisfied by this function y, and verifying the relation

$$\delta^2 y_j = (\delta x)^2 [y_j'' + \tfrac{1}{12}\delta^2 y_j'' - \tfrac{1}{240}\delta^4 y_j''] + O(\delta x)^8.$$

5. Show that the function $y = (\sin x - x \cos x)/x$ satisfies the differential equation $y'' + (1 - 2/x^2)y = 0$.

Evaluate this function to five decimals, for $x = 0(0.1)2.2$, from its power series expansion, and check the results by use of the differential equation.

6. Calculate $\sum_n x_n \Big/ \sum_n x_n^2$ on a desk machine for $x_1 = 1.274, x_2 = 0.984, x_3 = 1.577$, $x_4 = 0.126$ without writing down any intermediate results.

7. Find $3 \times (£3. 8s. 7d.) + 19 \times (£1. 17s. 9d.) + 16 \times (£2. 2s. 11d.)$ using an ordinary desk machine, setting the sterling amounts in £. s. d. and exhibiting the results in £. s. d., without writing down any intermediate results.

(*Note*: Assign the three right-hand places on the setting levers or keyboard to pence, the next three to shillings, and the rest to pounds. After forming the sum, reduce the number of pence by a multiple of 12, and add that same multiple to the shillings, by adding 988 in the right-hand three places until the number of pence in the result is less than 12. Treat the shillings similarly.)†

8. Build up the cubic $f(x) = x^3 - 5x^2 + 6x + 1$ between $x = 2$ and $x = 3$ at intervals of 0·1 by means of a difference table. From these results estimate the position x_m and magnitude of the minimum of $f(x)$ near $x = 2·5$. Verify by solving the quadratic for x_m and evaluating $f(x_m)$.

(*Note*: Change to $\xi = x - 2$ as variable, verifying the transformed form of the cubic by evaluating it for $\xi = 0, \pm 1, \pm 2$ and comparing with the values of $f(x)$ on p. 43.)

9. Evaluate $0·623x^3 - 1·876x^2 + 5·623x + 2·875$ to three decimals for

$$x = 0(0·32)2·56$$

and check the results by differencing.

10. The following values are alleged to be copied from a table of $x^{\frac{1}{2}}$. Locate and correct the mistakes by examination of the differences.

x	$f(x)$	x	$f(x)$
27	3·00000	35	3·27107
28	·03659	36	·30193
29	·07232	37	·33332
30	·10723	38	·36198
31	·14318	39	·39121
32	·17480	40	·41995
33	·20753	41	·44852
34	3·23961	42	3·47603

11. Using 6-figure tables of $\sin x°$, calculate the function

$$y = \sin x° + 2 . 10^{-4} \left[\frac{\sin(x - 50)\pi/10}{(x - 50)\pi/10} \right] \exp[-(x - 50)^2/100]$$

for $x = 30(1)70$, and round off to five decimals.

Compare the second and fourth differences of the rounded values of y with those of five-figure values of $\sin x°$.

Repeat for $x = 25(5)75$ and for $x = -20(10)120$.

(*Note*: $y - \sin x°$ can be regarded as an 'error' in a table of $\sin x°$. The purpose of this example is to illustrate that smooth differences do not necessarily imply freedom from error; the differences of y at intervals 1 in x are no more irregular than those of $\sin x$. It also shows that a table may appear smooth on a small scale as represented by the differences at a small interval of x, but unsmooth on a large scale.)

† This procedure for using a decimal machine for certain calculations in sterling was shown to me by Dr. L. J. Comrie.

12. Show that the sum $\sum_{j=0}^{J-1} \delta^2 f_{2j+1}$, of *alternate* second differences, can be expressed in terms of the operator $U = (\delta x)d/dx$ as $(\tanh \frac{1}{2}U)(f_{2J}-f_0)$.

Deduce the value of this sum when f is a periodic function which is an even function both of $(x-x_0)$ and of $(x-x_{2J})$, and examine whether or not this result is independent of rounding errors in the f values.

13. From the table of the function y calculated in example 4:

(i) Use the 'half-way' interpolation formula to obtain y at $x = 0\cdot7, 0\cdot9, 1\cdot1, 1\cdot3$.
(ii) Interpolate y for $x = 0\cdot95(0\cdot01)1\cdot00$ by Everett's formula.
(iii) Find the value of x for which $y = 0\cdot5$

    (a) by inverse interpolation using the values at $0\cdot1$ intervals only;
    (b) by inverse interpolation using the values at $0\cdot01$ intervals calculated under (ii).

14. From a table of $\sin x$ at intervals of $10°$ in x (see p. 61):

(i) Find $\sin 23° 20'$ and $\sin 26° 40'$.
(ii) Find $\sin^{-1} 0\cdot40$

    (a) by inverse interpolation using a formula involving the differences of $\sin x$ as a function of x;
    (b) by using Lagrange's interpolation formula, treating x as a function of $\sin x$, and verifying by interpolating in the table of $\sin x$ for the value of $\sin^{-1} 0\cdot40$ obtained;
    (c) by using the divided differences of x as a function of $\sin x$.

15. Construct a table of values of $\log(n!)$ to five decimals for $n = 5(1)12$. Use this table to interpolate $\log(x!)$ for $x = 8\frac{1}{2}$ and $9\frac{1}{2}$, and verify that the interpolated values satisfy the relation $(9\frac{1}{2})!/(8\frac{1}{2})! = 9\frac{1}{2}$.

Derive a value for $(\frac{1}{2})! = \frac{1}{2}\sqrt{\pi}$, and hence a value of π.

16. Given the values

$x =$	0	1	2	3	4	5
$y =$	0	1	8	27	64	125

examine the result of attempting to interpolate x for $y = 20$ by a six-point Lagrange formula for x as a function of y.

If the calculation were done by the use of divided differences what symptoms would suggest that the result should be accepted with suspicion?

17. Continue to $x = 0\cdot80$ the subtabulation started in the example in § 5.61.

18. Continue to $x = 1\cdot6$, by intervals $x = 0\cdot05$, the evaluation of $\int_0^x e^{w^2}\, dw$ started in the example in § 6.4.

19. Show that

$$\int_{x_{-2}}^{x_2} f(x)\, dx = 4(\delta x)[1 + \tfrac{2}{3}\delta^2 + \tfrac{7}{90}\delta^4 - \tfrac{2}{945}\delta^6 + \tfrac{13}{56700}\delta^8]f_0 + O(\delta x)^{11}.$$

20. Show that if for integration over a *given* range $x = a$ to $x = b$, this range is divided into $2J$ equal intervals $\delta x = (b-a)/2J$, then

$$\int_a^b f(x)\,dx = [(b-a)/J]\left[\sum_{j=0}^{J-1} f_{2j+1} + \tfrac{1}{6}\sum_{j=0}^{J-1}\delta^2 f_{2j+1} - \tfrac{1}{180}\sum_{j=0}^{J-1}\delta^4 f_{2j+1} + \right.$$

$$\left. + \tfrac{1}{1512}\sum_{j=0}^{J-1}\delta^6 f_{2j+1}\right] + O(1/J^8),$$

the sums being sums of *alternate* values of the function and of its differences of even order.

(*Note*: For the evaluation of an integral over a given range this formula, taken as far as the $\delta^2 f$ term, is probably the most convenient form of Simpson's rule for practical work; higher-difference terms can easily be included if appreciable.)

21. The function erfc x is defined by

$$\text{erfc}\, x = (2/\pi^{\frac{1}{2}})\int_x^\infty e^{-w^2}\,dw.$$

Evaluate erfc x for $x = 0(0\cdot1)1\cdot2$ to five decimals by quadrature. Evaluate $2\int_x^\infty \text{erfc}\, w\,dw$ for $x = 0(0\cdot1)1\cdot0$ by quadrature and check by use of the relation

$$2\int_x^\infty \text{erfc}\, w\,dw = (2/\pi^{\frac{1}{2}})e^{-x^2} - 2x\,\text{erfc}\,x.$$

(*Notes*: (i) erfc $0 = 1$; $2\int_0^\infty \text{erfc}\, w\,dw = 2/\pi^{\frac{1}{2}} = 1\cdot128379$; (ii) the relation between $\int_x^\infty \text{erfc}\, w\,dw$ and erfc x is obtained by integrating by parts.)

22. Evaluate $\int_0^\infty [e^{-x^2}/(x+1)]\,dx$ and $\int_0^\infty [e^{-x^2}/(x+2)]\,dx$ to five decimals by quadrature. Check by evaluating the difference $\int_0^\infty [e^{-x^2}/(x+1)(x+2)]\,dx$ between these integrals by an independent quadrature.

23. Evaluate $y = (1/\pi)\int_0^\pi \cos(x\sin\theta)\,d\theta$, to four decimals, by quadrature for $x = 0(\tfrac{1}{4}\pi)\tfrac{5}{4}\pi$. Estimate, as closely as you can from the results, the smallest positive value of x for which $y = 0$.

24. Continue to $x = 1\cdot6$ the integration of the equation $y'' = (1-x^2)y$ started in the worked example in § 7.2.

25. Continue to $x = 2\cdot0$ the integration of the equation $y' = 1 - 2xy$ started in the example in § 7.3. The solution of this equation is $y = e^{-x^2}\int_0^x e^{w^2}\,dw$. Compare the results of the integration of this differential equation with those of the worked example in § 6.4 and its continuation in Example 18.

26. The function $f(x) = \int\limits_0^\infty e^{-u^2}/(x+u)\, du$ satisfies the differential equation

$$f' + 2xf = -\frac{1}{x} + \pi^{\frac{1}{2}} \quad \text{(see § 6.56)}.$$

Starting from the value of $f(1)$ obtained in Example 22, integrate this equation as far as $x = 2$. Compare the value of $f(2)$ obtained by integration with the value of $f(2)$ obtained in Example 22.

27. Evaluate $y = (3/\pi) \int\limits_0^{\frac{1}{2}\pi} e^{ix\cos\theta}\, d\theta$ to four decimals for $x = 0(\frac{1}{2})2$

   (a) by expanding the integrand in series, integrating term by term with respect to θ, and evaluating the resulting series in x;

   (b) by quadrature;

   (c) by obtaining a second-order differential equation satisfied by y as a function of x, and evaluating the appropriate solution by numerical integration.

28. Find, to two decimals, the solution of the equations

$$18x - 4y + 3z = 53,$$
$$10x + 16y + 2z = 87,$$
$$5x + 3y + 9z = 21$$

(a) by elimination; (b) by relaxation.

29. A cubic $y = a_0 x^3 + a_1 x^2 + a_2 x + a_3$ takes the values $y = 12, 6, 0, 12$ for $x = -2, 0, 1, 3$ respectively. Find the values of the coefficients a_0, a_1, a_2, a_3

   (i) by substituting $x = -2, 0, 1, 3$ and solving the resulting simultaneous equations for the coefficients;

   (ii) by use of divided differences (see § 5.72).

30. Use Milne's method (§ 6.7) to obtain an expression for the error term of the integration formula

$$\int\limits_{x_0}^{x_1} f(x)\, dx = \tfrac{1}{2}(\delta x)[f_0 + f_1 - \tfrac{1}{6}(\delta x)(f_1' - f_0')].$$

31. (i) Invert the matrix

$$\begin{pmatrix} 5 & 7 & 6 & 5 \\ 7 & 10 & 8 & 7 \\ 6 & 8 & 10 & 9 \\ 5 & 7 & 9 & 10 \end{pmatrix}$$

   (ii) Find the characteristic values and characteristic vectors of this matrix.

32. Construct the inverse of the matrix

$$\begin{pmatrix} -23 & 11 & 1 \\ 11 & -3 & 2 \\ 1 & 2 & 1 \end{pmatrix}$$

from its characteristic vectors and the reciprocals of its characteristic values as determined in § 8.63.

(*Note*: This is the matrix whose inverse is found by elimination in the worked example in § 8.3.)

33. Solve the equations

$$14x_1 + 7x_2 + 17x_3 + 8x_4 = 134,$$
$$7x_1 + 11x_2 + 13x_3 + 4x_4 = 70,$$
$$17x_1 + 13x_2 + 42x_3 - 11x_4 = 77,$$
$$8x_1 + 4x_2 - 11x_3 + 30x_4 = 70.$$

34. Find the solution of the equation $y'' = x^2 y - 1$ for which $y = 0$ at $x = \pm 2$

(i) by evaluating a particular integral and a complementary function by step-by-step integration and forming the appropriate linear combination;

(ii) by a relaxation method.

35. Work out a relaxation method for finding a solution of $\nabla^2 V = 0$ for a system with symmetry about an axis. Apply it to find an approximate solution of $\nabla^2 V = 0$ for the axially-symmetrical system formed by rotating Fig. 20 (p. 225) about its axis of symmetry.

36. $\nabla^2 V = 0$ in the space between the planes $z = 0, a$. On the plane $z = 0$, $V = 0$ for $r > a$ and $V = J_0(kr)$ for $r < a$, where ka is the first root of $J_0(x) = 0$; on the plane $z = 2a$, $V = 0$. Find to two decimals the variation of V in the space between the planes.

37. V satisfies $\nabla^2 V = 2/a^2$ inside a square of side a, and $V = 0$ on the boundary of the square. Find to three decimals the value of V at the centre of the square.

38. Find to two decimals the other roots of the simultaneous non-linear equations of which one root is found in § 9.6.

39. Use the iterative formulae

$$(a) \ y_{n+1} = \tfrac{1}{2}[y_n + (a/y_n)], \qquad (b) \ y_{n+1} = y_n(3a - y_n^2)/2a$$

for $a^{\frac{1}{2}}$ to evaluate $\sqrt{5}$ and $\sqrt[3]{60}$.

40. Show that the formula

$$y_{n+1} = y_n[p + 1 - ay_n^p]/p$$

gives a second-order iterative process for $1/a^{1/p}$.

41. Devise a second-order iterative method on the lines of Example 40 to find $(1/9a)^{1/9}$. Use it to find $(8/9)^{1/9}$ and $(1/9)^{1/9}$ to eight decimals; check by verifying that the ratio of the results is $2^{1/3}$.

BIBLIOGRAPHY

THIS bibliography includes, as suggestions for further reading, some books and papers not referred to in the text. Page numbers in italics at the end of an entry indicate the reference in the text to the book or paper listed.

AITKEN, A. C., 'On interpolation by proportional parts, without the use of differences', *Proc. Edin. Math. Soc.* (2), **3** (1932), 56—*84*.

—— 'Studies in practical mathematics, II. The evaluation of the latent roots and the latent vectors of a matrix', *Proc. Roy. Soc. Edin.* **57** (1937), 269.

—— 'Studies in practical mathematics, III. The application of quadratic extrapolation to the evaluation of a derivative and to inverse interpolation', ibid. **58** (1938), 161.

—— 'Studies in practical mathematics, V. On the iterative solution of a system of linear equations', ibid. **63** A (1950), 52.

—— 'Studies in practical mathematics, VI. On the factorization of polynomials by iterative methods', ibid. **63** A (1951), 174—*203*.

Barlow's Tables of Squares, Cubes, etc. (edited by L. J. COMRIE, fourth edition, Spon, 1941)—*20, 193*.

BICKLEY, W. G., 'Difference and associated operators, with some applications', *Journ. of Math. and Phys.* **27** (1948), 183—*56*.

—— 'Finite difference formulae for the square lattice', *Quart. J. Mech. and Applied Math.* **1** (1948), 35—*216*.

BICKLEY, W. G., and MILLER, J. C. P., 'The numerical summation of slowly convergent series of positive terms', *Phil. Mag.* (7), **22** (1936), 754—*243*.

BICKLEY, W. G. See TEMPLE and BICKLEY.

BIRKHOFF, G. D., and YOUNG, D. M., 'Numerical quadrature of analytic and harmonic functions', *Journ. of Math. and Phys.* **29** (1950), 217—*219*.

British Association Mathematical Tables, Part-volume B, *The Airy Integral* (1946) —*77, 119, 137*.

BROMWICH, T. J. I'A., *Theory of Infinite Series* (Macmillan, second edition, 1926)—*65*.

Chambers's Six-figure Mathematical Tables (edited by L. J. COMRIE), vol. 2 (1949) —*20, 47, 68, 70, 71, 72, 75, 76, 84, 111, 195, 214*.

CHERRY, P. M., 'Summation of slowly convergent series', *Proc. Camb. Phil. Soc.* **46** (1950), 436—*243*.

COLLATZ, L., *Numerische Behandlung von Differentialgleichungen* (Springer, 1951).

COMRIE, L. J., 'On the construction of tables by interpolation', *Month. Notices, Royal Astron. Soc.* **88** (1928), 506—*79*.

—— 'Inverse interpolation and scientific applications of the National accounting machine', *Journ. Roy. Stat. Soc.*, supplement, **3** (1936), 87—*24, 83*.

—— See *Chambers's Six-figure Mathematical Tables*.

CRANK, J., and NICOLSON, P., 'A practical method for numerical evaluation of partial differential equations of the heat conduction type', *Proc. Camb. Phil. Soc.* **43** (1947), 50—*235*.

CROUT, P. D., 'A short method of evaluating determinants and solving sets of linear equations with real or complex coefficients', *Trans. Amer. Inst. Elect. Eng.* **60** (1941), 1235—*164*.

DOODSON, A. T., 'A method for the smoothing of numerical tables', *Quart. J. of Mech. and Applied Math.* **3** (1950), 217—*251*.

DWYER, P. S., *Linear Computations* (John Wiley, 1951).

ECKERT, W. J., *Punched Card Methods in Scientific Computation* (Columbia Univ., 1940), *25*.

EYRES, N. R., *et al.* 'The calculation of variable heat flow in solids', *Phil. Trans. Roy. Soc.* **240** (1946), 1—*233*.

FLETCHER, A., MILLER, J. C. P., and ROSENHEAD, L., *Index of Mathematical Tables* (Scientific Computing Service, 1946)—*21, 70, 75, 200*.

FOX, L., 'Some improvements in the use of relaxation methods for the solution of ordinary and partial differential equations', *Proc. Roy. Soc.* A, **190** (1947), 31—*224*.

—— 'A short summary of relaxation methods', *Quart. J. Mech. and Applied Math.* **1** (1948), 253.

—— 'The solution by relaxation methods of ordinary differential equations', *Proc. Camb. Phil. Soc.* **45** (1949), 50—*172, 174, 189*.

—— 'Practical methods for the solution of linear equations and the inversion of matrices', *Journ. Roy. Stat. Soc.* B, **12** (1950), 120—*166*.

FOX, L., and GOODWIN, E. T., 'Some new methods for the integration of ordinary differential equations', *Proc. Camb. Phil. Soc.* **45** (1949), 373—*142*.

FOX, L., HUSKEY, H. D., and WILKINSON, J. H., 'Notes on the solution of algebraic linear simultaneous equations', *Quart. J. Mech. and Applied Math.* **1** (1948), 149—*164*.

FRIEDMAN, B., 'Note on approximating complex zeros of a polynomial', *Commun. on Pure and Applied Mathematics*, **2** (1949), 195—*203*.

GOODWIN, E. T., 'The evaluation of integrals of the form $\int\limits_{-\infty}^{\infty} f(x)e^{-x^2}\,dx$', *Proc. Camb. Phil. Soc.* **45** (1949), 241—*112, 113*.

GOODWIN, E. T., and STATON, J., 'Table of $\int\limits_{0}^{\infty} [e^{-u^2}/(u+x)]\,du$', *Quart. J. Mech. and Applied Math.* **1** (1948), 319—*114*.

HARTREE, D. R., 'Notes on iterative processes', *Proc. Camb. Phil. Soc.* **45** (1948), 230—*197*.

—— 'A solution of the laminar boundary layer equation for retarded flow', *Aero. Res. Comm., Rep. and Mem.*, No. 2426 (1939, issued 1949)—*235*.

HARTREE, D. R., KRONIG, R. DE L., and PEDERSEN, H., 'A theoretical calculation of the fine structure for the K-absorption band of Ge in $GeCl_4$', *Physica*, **1** (1934), 895—*148*.

HARTREE, D. R., and WOMERSLEY, J. R., 'A method for the numerical or mechanical solution of certain types of partial differential equations', *Proc. Roy. Soc.* **161** (1937), 363—*234*.

Index of Mathematical Tables. See FLETCHER, A.

Interpolation and Allied Tables (H.M.S.O. 1947)—*20, 21, 70, 71*.

KILBURN, T., 'The University of Manchester universal high-speed digital computing machine', *Nature*, **164** (1949), 684.

LANCZOS, C., 'Trigonometric interpolation of empirical and analytic functions', *Journ. of Math. and Phys.* **17** (1938), 123.

—— 'An iteration method for the solution of the eigenvalue problem of linear differential and integral operators', *Journ. of Research, Nat. Bur. Standards*, **45** (1950), 255.

LIEBMANN, H., 'Die angenäherte Ermittelung harmonischer Funktionen und konformer Abbildung', *Sitz. Bayer. Akad. München* (1918), 385—*232*.

MACFARLANE, G. G., 'The application of Mellin transforms to the summation of slowly convergent series', *Phil. Mag.* (7), **40** (1949), 188—*243*.

MADELUNG, E., 'Über eine Methode zur schnellen numerischen Lösung von Differentialgleichungen zweiter Ordnung', *Zeit. f. Phys.* **67** (1931), 516—*148*.

MANNING, M. F., and MILLMAN, J., 'Note on numerical integration', *Phys. Rev.* **53** (1938), 673—*133*.

MICHEL, J. G. L., 'Central difference formulae obtained by means of operator expansions', *Journ. Inst. of Actuaries,* **72** (1946), 470—*65*.

MILLER, J. C. P., 'Checking by differences', *Math. Tables and Aids to Comp.* **4** (1950), 3—*48*.

—— 'A method for the determination of converging factors, applied to the asymptotic expansions of the parabolic cylinder functions', *Proc. Camb. Phil. Soc.* **48** (1952), 243.

—— See also *Brit. Assn. Math. Tables*, BICKLEY, and FLETCHER.

MILNE, W. E., *Numerical Analysis* (Univ. of Princeton Press, 1950)—*94, 121*.

—— 'Numerical determination of characteristic numbers', *Journ. of Research, Nat. Bur. Standards,* **45** (1950), 245—*147*.

MORRIS, J., 'An escalator process for the solution of linear simultaneous equations', *Phil. Mag.* (7), **37** (1946), 106—*154*.

NEVILLE, E. H., 'Iterative interpolation', *Journ. Indian Math. Soc.* **20** (1934), 87—*85*.

OLVER, F. W. J., 'A new method for the evaluation of zeros of Bessel functions and of other solutions of second-order differential equations', *Proc. Camb. Phil. Soc.* **46** (1950), 570—*142*.

—— 'The evaluation of zeros of high-degree polynomials', *Phil. Trans. Roy. Soc.* **244** (1952), 385—*200*.

RICHARDSON, L. F., 'The approximate arithmetical solution by finite differences of physical problems involving differential equations', ibid. **210** (1910), 307—*232*.

—— 'The deferred approach to the limit', ibid. **226** (1927), 300—*125, 140*.

—— 'A purification method for computing the latent columns of numerical matrices and some integrals of differential equations', ibid. **242** (1950), 439—*183*.

SAMUELSON, P. A., 'Iterative computation of complex roots', *Journ. of Math. and Phys.* **28** (1949), 259—*201*.

SOUTHWELL, R. V., 'Stress calculations in frameworks by the method of "systematic relaxation of constraints"', *Proc. Roy. Soc.* A, **151** (1935), 56—*167, 172*.

—— 'On relaxation methods; a mathematics for engineering science' (Bakerian Lecture), ibid. **184** (1945), 253—*167*.

—— *Relaxation Methods in Engineering Science* (Oxford, 1940)—*167*.

—— *Relaxation Methods in Theoretical Physics* (Oxford, 1946)—*230*.

SPENCER, J., 'On the graduation of the rate of sickness and mortality presented by the experience of the Manchester Unity of Oddfellows during the period 1893–97', *J. Inst. Actuaries,* **38** (1904), 334—*250*.

STIEFEL, L., 'Über einige Methoden der Relaxationsrechnung', *Zeit. f. angew. Math. und Phys.* **3** (1952), 1—*230*.

SZÁSZ, O., 'Summation of slowly convergent series', *Journ. of Math. and Phys.* **28** (1949), 272—*243*.

TEMPLE, G., 'The general theory of relaxation methods applied to linear systems', *Proc. Roy. Soc.* A, **169** (1938), 476—*171*.

TEMPLE, G., and BICKLEY, W. G., *Rayleigh's Principle* (Oxford, 1933)—*147, 180*.

TURING, A. M., 'Rounding-off errors in matrix processes', *Quart. J. Mech. and Applied Math.* **1** (1948), 287—*153, 164*.

WHEELER, D. J., 'Programme organization and initial orders for the EDSAC', *Proc. Roy. Soc.* A, **202** (1950), 573—*262, 271.*

WHITEHEAD, A. N., *Introduction to Mathematics* (Home University Library Series, No. 18; Oxford, 1948)—*2.*

WHITTAKER, E. T., and ROBINSON, G., *Calculus of Observations* (Blackie, fourth edition, 1944)—*116, 250.*

WHITTAKER, E. T., and WATSON, G. N., *Modern Analysis* (Camb. Univ. Press, fourth edition, 1927)—*99, 246.*

WILKES, M. V., 'A method of solving second-order simultaneous linear differential equations using the Mallock machine', *Proc. Camb. Phil. Soc.* **36** (1940), 204—*133.*

—— 'Electronic calculating machine development at Cambridge', *Nature,* **164** (1949), 557—*261.*

—— 'Programme design for a high-speed automatic calculating machine', *Journ. Sci. Insts.* **26** (1949), 217—*262.*

WILKES, M. V., and RENWICK, W., 'The EDSAC, an electronic calculating machine', *Journ. Sci. Insts.* **26** (1949), 385—*261.*

WILKES, M. V., WHEELER, D. J., and GILL, S., *Preparation of Programs for an Electronic Digital Computer* (Addison-Wesley Press, 1951)—*262.*

WOODWARD, P. M., 'Tables of interpolation coefficients for use in the complex plane', *Phil. Mag.* (7), **39** (1948), 594—*219.*

WOODWARD, P. M., and WOODWARD, A. M., 'Four-figure tables of the Airy function in the complex plane', ibid. **37** (1946), 236—*219.*

ADDITIONAL REFERENCES

ALLEN, D. N. DE G., *Relaxation Methods* (McGraw-Hill, 1954).

FOX, L., and GOODWIN, E. T., 'The numerical solution of non-singular linear integral equations', *Phil. Trans. Roy. Soc.* **245** (1953), 501.

HOUSEHOLDER, A. S., *Principles of Numerical Analysis* (McGraw-Hill, 1953).

MILNE, W. E., *Numerical Integration of Differential Equations* (Wiley, 1953).

MINEUR, H., *Technique de Calcul Numérique* (Ch. Béranger, 1952).

NATIONAL PHYSICAL LABORATORY. *Proceedings of a Symposium on Automatic Digital Computation*, March 1953 (H.M.S.O., 1954), especially: Paper 18. J. H. Wilkinson, 'Linear algebra on the pilot ACE'; Paper 19. L. Fox and H. H. Robertson, 'The numerical solution of differential equations'.

TAUSSKY, O., 'Note on the condition of matrices', *Math. Tables and Aids to Comp.* **4** (1950), 111—*155.*

WILKINSON, J. H., 'The calculation of latent roots and vectors of matrices on the pilot model of the ACE', *Proc. Camb. Phil. Soc.* **50** (1954), 536.

INDEX

PRINTED IN
GREAT BRITAIN
AT THE
UNIVERSITY PRESS
OXFORD
BY
CHARLES BATEY
PRINTER
TO THE
UNIVERSITY